Prentice Hall LITERATURE

PENGUIN EDITION

Reader's Notebook

D1301178

Grade Nine

PEARSON

Upper Saddle River, New Jersey
Boston, Massachusetts
Chandler, Arizona
Glenview, Illinois

ACKNOWLEDGMENTS

Grateful acknowledgment is made to the following for copyrighted material:

Arte Publico Press, Inc.
"A Voice" by Pat Mora from *Communion*. Copyright © 1991 Arte Publico Press—University of Houston. Used by permission of the publisher.

The Battalion Online
"About The Event" from http://bigevent.tamu. edu/?q=node/2. Copyright © 2003–2008 The Battalion Online. Used by permission of The Battalion, Texas A&M University.

Susan Bergholz Literary Services
"Twister Hits Houston" from *My Wicked Wicked Ways*. Copyright © 1987 by Sandra Cisneros. Published by Third Woman Press and in hardcover by Alfred A. Knopf. From *A Celebration of Grandfathers*. Copyright © 1983 by Rudolfo Anaya. First published in New Mexico Magazine, March 1983. Used by permission of Third Woman Press and Susan Bergholz Literary Services, New York, NY and Lamy, NM. All rights reserved.

Gary L. Blackwood
From *The Shakespeare Stealer* by Gary L. Blackwood. Copyright © 2003 by Gary L. Blackwood. Used by permission of the author.

Brandt & Hochman Literary Agents, Inc.
"The Most Dangerous Game" from *The Most Dangerous Game* by Richard Connell. Copyright © 1924 by Richard Connell. Copyright renewed © 1952 by Louise Fox Connell. "Sonata For Harp and Bicycle" from *The Green Flash and Other Tales of Horror* by Joan Aiken. Copyright © 1957, 1958, 1959, 1960, 1965, 1968, 1969, 1971 by Joan Aiken. Used by permission of Brandt & Hochman Literary Agents, Inc. Any copying or redistribution of the text is expressly forbidden.

Curtis Brown, Ltd.
"Uncoiling" by Pat Mora. First appeared in *Daughters of the Fifth Sun*, published by Riverhead Press. Copyright © 1995. Used by permission of Curtis Brown, Ltd.

The Bryan-College Station Eagle
"A&M students help out in a 'big' way" from *http://www.theeagle.com/PrinterFriendly/A-amp-amp-M-students-help-out-in-a--big--way*. Copyright © 2008 The Bryan-College Station Eagle. Used by permission.

The Bukowski Agency
"The Jade Peony" by Wayson Choy. First published in the *UBC Alumni Chronicle*, Vol. 34, No. 4, Winter 1979. Copyright by Wayson Choy 1977. The novel The Jade Peony, based on this story, is published in the United States by The Other Press. Used by permission of The Bukowski Agency.

Catherine Costello
"There is No Word for Goodbye" by Mary Tall Mountain from *There Is No Word for Goodbye: Poems by Mary Tall Mountain*. Copyright © 1994 by Tall Mountain Estate. Used by permission of Catherine Costello. All rights reserved.

(Acknowledgments continue on page V71, which constitutes an extensions of this copyright page.)

PEARSON

ISBN-13: 978-0-13-371359-6
ISBN-10:   0-13-371359-8

3 4 5 6 7 8 9 10   V001   13 12 11 10

CONTENTS

© Pearson Education

CONTENTS

CONTENTS

CONTENTS

CONTENTS

UNIT 4 Poetry

CONTENTS

CONTENTS

UNIT 5 Drama

MODEL SELECTION

excerpt from **The Shakespeare Stealer** by Gary L. Blackwood

The Tragedy of Romeo and Juliet, Act I by William Shakespeare

The Tragedy of Romeo and Juliet, Act II Scene ii by William Shakespeare

The Tragedy of Romeo and Juliet, Act III by William Shakespeare

The Tragedy of Romeo and Juliet, Act IV by William Shakespeare

CONTENTS

CONTENTS

CONTENTS

PART 2 Vocabulary Building Tools

As you read your hardcover student edition of *Prentice Hall Literature* use the **Reader's Notebook** to guide you in learning and practicing the skills presented. In addition, many selections in your student edition are presented here in an interactive format. The notes and instruction will guide you in applying reading and literary skills and in thinking about the selection. The examples on these pages show you how to use the notes as a companion when you read.

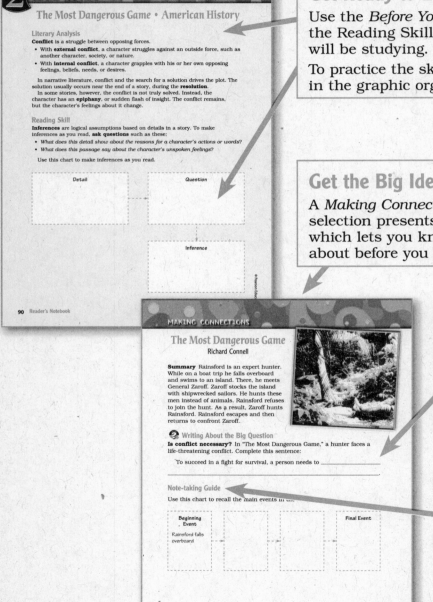

Get Ready to Learn

Use the *Before You Read*: page to learn about the Reading Skill and Literary Analysis you will be studying.

To practice the skills, you can write directly in the graphic organizer as you read.

Get the Big Idea

A *Making Connections* page for every selection presents a selection summary, which lets you know what the selection is about before you read.

Build Your Vocabulary

Sentence starters help you think about the Big Question. These sentences use vocabulary introduced in the student edition.

Be an Active Reader

A *Note-taking Guide* helps you organize the main ideas of the selection. Complete the guide as you read to track your understanding.

Take Notes

Side-column questions accompany the selections that appear in the Reader's Notebooks. These questions are a built-in tutor to help you practice the skills and understand what you read.

Mark the Text

Use write-on lines to answer questions in the side column. You may also want to use the lines for your own notes.

When you see a pencil, you should underline, circle, or mark the text as indicated.

Check Your Understanding

Questions after every selection help you think about the selection. You can use the write-on lines and charts to answer the questions. Then, share your ideas in class discussions.

Go Beyond the Selection

This page provides step-by-step guidance for completing the Writing and Extend Your Learning activities presented in your student edition.

TAKE NOTES

The Most Dangerous Game
Richard Connell

Activate Prior Knowledge
Describe a time when someone else had different rules for playing a game. What happened?

Reading Skill
When you make an **inference** you use information in the story to make a logical guess. What can you infer from the name Ship-Trap Island?

Literary Analysis
Underline details that show how Rainsford and Whitney feel about hunting. How is Rainsford's attitude in **conflict** with Whitney's?

Reading Check
What two classes does Rainsford believe make up the world? Underline your answer.

"Off there to the right—somewhere—is a large island," said Whitney. "It's rather a mystery—"

"What island is it?" Rainsford asked.

"...it Ship-Trap Island," Whitney replied. "A suggestive name, isn't it? Sailors have a curious dread of the place. I don't know why. Some superstition—"

"Can't see it," remarked Rainsford, trying to peer through the dank tropical night that was palpable as it pressed its thick warm blackness in upon the yacht.

"You've good eyes," said Whitney, with a laugh, "and I've seen you pick off a moose moving in the brown fall bush at four hundred yards, but even you can't see four miles or so through a moonless Caribbean[1] night."

"Not four yards," admitted Rainsford. "Ugh! It's like moist black velvet."

"It will be light in Rio," promised Whitney. "We should make it in a few days. I hope the jaguar guns have come from Purdey's. We should have some good hunting up the Amazon. Great sport, hunting."

"The best sport in the world," agreed Rainsford.

"For the hunter," amended Whitney. "Not for the jaguar."

"Don't talk rot, Whitney," said Rainsford. "You're a big-game hunter, not a philosopher. Who cares how a jaguar feels?"

"Perhaps the jaguar does," observed Whitney.

"Bah! They've no understanding."

"Even so, I rather think they understand one thing—fear. The fear of pain and the fear of death."

"Nonsense," laughed Rainsford. "This h... ...er is making you soft, Whitney. Be a re... ...he world is made up of two classes—the hunt... ...nd the huntees. Luckily, you and I are the h... ...s. Do you think we've passed that island yet?"

"...n't tell in the dark, I hope so."

"...why?" asked Rainsford.

"The place has a reputation—a bad one."

"Cannibals?" suggested Rainsford.

"Hardly. Even cannibals wouldn't live in such a God-forsaken place. But it's gotten into sailor lore, somehow.

Vocabulary Development
palpable (PAL puh buhl) *adj.* able to be felt; easily perceived

1. **Caribbean** (kar uh BEE uhn) the Caribbean Sea, a part of the Atlantic Ocean, bounded by the north coast of South America, Central America, and the West Indies.

92 Reader's Notebook

AFTER YOU READ

The Most Dangerous Game

1. **Respond:** What do you like or dislike about Rainsford? Explain.

2. **Speculate:** How might Rainsford's experience on the island change him? Use evidence from the text to support your answer.

...o record details that reveal **conflicts** in the

Rainsford vs. himself

...rence you made about Whitney.

The Most Dangerous Game 113

SUPPORT FOR WRITING AND EXTEND YOUR LEARNING

Writing: Alternative Ending
Write an **alternative ending** to "The Most Dangerous Game." Use your notes from the following questions to help create your ending.

• If the general, rather than his dog, had fallen into the trap, how might the story have ended?

• If Rainsford had not jumped into the sea, how might the story have ended?

Listening and Speaking: Oral Presentation
Use the following lines to create an oral presentation about two or three-big game species mentioned in the story "The Most Dangerous Game."

Species #1: _____

Facts about this species: _____

Species #2: _____

Facts about this species: _____

Species #3: _____

Facts about this species: _____

Sources used: _____

114 Reader's Notebook

Selections and Skills Support

The pages in your *Reader's Notebook* go with the pages in the hardcover student edition. The pages in the *Reader's Notebook* allow you to participate in class instruction and take notes on the concepts and selections.

Before You Read

Build Skills Follow along in your *Reader's Notebook* as your teacher introduces the **Reading Skill** and **Literary Analysis** instruction. The graphic organizer is provided on this page so that you can take notes right in your *Reader's Notebook*.

Preview Use this page for the selection your teacher assigns.

- The **Summary** gives you an outline of the selection.
- Use the **Reading-Writing Connection** to understand the big idea of the selection and join in the class discussion about the ideas.
- Use the **Note-taking Guide** while you read the story. This will help you organize and remember information you will need to answer questions about the story later.

While You Read

Selection Text and Sidenotes You can read the full text of one selection in each pair in your *Reader's Notebook.*

- You can write in the *Reader's Notebook.* Underline important details to help you find them later.
- Use the **Take Notes** column to jot down your reactions, ideas, and answers to questions about the text. If your assigned selection is not the one that is included in the *Reader's Notebook,* use sticky notes to make your own **Take Notes** section in the side column as you read the selection in the hardcover student edition.

After You Read

Apply the Skills Use this page to answer questions about the selection right in your *Reader's Notebook.* For example, you can complete the graphic organizer that is in the hardcover student edition right on the page in your *Reader's Notebook.*

Support for Writing and Extend Your Learning Use this page to help you jot down notes and ideas as you prepare to do one or more of the projects assigned with the selection.

Other Features in the *Reader's Notebook* You will also find note-taking opportunities for these features:

- Learning About the Genre
- Support for the Model Selection
- Support for Reading Informational Materials

Characteristics of Fiction

Fiction is prose writing that tells a story about imaginary events. Fiction has these elements:

- invented people called **characters**. These people experience a series of events called the **plot**. The plot starts with a **conflict**, or problem, that the characters face.
- a **setting**, which is the time and place of the plot
- the **point of view** of the character who narrates, or tells, the story. The narrator may or may not take part in the story's events.
- a **theme**, which is the message the author wants to tell you about life or human nature

Types of Fiction

Type	Length	Coverage
Novel	long work usually presented in chapters	• has many characters, settings, and conflicts • may contain subplots, which are separate but related stories
Novella	shorter than a novel but longer than a short story	• may have several characters and settings • usually has one conflict • usually does not have subplots
Short story	brief enough to be read in one sitting	• may have several characters • usually has one setting • has one main plot driven by a single conflict

Characteristics of Nonfiction

Nonfiction is prose writing that tells about real people, places, and events. Nonfiction has these elements:

- Nonfiction is told by an author who is a real person.
- Nonfiction presents facts, discusses ideas, or describes true-life experiences.
- Nonfiction is written for a specific **audience**, or group of readers.
- Nonfiction authors write for a specific reason, or **purpose**.
- Nonfiction authors display their **tone**, or attitude toward the subject or reader, through word choice.

Types of Nonfiction

Type	Characteristics	Examples
Literary Nonfiction	• tells stories of real-life events • a type of narrative nonfiction • tells the writer's thoughts and feelings about personal experiences or ideas	• autobiographies • memoirs • literary essays • journals
Informational Text—Expository	• informs or explains	• analytical essays • research reports
Informational Text—Persuasive	• presents reasons and evidence to persuade readers to act or think in a certain way	• editorials • political speeches
Informational Text—Procedural	• provides information or steps that can be used to complete a task	• instructions • consumer publications

from The Giant's House
Elizabeth McCracken

Summary James is an unusually tall young man. One day, he asks Peggy, the librarian, for help finding books. He is looking for information about people like him. James and Peggy look under different topics to find what James wants to know.

Note-taking Guide

As you read, fill in this chart that tells what James says, does, and thinks. Then, tell what others say about him.

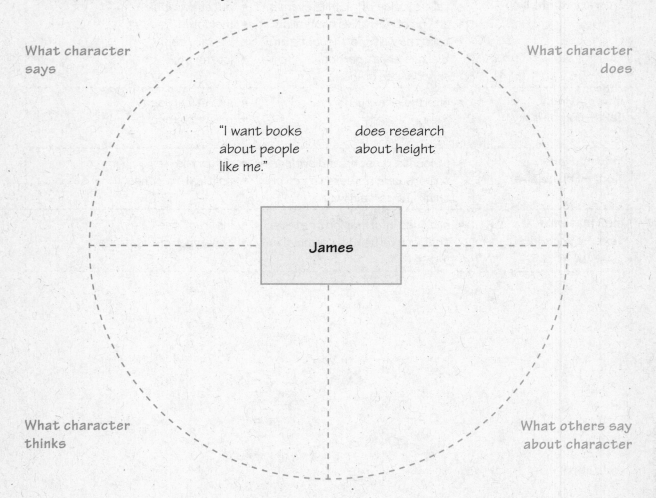

What character says

What character does

"I want books about people like me."

does research about height

James

What character thinks

What others say about character

from The Giant's House
Elizabeth McCracken

James took out books on astronomy, ornithology:[1] sciences at once about tininess and height. He approached the desk with books he'd liked and asked for more—he knew it was easier to find more books with a good example in hand.

Then one day, in the first months of 1955—I remember looking over his head at some awful persistent Christmas decoration Astoria had stuck to the ceiling—he came to me without books. His height had become unwieldy; he reached out to touch walls as he walked, sometimes leaving marks way above where the other teenage boys smudged their hands. "I want books about people like me," he said.

I thought I knew what he was talking about, but I wanted to be cautious. "What exactly about you?" I asked. I made myself think of all the things he could have meant: Boy Scouts, basketball players. Never jump to conclusions when trying to answer a reference question. Interview the patron.

"Tall people," he said.

"Tall people? Just tall people in general?"

"Very tall people. Like *me*," he said, clearly <u>exasperated</u> with my playing dumb. "What they do."

"Okay," I told him. "Try the card catalog. Look in the big books on the table—see those books?" I pointed. "Those are books of subject headings for the card catalog. Look under words that you think describe your topic." James was used to me doing this: I gave directions but would not pull the books off the shelf for him. My job was to show people—even people I liked—how to use the library, not to use it for them. "Dig around," I said. "Try height, try stature. Then look in the catalog for books."

He nodded, leaned on the desk, and pushed off.

An hour later he headed out the door.

"Did you find what you needed?" I asked.

"There isn't anything," he said. "There was one book that sort of was about it, but I couldn't find it on the shelf."

"There's something," I told him. "Come back. We'll look for it together."

© Pearson Education

Vocabulary Development

exasperated (ig ZAS puh ray tid) *adj.* annoyed

---

1. **astronomy, ornithology** Astronomy is the study of the stars and planets. Ornithology is the study of birds.

Activate Prior Knowledge

When you think about giants, what words and ideas come to mind?

_____

_____

_____

Fiction

The **setting** is the time and place in which a story happens. Underline words in the bracketed passage that tell you when this story occurs.

Fiction

Readers get to know **characters** by looking at what they say, do, think, and feel. Write two things you learn about Peggy, the librarian.

_____

_____

_____

Fiction

As the narrator of the story, Peggy tells readers about both herself and James. Underline words and groups of words in the bracketed passage that tell how she feels about her job.

Stop to Reflect

Why does the librarian say that she could not bear to tell James to look under the word *giant*?

_____

_____

_____

Fiction

Conflict is the problem characters try to solve as the story progresses. What problem does Peggy have?

_____

_____

_____

Reading Check

James has a hard time finding what he needs. Circle the words in the text that Peggy uses to look up information for James.

That night after closing, I hunted around myself. The only thing under *stature* was a book about growth and nutrition. I tried our two encyclopedias under height and found passing references. Not much.

In truth, my library was a small-town place, and this was a specialized topic. Still, I was certain I could find more. I got that familiar mania—there is information somewhere here, and I can find it, I have to. A good librarian is not so different from a prospector, her whole brain a divining rod. She walks to books and stands and wonders: here? Is the answer here? The same blind faith in finding, even when hopeless. If someone caught me when I was in the throes of tracking something <u>elusive</u>, I would have told them: but it's out there. I can feel it. God *wants* me to find it.

That night I wandered the reference department, eyed the bindings of the encyclopedias, dictionaries, atlases. James was so big I almost expected to locate him in the gazetteer.[2] I set my hands upon our little card catalog, curled my fingers in the curved handles of the drawers. Then I went to the big volumes of subject headings.

Looking under *height* and *stature* turned up nothing; *anthropometry* was not quite right. Then I realized the word I was looking for: *Giant*.

Giant described him. *Giant*, I knew, would lead me to countless things—not just the word, located in indexes and catalogs and encyclopedias, but the idea of Giant, the knowledge that the people that James wanted to read about, people who could be described as like him, were not just tall but giants. I sat in a spindle-backed chair in the reference room, waiting for a minute. Then I checked the volume of the Library of Congress headings. *Giants. See also: dwarfs.*

We did not have a book, but I found several encyclopedia entries. Nowadays I could just photocopy; but that night I wrote down the page and volume numbers, thinking I could not bear to tell him the word to look under. Most of the very tall people mentioned in the encyclopedia had worked in the circus as professional giants, so I went to our books on the circus.

The photographs showed enormous people. Not just tall, though of course they were that, often with an ordinary person posed beside them. The tall people looked

Vocabulary Development

elusive (i LOO siv) *adj.* hard to grasp or retain mentally

2. **gazetteer** (ga zuh TEER) *n.* dictionary or index of geographical names.

twice as big as the ambassador from the normal-sized, as if they were an entirely different race. The books described weak stomachs and legs and bones. Sometimes what made them tall showed in their faces: each feature looked like something disturbed in an avalanche, separate from the others, in danger of slipping off.

Anna Swann, the Nova Scotia Giantess, married Captain Bates, the Kentucky Giant. As a young woman at Barnum's Dime Museum in New York, Miss Swann had been in two fires; in the second she had to be lifted out by a crane. No ordinary over-the-shoulder rescue for a woman better than seven feet tall. She and her husband retired to Ohio, to a specially made house. Their church installed an extra-large pew.

Byrne, the Irish Giant, lived in fear of a certain doctor who lusted after his skeleton; he imagined the doctor's giant kettle ready to boil his bones.

Jack Earle was over seven feet tall, traveled with the circus for years; after his retirement he wrote poetry.

I took comfort in Anna Swann and her husband. They were solid-looking people. Respectable. They'd had two children, though neither survived. The book described them as *in love*, and you could believe that from the pictures: their complementary heights were just a lovely coincidence to their love affair. I found myself that late night a little jealous of Anna Swann and her handsome, bearded captain.

The books said that giants tended to exaggerate their heights for exhibition purposes. I did not know it then, but every person I read about was shorter than James grew to be.

The worst book was called *Medical Curiosities*. I say worst now. That is hindsight. The night I looked, I thought, in fact, that it was the best book—not because it was good or even accurate, but because it had the most pages on the subject I was researching. I found it under the subject heading *Abnormalities, human*. A terrible phrase, and one I knew I could not repeat to James. It was a late-nineteenth-century medical book, described two-headed people and parasitic twins and dwarfs. And giants. Not exactly information, but interesting: giants who had enormous or usual appetites; ones who grew throughout their lives or only after adolescence; professional giants and private citizens.

Vocabulary Development

ambassador (am BAS uh der) *n.* an official who represents his or her country in another country

avalanche (AV uh lanch) *n.* the fall of a large amount of snow and ice down the side of a mountain

Fiction

Peggy is the narrator. The story is told from her **point of view**. Is she a part of the events in Anna Swann's life? Explain your answer.

_____

_____

_____

Stop to Reflect

Why do you think Peggy does not want James to realize where she found the most information?

_____

_____

_____

Fiction

Circle words and groups of words in the bracketed paragraph that show how Peggy feels about the books she finds.

© Pearson Education

Fiction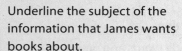

What does the first bracketed paragraph tell you about Peggy's **character**?

_____

_____

_____

Fiction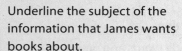

Read the second bracketed passage. Explain the **conflict** that James seems to be having.

_____

_____

_____

_____

Reading Check

Underline the subject of the information that James wants books about.

_____

_____

So I took that book, and the circus books, marked the <u>pertinent</u> places with the old catalog cards I used for scrap, and set them aside. Ready for him, so that he did not have to look in the index, or wander through the pages at all.

"Your tall friend is here," Astoria said to me the next week. I was in my office, reading reviews. "He's looking for you."

James waited for me at the circ desk. "You said we could—"

"I looked," I said. I'd stowed the books beneath the shelf. "Try these out."

He took them to the big table in the front room. Read them. He made the sturdy chair, the same chair I'd sat in the night before, seem tiny.

Afterward he came up to me.

"How were they?" I asked. "Would you like to take them home?"

He shook his head.

"No," he said. "Thanks."

"Nothing useful here at all?"

"No," he said.

I tried to catch his eye. "Close?"

"Close. I guess." He pointed at *Medical Curiosities*. "I guess that's close."

I picked up the book and opened it to where the marker was, but he'd moved it to another page. A line drawing of a double-bodied baby looked up at me. Horrible. I snapped the book shut.

"I meant medical books," he said. "But new ones. Ones that say what goes wrong. How to cure it."

"Cures," I said. "Oh." Cures for giants? No such thing. No cure for height. Only preventive medicine. I said it as a question. "Cures? For tall people?"

"Yes," he said.

All I wanted was for him to explain it to me. It seemed <u>presumptuous</u> to come to any conclusions myself. I knew what he was talking about. I did. But what he wanted, I couldn't help him with.

Darla, the shelver, came rattling up with her metal cart. "Shelve these?" she said, pointing at the books. The catalog cards I'd used stuck out from the pages; James had lined them up, like a pack of cards he'd shuffled into them. "Hi, Jim," she said.

Vocabulary Development

pertinent (PERT n uhnt) *adj.* relevant; having a connection to the matter at hand

presumptuous (pri ZUMP choo uhs) *adj.* seeming disrespectful because one is overly confident

"Hi." He squinted down at her.

She stared at me; I waited for her to get back to shelving.

"Peggy. Shelve them, or not?"

"Not yet," I said. She sighed and pushed the cart off.

James stood in silence on the other side of the desk. He looked ready to leave.

"You mean how to stop growing," I said.

"Yes." Now he looked at me. "Medicine, or operations, or something."

"I'm not sure we have anything here," I said. That was a lie. I knew we didn't. "A medical library somewhere, perhaps. Or a university library. But really—" I started pulling the bookmarks from the books. I tried to sound gentle. "Really, you should ask your doctor."

"I have," he said. "I've asked a lot of doctors."

Reader's Response: How would you feel if you were James? Explain.

_____

_____

_____

_____

_____

TAKE NOTES

Fiction

Theme is the message the author wants you to understand about life or human nature. Circle words or groups of words on this page that give you clues about the theme.

What is the theme of this excerpt from *The Giant's House*? Think about why James is so worried about his height.

_____

_____

Desiderata
Elizabeth McCracken

Summary In this essay, the author explores the importance of family papers. Letters and even shopping lists move her to write stories. McCracken's wish to be a writer came from the words family members left behind.

Note-taking Guide

Nonfiction authors may write for several different purposes. As you read "Desiderata," use this chart to take notes on the reasons Elizabeth McCracken wrote this essay.

Author's Purpose	Examples from Text
To inform	Author's collection of desiderata includes grandfather's genealogy, grandmother's letter collection, diplomas, diaries, and laundry lists.
To entertain	
To persuade	
To reflect	

Desiderata
Elizabeth McCracken

Desiderata, I learned in library science school, were the items you needed for an <u>archive</u> to make it useful. Useful, not complete, because there is no such thing as a complete archive. There's always a letter out there you want and need, either in someone else's collection or in an attic or just unfound. You need and want things you don't even know exist. That's how collections work.

I come from a family strong on documents. I have a small archive myself. My grandfather McCracken was a <u>genealogist</u>—I have his history of the McCrackens, a lovely compilation of research on early ancestors and personal remembrances of his own relatives. His wife, my grandmother, wrote stories and poems; I have copies of those, and remember once opening a drawer full of letters she wrote to God, part prayer and part daily <u>correspondence</u> to Someone dear. I have my grandmother Jacobson's collection of family letters; she had 11 brothers and sisters, some who wrote often and some just now and then. I have diplomas of relatives I never met. I have diaries and laundry lists. I love anything written by a relative, any evidence of what they really thought.

And I read these documents fairly regularly. Besides letters from her family, my grandmother also saved letters from Martha, her children's nanny. My mother, who says she had the happiest childhood on record, remembers Martha and her letters as lovely and slightly daffy. Her twin sister, my aunt Carolyn, remembers the letters and the woman as dark and Dickensian,[1] longing for a time that never really existed. I'd always assumed that the truth was somewhere in the middle, but I have the letters and now know that Martha was, at best, weird. She wrote to my travelling grandmother that the twins—The Dollies, she called them—didn't miss her at all. She reported that she took them out to her mother's farm, and couldn't

Vocabulary Development

archive (AHR kyv) *n.* storage area for historical or family objects and documents
genealogist (jee nee AHL uh jist) *n.* someone who studies the history of a family
correspondence (kawr uh SPAHN duhns) *n.* communication through written letters

1. **Dickensian** of or relating to English novelist Charles Dickens (1812–1880).

Activate Prior Knowledge

What could you learn from an old shopping list? What could you learn from an old family letter?

_____

_____

_____

_____

Nonfiction

Early in the essay, the author gives you important facts. She helps you understand the kinds of papers she collects. She states what an archive includes. Underline words and groups of words in the bracketed passage that tell you the kinds of documents she collects.

Stop to Reflect

Why does Elizabeth McCracken like hearing different sides of the same story?

_____

_____

_____

_____

Nonfiction

Literary nonfiction uses character sketches. List the words the author uses to describe her grandmother's sisters.

_____

_____

_____

Nonfiction

Circle the facts the author gives about grandmother Jacobson. Double underline her thoughts and feelings about her grandmother.

Reading Check

What is the author's major frustration about collecting family papers? Underline the words in the text that tell you.

understand why the girls were so upset to be served for dinner the chicken they'd met earlier. She reported on The Dollies' toilet training as if it were grand opera, and the Dollies heroines who wanted only, desperately, to triumph.

I'm glad to know this, I think. Certainly, it's a whole different Martha than the one I knew from my mother's stories. I know Martha now because of all that she reveals of herself, not knowing she was doing it, in her letters.

Still, there are many frustrations to family papers. First of all, you may learn things you don't want to know. For instance: some of my grandmother's sisters wanted to sue the widow of one of their brothers. Even in letters from the litigious[2] sisters themselves, this comes across as merely petty and <u>vindictive</u>. There are letters that can break your heart: my Aunt Edna, writing to my grandmother, <u>lamented</u> how poor her health was, how the doctors told her to slow down; I know from the dates that Edna died two weeks later, of a heart attack.

But the major frustration is how incomplete everything is, how incomplete *people* are if you try to meet them this way. The great-aunt who wanted to sue only happened to write it down; maybe she gave up the idea. Maybe she was suffering otherwise—her life was continually tragic in small ways, I know that. Some of the great-aunts I barely know, because they barely wrote. Or rather, I *think* they barely wrote—my grandmother saved every letter some years, and selected letters others. Perhaps those great-aunts simply never made it into the collection.

And then there's my grandmother Jacobson herself. She was a wonderful and complex woman, an attorney and small businessperson who died at home at the age of 90. The pieces of paper I have from her don't conjure her up at all. Her diary (which I don't own but have read) is a very careful record of daily events, nothing more. She doesn't detail worries or doubts, and the fact is she was a worried and somewhat doubtful person. I think she knew that we'd read it, eventually, and didn't want to tell us in her diary anything she hadn't told us already.

One piece of paper I do have: a post-it note from late in her life, which she used to mark a recipe in *The Jewish Cookbook*. It says:

coffee
bananas

Vocabulary Development

vindictive (vin DIK tiv) *adj.* revengeful; inclined to seek revenge
lamented (luh MEN tid) *v.* expressed sadness and disappointment

2. **li igi us** (li TIJ uhs) *adj.* given to carrying out lawsuits; quarrelsome.

bread
milk
wax beans?
and then, in the corner, written diagonally and underlined,
lottery ticket.

I know that this dates to a time when she was both worried about money and had become very serious about luck. I don't know how superstitious she'd previously been, but about two years before she died, she began to see luck good and bad, in everything: she read her <u>horoscope</u>, her children's horoscope, the horoscope of everyone who might touch her life that day. She believed in fortune cookies. She told her own fortune playing solitaire. And she bought lottery tickets, not so much because she believed she might win but because not playing meant she did not believe that sudden good things could happen. She was a businessperson, after all: she knew what a bad investment that weekly dollar was.

I love that little green piece of paper. *Desideratum* to me, though less than ephemera[3] to anyone else.

I could tell dozens of other stories from the pages of family papers: my aunt Blanche's <u>pell-mell</u> record of taking care of her favorite sister, Elizabeth, who was dying of Alzheimer's; Blanche has that disease herself now, and you can see the early signs in these notes. My great-uncles' cheery letters from Europe during World War II. A letter my brother wrote to my grandmother when I was four and he was six, thanking her for a gift and then recording that I was resisting writing a thank-you note myself.

Here's a last story. My father's parents were, when I knew them, quiet people. I know now that my version of them is different from anyone else's, but they were my grandparents and I never questioned who I understood them to be. After their deaths, I inherited a cherry chest-of-drawers from their house. I owned this imposing piece of furniture for a few years before I lifted some paper lining from one of the drawers and found a letter. Part of a letter, actually, written by my grandfather to my grandmother before their marriage.

Nonfiction

The author says that grandmother Jacobson thought about good and bad luck. Which facts in the first bracketed paragraph support that statement?

_____

_____

_____

Nonfiction

What do you think McCracken's **purpose** is in using the example of her brother's thank-you note?

_____

_____

Nonfiction

How does McCracken see her grandparents in the second bracketed paragraph? Underline the groups of words that tell you.

Vocabulary Development

horoscope (HAWR uh scohp) *n.* a description of character and prediction of future events for someone that is based on the positions of the stars and planets when that person was born

pell-mell (pel mel) *adj.* jumbled

---

3. **ephemera** (e FEM er uh) *n.* something, often printed material, meant to last for only a short time.

Nonfiction

Literary nonfiction shows the author's thoughts and feelings. Circle the feelings and thoughts the author expresses in the bracketed paragraph.

Reading Check

Why was the author's father less excited about the love letter than the author was? Underline the text that tells you.

Stop to Reflect

Why is the letter about her grandparents important to the author?

_____

_____

_____

_____

It was one of the most beautiful love letters I've ever read, full of delight for her person and for their love together. It was passionate and thrilled and almost disbelieving of his great fortune, to have found her. I never imagined my grandfather, my quiet careful grandfather, was the sort of man who'd write any kind of love letter, never mind this kind. Wrong again. And my grandmother had saved it for more than fifty years. I wondered whether she took it out and reread it from time to time, or whether she'd forgotten where she'd put it.

My parents were out of town that weekend, and as it happened I'd agreed to pick them up at the airport. I brought the letter to give to my father—if it meant that much to me, I couldn't imagine what it would mean to him. And so, sitting on a bench in Logan,[4] I gave it to him. "Look what I found," I said.

"Oh," he said, perfectly pleased but not surprised. "Another letter. I'll put it with the others."

Turns out there were many more—my grandparents had written each other several times a day during their courtship. Which makes it, of course, a happier story.

My question is: was that letter more a *desideratum* for me, or my father? He had the collection, I didn't. Sometimes I regret giving it to him. I've forgotten the exact words my grandfather used, but it doesn't seem right to ask for someone else's love letter back. Someday I'll see it again, I know. Meanwhile, I need it and desire it. I need and desire everything that belongs to my family, and in some ways, I think, that's what I do with my days, writing fiction. I am writing love letters to diaries and post-it notes and telegrams and birthday cards. I am writing love letters to love letters.

Reader's Response: Does this essay affect your ideas about family photographs and writings? Why or why not?

_____

_____

_____

_____

Vocabulary Development

courtship (KAWRT ship) *n.* period of a romantic relationship before marriage

4. **Logan** Boston's Logan International Airport, named for General Edward Lawrence Logan.

from The Giant's House • Desiderata

1. **Analyze:** Does Peggy feel as if she is being a helpful librarian to James? Why or why not?

_____

_____

_____

2. **Speculate:** Help James find information about his condition in our more scientifically advanced world. Complete the chart by writing research questions and possible sources (including the Internet and the library) that he might use.

Research Question	Possible Source

3. **Fiction:** How does the **setting** of _The Giant's House_ affect James's problem?

_____

_____

_____

_____

4. **Nonfiction:** In her **nonfiction** essay, is McCracken's main **purpose** to persuade, to inform, or to reflect? Explain.

_____

_____

_____

_____

Oral Report

Create an **oral report** to discuss McCracken's interest in libraries, documents, and research. The following bullets will help you find information for your report.

- Read some of the author's other works. *Niagara Falls All Over Again*, *The American Child*, and *Here's Your Hat, What's Your Hurry?* are fictional pieces, and her essays appear in the collections *Family: American Writers Remember Their Own* and *A Few Thousand Words About Love*.

  What I learned from McCracken's fiction and nonfiction:

  _____

  _____

  _____

- Search the Internet.

  What I learned from information about McCracken:

  _____

  _____

  _____

- Watch the video interview with Elizabeth McCracken. Use it and your source material to answer these questions.

1. What did you learn about McCracken's library background? How did her background affect her writing?

   _____

   _____

   _____

2. What did you learn about McCracken's interest in documents?

   _____

   _____

   _____

The Washwoman • New Directions

Literary Analysis

A **literary essay** is a short piece of nonfiction that tells a story about a real person or event. In a narrative essay, the author chooses to include **significant details** that help move the story forward or that help make his or her point about the subject. For example, if an author writing about a famous singer wants to stress that the singer comes from a musical family, the essay might mention that the singer's father plays guitar. The essay probably would not mention that the singer's father collects stamps. As you read, notice how the author's choice of significant details influences your impressions of the people and events he or she describes.

Reading Skill

A **prediction** is an informed idea about what might happen later in a narrative. Predictions are based on details in the text and your own experience. When you **verify predictions**, you read on to see whether the prediction is correct.

Pause periodically to reflect on your understanding while reading. **Ask questions** about text details and events.

• Why does the author mention this detail?

• How might it become important later on?

Look for the answers as you read on. Use this chart to record your predictions and whether they are accurate.

Detail	Question

Prediction	Verification?

The Washwoman
Isaac Bashevis Singer

Summary The author recalls the old woman who washed his family's laundry. She was a dedicated, hard worker. She overcame great obstacles to do her job. The author shows how, even to the end of her days, her sense of duty and her honor prevailed.

? Writing About the Big Question

Can truth change? In "The Washwoman," a Jewish family learns to appreciate a Christian washwoman whose son has abandoned her. Complete these sentences:

A mother's relationship with her son can be distorted because of

_____. They could gain insight into each

other's perspective by _____.

Note-taking Guide

Use this chart to write details that tell or show what the washwoman looks like and how she behaves.

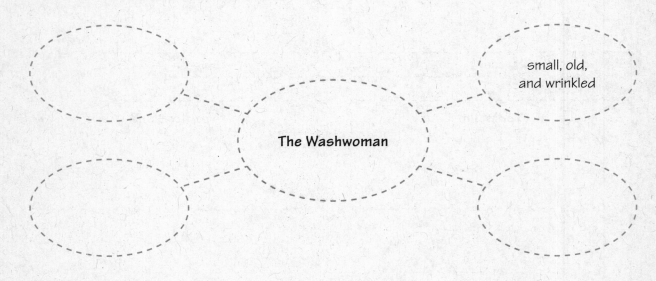

small, old, and wrinkled

The Washwoman

The Washwoman

1. **Draw Conclusions:** After a long absence, the washwoman returns to the family. What does her return tell you about her character?

_____

_____

_____

2. **Speculate:** What kind of information about the washwoman might the author have included but did not include?

_____

_____

_____

3. **Literary Analysis:** Identify three **significant details** that the author uses to describe the washwoman and her son. Use this chart.

The Washwoman	The Washwoman's Son

4. **Reading Skill:** Write one **prediction** you made while reading "The Washwoman." What details did you use to make the prediction?

_____

_____

_____

_____

Writing: Anecdote

Write an **anecdote**, or short narrative, about a person you know and admire. Answer the following questions. Then, use your notes to help write your anecdote.

- What do you admire about the person?

  _____

  _____

- What event or action shows this characteristic?

  _____

  _____

- How did the event or action make you feel?

  _____

  _____

- What did you learn from it?

  _____

  _____

Listening and Speaking: Personal Interview

In the first column of the following chart, write down some questions that you plan to ask during your interview. Use the second column to jot down your interviewee's responses.

Questions I plan to ask	How the interviewee responded
1.	1.
2.	2.
3.	3.

New Directions
Maya Angelou

Summary A young woman named Annie Johnson decides to separate from her husband and change her life. To support her family, she decides to sell meat pies. She carries the food long distances each day and never disappoints her customers. Slowly, her success grows.

 Writing About the Big Question

Can truth change? In "New Directions," Mrs. Annie Johnson finds herself on her own with two young children. Complete this sentence:

The truth about a person can change as a result of _____

_____.

Note-taking Guide
Use this chart to write details describing Annie Johnson's character.

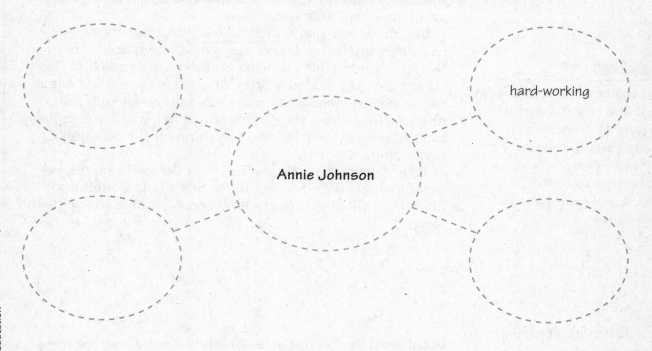

hard-working

Annie Johnson

Activate Prior Knowledge

Think of a difficult problem you have faced. How did you work through the problem to a solution?

_____

_____

_____

Literary Analysis

A **literary essay** is a short piece of nonfiction that tells a story about a real person or an event. In this literary essay, underline the words that explain the problem that Annie Johnson faces. How does this problem move the story forward?

_____

_____

_____

Reading Skill

A **prediction** is an informed idea about what might happen later in a narrative. Predictions are based on details in the text and your own experience. Read the bracketed passage. What prediction do you make about Annie's plans?

_____

_____

_____

Circle the details that you based your prediction on.

New Directions
Maya Angelou

In 1903 the late Mrs. Annie Johnson of Arkansas found herself with two toddling sons, very little money, a slight ability to read and add simple numbers. To this picture add a disastrous marriage and the burdensome fact that Mrs. Johnson was a Negro.

When she told her husband, Mr. William Johnson, of her dissatisfaction with their marriage, he conceded that he too found it to be less than he expected, and had been secretly hoping to leave and study religion. He added that he thought God was calling him not only to preach but to do so in Enid, Oklahoma. He did not tell her that he knew a minister in Enid with whom he could study and who had a friendly, unmarried daughter. They parted amicably, Annie keeping the one-room house and William taking most of the cash to carry himself to Oklahoma.

Annie, over six feet tall, big-boned, decided that she would not go to work as a domestic and leave her "precious babes" to anyone else's care. There was no possibility of being hired at the town's cotton gin or lumber mill, but maybe there was a way to make the two factories work for her. In her words, "I looked up the road I was going and back the way I come, and since I wasn't satisfied, I decided to step off the road and cut me a new path." She told herself that she wasn't a fancy cook but that she could "mix groceries well enough to scare hungry away and from starving a man."

She made her plans meticulously and in secret. One early evening to see if she was ready, she placed stones in two five-gallon pails and carried them three miles to the cotton gin. She rested a little, and then, discarding some rocks, she walked in the darkness to the saw mill five miles farther along the dirt road. On her way back to her little house and her babies, she dumped the remaining rocks along the path.

That same night she worked into the early hours boiling chicken and frying ham. She made dough and filled the rolled-out pastry with meat. At last she went to sleep.

Vocabulary Development
amicably (AM i kuh blee) *adv.* in a friendly way
meticulously (muh TIK yuh luhs lee) *adv.* very carefully and precisely

The next morning she left her house carrying the meat pies, lard, an iron brazier, and coals for a fire. Just before lunch she appeared in an empty lot behind the cotton gin. As the dinner noon bell rang, she dropped the savors into boiling fat and the aroma rose and floated over to the workers who spilled out of the gin, covered with white lint, looking like specters.

Most workers had brought their lunches of pinto beans and biscuits or crackers, onions and cans of sardines, but they were tempted by the hot meat pies which Annie ladled out of the fat. She wrapped them in newspapers, which soaked up the grease, and offered them for sale at a nickel each. Although business was slow, those first days Annie was determined. She balanced her appearances between the two hours of activity.

So, on Monday if she offered hot fresh pies at the cotton gin and sold the remaining cooled-down pies at the lumber mill for three cents, then on Tuesday she went first to the lumber mill presenting fresh, just-cooked pies as the lumbermen covered in sawdust emerged from the mill.

For the next few years, on balmy spring days, blistering summer noons, and cold, wet, and wintry middays, Annie never disappointed her customers, who could count on seeing the tall, brown-skin woman bent over her brazier, carefully turning the meat pies. When she felt certain that the workers had become dependent on her, she built a stall between the two hives of industry and let the men run to her for their lunchtime provisions.

She had indeed stepped from the road which seemed to have been chosen for her and cut herself a brand-new path. In years that stall became a store where customers could buy cheese, meal, syrup, cookies, candy, writing tablets, pickles, canned goods, fresh fruit, soft drinks, coal, oil, and leather soles for worn-out shoes.

Each of us has the right and the responsibility to assess the roads which lie ahead, and those over which we have traveled, and if the future road looms ominous

Vocabulary Development

brazier (BRAY zhuhr) *n.* a metal pan, bowl, or similar item to hold burning coals or charcoal, as for grilling food

assess (uh SES) *v.* to make a judgment about a situation after thinking carefully about it

ominous (AHM uh nuhs) *adj.* threatening

TAKE NOTES

Reading Skill

A reader should pause while reading to **ask questions** about text details and events. Read the underlined sentence. Then, answer the following questions: Why does the author mention this detail?

_____

_____

How might it become important later on?

_____

_____

Stop to Reflect

What does Annie Johnson's achievement suggest about the human spirit?

_____

_____

_____

_____

Reading Check

Circle the sentence that describes what Annie Johnson's business becomes.

Literary Analysis 🔍

In a **literary essay,** the author includes **significant details** that help make his or her point about the subject. What point do you think the author makes in this literary essay?

_____

_____

_____

_____

Which details in the essay best support this point?

_____

_____

_____

or unpromising, and the roads back uninviting, then we need to gather our resolve and, carrying only the necessary baggage, step off that road into another direction. If the new choice is also <u>unpalatable</u>, without embarrassment, we must be ready to change that as well.

Reader's Response: What do you find most inspiring in Annie Johnson's story? Explain.

_____

_____

_____

_____

_____

_____

_____

Vocabulary Development

unpalatable (un PAL it uh buhl) *adj.* distasteful; unpleasant

New Directions

1. **Evaluate:** How would you describe Annie Johnson's abilities as a businessperson? Explain.

   _____

   _____

   _____

2. **Make a Judgment:** Do you think that taking a "new direction" in life is worth the risk of failure? Explain.

   _____

   _____

   _____

3. **Literary Analysis:** Use this chart to record three significant details to describe Annie Johnson and her husband.

Annie Johnson	Annie Johnson's Husband

4. **Reading Skill:** A **prediction** is an informed guess about what might happen later. Write three predictions you made while reading "New Directions."

   _____

   _____

   _____

   _____

   _____

Writing: Anecdote

Write an **anecdote**, or short narrative, about a person you know and admire.

- Write a list of four characteristics that you admire in people.

  _____

  _____

- In the chart, list three people you know and admire. Write the characteristic he or she has that you admire beneath his or her name. Choose one of the persons you admire as a subject for your anecdote.

Name:	Name:	Name:

Listening and Speaking: Job Interview

In the first column of the following chart, write down some questions you would ask Annie Johnson during your interview. In the second column, write what you think she might reply.

Questions I would ask Annie Johnson	How Annie Johnson might reply
1.	1.
2.	2.
3.	3.

Sonata for Harp and Bicycle • The Cask of Amontillado

Literary Analysis

Plot is the sequence of events in a narrative. It is structured around a **conflict**, or problem. It can be divided into the following parts:

- **Rising Action:** central conflict is introduced
- **Climax:** high point of intensity in the conflict is reached
- **Falling Action:** conflict decreases in intensity
- **Resolution:** conflict concludes and loose ends are tied up

Writers use a variety of techniques to keep readers interested in the plot. One of these, **foreshadowing**, is the use of clues to hint at events that will happen later in a story. Authors use foreshadowing to create **suspense**, a feeling of tension that keeps readers wondering what will happen next.

Reading Skill

A **prediction** is an informed guess about what will happen later in a narrative. Notice details that may foreshadow future events. Make predictions based on those details, and then **read on to verify your predictions**. If a prediction turns out to be wrong, evaluate your reasoning.

- Did you misread details?
- Did the author purposely create false expectations in order to surprise you later in the story?

Revise, or change, your prediction based on your evaluation. Use this chart to record your predictions and evaluate their accuracy. Analyze any inaccurate predictions to determine why they were incorrect.

Prediction	Outcome

Analysis of Prediction

Sonata for Harp and Bicycle

Joan Aiken

Summary Jason Ashgrove wonders about the nightly routine in the building where he works. He finds out there are ghosts in the building at night. With the help of Berenice Golden, Jason learns why the ghosts are there. He then sets out to solve the situation.

 Writing About the Big Question

Can truth change? In "Sonata for Harp and Bicycle," miscommunication leads to tragedy and a curse on a building. Complete this sentence:

You can change your own fate by _____.

Note-taking Guide

Use this diagram to recall the clues that help Jason solve the mystery.

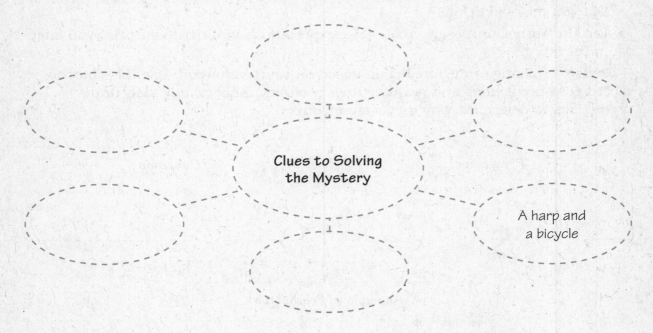

Clues to Solving
the Mystery

A harp and
a bicycle

Sonata for Harp and Bicycle
Joan Aiken

"No one is allowed to remain in the building after five o'clock," Mr. Manaby told his new assistant, showing him into the little room that was like the inside of a parcel.

"Why not?"

"Directorial policy," said Mr. Manaby. But that was not the real reason.

Gaunt and sooty, Grimes Buildings lurched up the side of a hill toward Clerkenwell.[1] Every little office within its dim and crumbling exterior owned one tiny crumb of light—such was the proud boast of the architect—but toward evening the crumbs were collected as by an immense vacuum cleaner, absorbed and demolished, yielding to an uncontrollable mass of dark that came tumbling in through windows and doors to take their place. Darkness infested the building like a flight of bats returning willingly to roost.

"Wash hands, please. Wash hands, please," the intercom began to bawl in the passages at a quarter to five. Without much need of prompting, the staff hustled like lemmings along the corridors to green- and blue-tiled washrooms that mocked with an illusion of cheerfulness the encroaching dusk.

"All papers into cases, please," the voice warned, five minutes later. "Look at your desks, ladies and gentlemen. Any documents left lying about? Kindly put them away. Desks must be left clear and tidy. Drawers must be shut."

A <u>multitudinous</u> shuffling, a rustling as of innumerable bluebottle flies might have been heard by the attentive ear after this injunction, as the employees of Moreton Wold and Company thrust their papers into cases, hurried letters and invoices into drawers, clipped statistical <u>abstracts</u> together and slammed them into filing cabinets, dropped discarded copy into wastepaper baskets. Two minutes later, and not a desk throughout Grimes Buildings bore more than its customary coating of dust.

"Hats and coats on, please. Hats and coats on, please. Did you bring an umbrella? Have you left any shopping

Activate Prior Knowledge

What movies have you seen or what books have you read that involved a mystery? What types of characters appear in mystery stories?

_____

_____

_____

_____

Literary Analysis

Suspense is a feeling of tension that keeps readers wondering what will happen next. How does the first sentence of the story create suspense?

_____

_____

_____

_____

Reading Skill

A **prediction** is an informed guess about what will happen later in a story. Readers use details from the story to make predictions. What do you predict will happen in the story? Underline details that helped you make your prediction.

_____

_____

_____

_____

Vocabulary Development

multitudinous (mul tuh TOOD n uhs) *adj.* very numerous; many

abstracts (AB strakts) *n.* short written statements containing only the most important ideas in speeches, articles, or other types of reports

1. **Clerkenwell** district of London.

© Pearson Education

Literary Analysis

What **conflict**, or problem, is Jason experiencing?

_____

_____

_____

_____

Reading Skill

Circle text clues about the relationship between Jason and Miss Golden. What can you **predict** about their relationship?

_____

_____

_____

Stop to Reflect

A **conflict** can occur when people do not share the same emotions. How are Jason's and Miss Golden's feelings about the mystery different?

_____

_____

_____

on the floor?" At three minutes to five the homegoing throng was in the lifts[2] and on the stairs; a clattering, staccato-voiced flood darkened momentarily the great double doors of the building, and then as the first faint notes of St. Paul's[3] came echoing faintly on the frosty air, to be picked up near at hand by the louder chimes of St. Biddulph's-on-the-Wall, the entire premises of Moreton Wold stood empty.

"But why is it?" Jason Ashgrove, the new copywriter, asked his secretary one day. "Why are the staff herded out so fast? Not that I'm against it, mind you; I think it's an admirable idea in many ways, but there is the liberty of the individual to be considered, don't you think?"

"Hush!" Miss Golden, the secretary, gazed at him with large and terrified eyes. "You mustn't ask that sort of question. When you are taken onto the Established Staff you'll be told. Not before."

"But I want to know now," Jason said in discontent. "Do you know?"

"Yes, I do," Miss Golden answered <u>tantalizingly</u>. "Come on, or we shan't have finished the Oat Crisp layout by a quarter to." And she stared firmly down at the copy in front of her, lips folded, candyfloss hair falling over her face, lashes hiding eyes like peridots,[4] a girl with a secret.

Jason was annoyed. He rapped out a couple of rude and witty rhymes which Miss Golden let pass in a withering silence.

"What do you want for your birthday, Miss Golden? Sherry? Fudge? Bubble bath?"

"I want to go away with a clear conscience about Oat Crisps," Miss Golden retorted. It was not true; what she chiefly wanted was Mr. Jason Ashgrove, but he had not realized this yet.

"Come on, don't tease! I'm sure you haven't been on the Established Staff all that long," he coaxed her. "What happens when one is taken on, anyway? Does the Managing Director have us up for a <u>confidential</u> chat? Or are we given a little book called *The Awful Secret of Grimes Buildings*?"

Vocabulary Development

tantalizingly (TAN tl yz ing lee) *adv.* in a teasing way

confidential (kahn fuh DEN shuhl) *adj.* secret and not intended to be shown or told to other people

2. **lifts** *n.* British term for elevators.

3. **St. Paul's** famous church in London.

4. **peridots** (PER uh dahts) *n.* yellowish-green gems.

Miss Golden wasn't telling. She opened her drawer and took out a white towel and a cake of rosy soap.

"Wash hands, please! Wash hands, please!"

Jason was frustrated. "You'll be sorry," he said. "I shall do something desperate."

"Oh no, you mustn't!" Her eyes were large with fright. She ran from the room and was back within a couple of moments, still drying her hands.

"If I took you out for a coffee, couldn't you give me just a tiny hint?"

Side by side Miss Golden and Mr. Ashgrove ran along the green-floored passages, battled down the white marble stairs among the hundred other employees from the tenth floor, the nine hundred from the floors below.

He saw her lips move as she said something, but in the clatter of two thousand feet the words were lost.

"—fire escape," he heard, as they came into the momentary hush of the carpeted entrance hall. And "—it's to do with a bicycle. A bicycle and a harp."

"I don't understand."

Now they were in the street, chilly with the winter dusk smells of celery on carts, of swept-up leaves heaped in faraway parks, and cold layers of dew sinking among the withered evening primroses in the bombed areas. London lay about them wreathed in twilit mystery and fading against the barred and smoky sky. Like a ninth wave the sound of traffic overtook and swallowed them.

"Please tell me!"

But, shaking her head, she stepped onto a scarlet homebound bus and was borne away from him.

Jason stood undecided on the pavement, with the crowds dividing around him as around the pier of a bridge. He scratched his head, looked about him for guidance.

An ambulance clanged, a taxi hooted, a drill stuttered, a siren wailed on the river, a door slammed, a brake squealed, and close beside his ear a bicycle bell tinkled its tiny warning.

A bicycle, she had said. A bicycle and a harp.

Jason turned and stared at Grimes Buildings.

Somewhere, he knew, there was a back way in, a service entrance. He walked slowly past the main doors, with their tubs of snowy chrysanthemums, and up Glass Street. A tiny furtive wedge of darkness beckoned him, a snicket, a hacket, an alley carved into the thickness of the building. It was so narrow that at any moment, it seemed,

Vocabulary Development

momentary (MOH muhn ter ee) *adj.* continuing for a very short period of time

furtive (FER tiv) *adj.* sneaky

TAKE NOTES

Literary Analysis ✎

Foreshadowing is the use of clues to hint at events that will happen later in a story. In the first bracketed passage, underline the details that may be important later in the story. How does the use of foreshadowing add to the story's **suspense**?

_____

_____

_____

_____

_____

_____

Literary Analysis 🔍

How do Jason's actions in the second bracketed passage increase the **suspense** of the narrative?

_____

_____

_____

Reading Check ✎

Does Miss Golden tell Jason the whole story of Grimes Buildings? Circle the text that tells you.

Reading Skill

Read the first bracketed passage. What do you **predict** will happen to Jason in Grimes Buildings?

_____

_____

_____

_____

_____

Literary Analysis

The **plot** of a story includes the **rising action**. The central conflict is introduced in the rising action. Is the second bracketed passage still part of the story's rising action? Explain.

_____

_____

_____

_____

_____

Reading Check

What noises does Jason hear inside Grimes Buildings? Underline the text that tells you.

the overtopping walls would come together and squeeze it out of existence.

Walking as softly as an Indian, Jason passed through it, slid by a file of dustbins,[5] and found the foot of the fire escape. Iron treads rose into the mist, like an illustration to a Gothic[6] fairy tale.

He began to climb.

When he had mounted to the ninth story he paused for breath. It was a lonely place. The lighting consisted of a dim bulb at the foot of every flight. A well of gloom sank beneath him. The cold fingers of the wind nagged and fluttered at the tails of his jacket, and he pulled the string of the fire door and edged inside.

Grimes Buildings were triangular, with the street forming the base of the triangle, and the fire escape the point. Jason could see two long passages coming toward him, meeting at an acute angle where he stood. He started down the left-hand one, tiptoeing in the cavelike silence. Nowhere was there any sound, except for the faraway drip of a tap. No night watchman would stay in the building; none was needed. Burglars gave the place a wide berth.

Jason opened a door at random; then another. Offices lay everywhere about him, empty and forbidding. Some held lipstick-stained tissues, spilled powder, and orange peels; others were still foggy with cigarette smoke. Here was a Director's suite of rooms—a desk like half an acre of frozen lake, inch-thick carpet, roses, and the smell of cigars. Here was a conference room with scattered squares of doodled blotting paper. All equally empty.

He was not sure when he first began to notice the bell. Telephone, he thought at first, and then he remembered that all the outside lines were disconnected at five. And this bell, anyway, had not the regularity of a telephone's double ring: there was a tinkle, and then silence; a long ring, and then silence; a whole volley of rings together, and then silence.

Jason stood listening, and fear knocked against his ribs and shortened his breath. He knew that he must move or be paralyzed by it. He ran up a flight of stairs and found himself with two more endless green corridors beckoning him like a pair of dividers.

Another sound now: a waft of ice-thin notes, riffling up an arpeggio[7] like a flurry of snowflakes. Far away down the passage it echoed. Jason ran in pursuit, but as he ran the music receded. He circled the building, but it always outdistanced him, and when he came back to the stairs he heard it fading away to the story below.

---

5. **dustbins** British term for garbage cans.

6. **Gothic** *adj.* mysterious.

7. **arpeggio** (ahr PEJ yoh) *n.* notes of a chord played one after the other instead of together.

He hesitated, and as he did so heard again the bell; the bicycle bell. It was approaching him fast, bearing down on him, urgent, menacing. He could hear the pedals, almost see the shimmer of an invisible wheel. Absurdly, he was reminded of the insistent clamor of an ice-cream vendor, summoning children on a <u>sultry</u> Sunday afternoon.

There was a little fireman's <u>alcove</u> beside him, with buckets and pumps. He hurled himself into it. The bell stopped beside him, and then there was a moment while his heart tried to shake itself loose in his chest. He was looking into two eyes carved out of expressionless air; he was held by two hands knotted together out of the width of dark.

"Daisy, Daisy?" came the whisper. "Is that you, Daisy? Have you come to give me your answer?"

Jason tried to speak, but no words came.

"It's not Daisy! Who are you?" The sibilants[8] were full of threat. "You can't stay here. This is private property."

He was thrust along the corridor. It was like being pushed by a whirlwind—the fire door opened ahead of him without a touch, and he was on the openwork platform, clutching the slender railing. Still the hands would not let him go.

"How about it?" the whisper mocked him. "How about jumping? It's an easy death compared with some."

Jason looked down into the smoky <u>void</u>. The darkness nodded to him like a familiar.[9]

"You wouldn't be much loss, would you? What have you got to live for?"

Miss Golden, Jason thought. She would miss me. And the syllables Berenice Golden lingered in the air like a chime. Drawing on some unknown deposit of courage he shook himself loose from the holding hands and ran down the fire escape without looking back.

Next morning when Miss Golden, crisp, fragrant, and punctual, shut the door of Room 492 behind her, she stopped short of the hat-pegs with a horrified gasp.

"Mr. Ashgrove, your hair!"

"It makes me look more distinguished, don't you think?" he said.

8. **sibilants** (SIB uh luhnts) *n.* hissing sounds.

9. **a familiar** a spirit.

Vocabulary Development

sultry (SUL tree) *adj.* referring to weather that is hot with air that feels wet

alcove (AL kohv) *n.* a small place in a wall of a room that is built farther back than the rest of the wall

void (voyd) *n.* an empty space where nothing exists

TAKE NOTES

Reading Skill

Revisit the **prediction** you made about what would happen to Jason in Grimes Buildings. Was your prediction correct? How did **reading on** help you **verify your prediction**?

_____

_____

_____

_____

Stop to Reflect

How would you feel if you met a ghost?

_____

_____

_____

Literary Analysis

Read the bracketed passage. Circle the details that explain why Jason had a sudden burst of courage. What possible event or relationship does this information **foreshadow**?

_____

_____

_____

Sonata for Harp and Bicycle **33**

Read the first bracketed passage. How does this new information increase the **suspense** of the narrative?

_____

_____

_____

Reading Skill

Read the second bracketed passage. What do you **predict** Jason will do next?

_____

_____

_____

Reading Check

What happened to Jason's hair? Circle the text that tells you.

_____

_____

It had indeed this effect, for his impeccable dark cut had turned to a stippled silver which might have been envied by many a diplomat.

"How did it happen? You've not—" her voice sank to a whisper—"*you've not been in Grimes Buildings after dark?*"

"Miss Golden—Berenice," he said earnestly. "Who was Daisy? Plainly you know. Tell me the story."

"Did you see him?" she asked faintly.

"Him?"

"William Heron—The Wailing Watchman. Oh," she exclaimed in terror, "I can see you did. Then you are doomed—doomed!"

"If I'm doomed," said Jason, "let's have coffee, and you tell me the story quickly."

"It all happened over fifty years ago," said Berenice, as she spooned out coffee powder with distracted extravagance. "Heron was the night watchman in this building, patrolling the corridors from dusk to dawn every night on his bicycle. He fell in love with a Miss Bell who taught the harp. She rented a room—this room—and gave lessons in it. She began to reciprocate his love, and they used to share a picnic supper every night at eleven, and she'd stay on a while to keep him company. It was an idyll,[10] among the fire buckets and the furnace pipes.

"On Halloween he had summoned up the courage to propose to her. The day before he had told her he was going to ask her a very important question, and he came to the Buildings with a huge bunch of roses and a bottle of wine. But Miss Bell never turned up.

"The explanation was simple. Miss Bell, of course, had been losing a lot of sleep through her nocturnal romance, and so she used to take a nap in her music room between seven and ten, to save going home. In order to make sure that she would wake up, she persuaded her father, a distant relative of Graham Bell,[11] to attach an alarm-waking fixture to her telephone which called her every night at ten. She was too modest and shy to let Heron know that she spent those hours in the building, and to give him the pleasure of waking her himself.

Vocabulary Development

impeccable (im PEK uh buhl) *adj.* completely perfect

extravagance (ik STRAV uh guhnts) *n.* a going beyond reasonable or proper limits in conduct or speech

reciprocate (ri SIP ruh kayt) *v.* return

10. **idyll** (YD l) *n.* a romantic scene, usually in the country.

11. **Graham Bell** Alexander Graham Bell (1847–1922), the inventor of the telephone.

"Alas! On this important evening the line failed, and she never woke up. The telephone was in its infancy at that time, you must remember.

"Heron waited and waited. At last, mad with grief and jealousy, having called her home and discovered that she was not there, he concluded that she had betrayed him; he ran to the fire escape, and cast himself off it, holding the roses and the bottle of wine.

"Daisy did not long survive him but pined away soon after. Since that day their ghosts have haunted Grimes Buildings, he vainly patrolling the corridors on his bicycle, she playing her harp in the room she rented. But they never meet. And anyone who meets the ghost of William Heron will himself, within five days, leap down from the same fatal fire escape."

She gazed at him with tragic eyes.

"In that case we must lose no time," said Jason, and he enveloped her in an embrace as prompt as it was ardent. Looking down at the <u>gossamer</u> hair sprayed across his pin-stripe, he added, "Just the same it is a <u>preposterous</u> situation. Firstly, I have no intention of jumping off the fire escape—" here, however, he repressed a shudder as he remembered the cold, clutching hands of the evening before—"and secondly, I find it quite nonsensical that those two inefficient ghosts have spent fifty years in this building without coming across each other. We must remedy the matter, Berenice. We must not begrudge our new-found happiness to others."

He gave her another kiss so impassioned that the electric typewriter against which they were leaning began chattering to itself in a frenzy of enthusiasm.

"This very evening," he went on, looking at his watch, "we will put matters right for that unhappy couple and then, if I really have only five more days to live, which I don't for one moment believe, we will proceed to spend them together, my <u>bewitching</u> Berenice, in the most advantageous manner possible."

She nodded, spellbound.

"Can you work a switchboard?" he added. She nodded again. "My love, you are perfection itself. Meet me in the switchboard room then, at ten this evening. I would say, have dinner with me, but I shall need to make one or two

Vocabulary Development

gossamer (GAHS uh mer) *adj.* light and thin

preposterous (pri PAHS ter uhs) *adj.* completely unreasonable or silly

bewitching (bi WICH ing) *adj.* referring to someone or something so interesting or attractive that you cannot think clearly

Stop to Reflect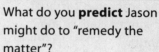

How do you think Daisy felt when she heard what Heron did?

_____

_____

_____

Reading Skill

What do you **predict** Jason might do to "remedy the matter"?

_____

_____

_____

_____

Reading Check

What happens to anyone who meets Heron's ghost? Circle the text that tells you.

Reading Skill

What do you **predict** Jason will
do with the two bunches of
roses? Why?

_____

_____

_____

Literary Analysis 🔍

Read the bracketed passage.
What might this information
foreshadow?

_____

_____

_____

Stop to Reflect

Jason is trying to solve the
mystery of Grimes Buildings. Do
you think it is worth the risk?
Why or why not?

_____

_____

_____

_____

purchases and see an old R.A.F.[12] friend. You will be safe
from Heron's curse in the switchboard room if he always
keeps to the corridors."

"I would rather meet him and die with you," she
murmured.

"My angel, I hope that won't be necessary. Now," he
said, sighing, "I suppose we should get down to our day's
work."

Strangely enough the copy they wrote that day,
although <u>engendered</u> from such agitated minds, sold more
packets of Oat Crisps than any other advertising matter
before or since.

That evening when Jason entered Grimes Buildings
he was carrying two bottles of wine, two bunches of red
roses, and a large canvas-covered bundle. Miss Golden,
who had concealed herself in the switchboard room before
the offices closed for the night, eyed these things with
surprise.

"Now," said Jason, after he had greeted her, "I want you
first to ring our own extension."

"No one will reply, surely?"

"I think she will reply."

Sure enough, when Berenice rang Extension 170 a
faint, sleepy voice, distant and yet clear, whispered,
"Hullo?"

"Is that Miss Bell?"

"Yes."

Berenice went a little pale. Her eyes sought Jason's
and, prompted by him, she said formally, "Switchboard
here, Miss Bell. Your ten o'clock call."

"Thank you," the faint voice said. There was a click and
the line went blank.

"Excellent," Jason remarked. He unfastened his
package and slipped its straps over his shoulders.
"Now plug into the intercom."

Berenice did so, and then said, loudly and clearly,
"Attention. Night watchman on duty, please. Night
watchman on duty. You have an urgent summons to
Room 492. You have an urgent summons to Room 492."
The intercom echoed and <u>reverberated</u> through the empty
corridors, then coughed itself to silence.

"Now we must run. You take the roses, sweetheart, and
I'll carry the bottles."

Vocabulary Development

engendered (in JEN derd) *v.* caused; brought about
reverberated (ri VER buh ray tid) *v.* caused a sound to be heard over and over
again

---

12. **R.A.F.** Royal Air Force.

Together they raced up eight flights of stairs and along the passages to Room 492. As they neared the door a burst of music met them—harp music swelling out, sweet and triumphant. Jason took a bunch of roses from Berenice, opened the door a little way, and gently deposited them, with a bottle, inside the door. As he closed it again Berenice said breathlessly, "Did you see anyone?"

"No," he said. "The room was too full of music." She saw that his eyes were shining.

They stood hand in hand, reluctant to move away, waiting for they hardly knew what. Suddenly the door opened again. Neither Berenice nor Jason, afterward, would speak of what they saw but each was left with a memory, bright as the picture on a Salvador Dali[13] calendar, of a bicycle bearing on its saddle a harp, a bottle of wine, and a bouquet of red roses, sweeping <u>improbably</u> down the corridor and far, far away.

"We can go now," Jason said.

He led Berenice to the fire door, tucking the bottle of Médoc in his jacket pocket. A black wind from the north whistled beneath them as they stood on the openwork platform, looking down.

"We don't want our evening to be spoiled by the thought of a curse hanging over us," he said, "so this is the practical thing to do. Hang onto the roses." And holding his love firmly, Jason pulled the rip cord of his R.A.F. friend's parachute and leaped off the fire escape.

A bridal shower of rose petals adorned the descent of Miss Golden, who was possibly the only girl to be kissed in midair in the district of Clerkenwell at ten minutes to midnight on Halloween.

> Reader's Response: Which parts of this story did you like? Which parts did you dislike? Would you change any elements of the plot?
>
> _____
>
> _____
>
> _____
>
> _____

TAKE NOTES

Literary Analysis

The **resolution** occurs when the conflict ends and loose ends are tied up. What is the resolution of the story?

_____

_____

_____

_____

Reading Skill

Do the events at the end of the story **verify your predictions**? Why or why not?

_____

_____

_____

_____

Reading Check

Were Jason and Berenice successful? Underline the text that supports your answer.

© Pearson Education

Vocabulary Development

improbably (im PRAHB uh blee) *adv.* in a slightly strange or surprising way

13. **Salvador Dali** (SAL vuh dawr DAH lee) modern artist (1904–1989) famous for his unusual paintings.

Sonata for Harp and Bicycle

1. **Infer:** Who is more worried about the curse—Jason or Miss Golden? Explain.

_____

_____

_____

2. **Generalize:** What lesson does William Heron's death teach about the danger of making rash decisions?

_____

_____

3. **Literary Analysis:** Use this chart to identify two key events in the **rising action**, one event in the **falling action**, and the event that marks the **climax**.

Climax: _____

Rising Action

Falling Action

Exposition: _____

Resolution: _____

4. **Reading Skill:** What **prediction** did you make when Jason entered Grimes Buildings and heard a bicycle bell?

_____

_____

Writing: Critique

Write a **critique** about the ending of "Sonata for Harp and Bicycle."

- Think about a story with an ending you liked. Why was the ending good? Write the title of the story and the reason you liked the ending.

_____

_____

- Now, think of a story ending you disliked. Why was the ending disappointing? Write the title of the story and the reason you did not like the ending.

_____

_____

- Think about the ending of "Sonata for Harp and Bicycle." Was the ending of this story good? Explain.

_____

_____

Use your notes as you write your critique.

Listening and Speaking: Retelling the Story

Plan your retelling of the story by answering the following questions.

1. From whose point of view will you retell the story? _____

_____

2. What facial expressions and gestures, or body movements, will you use? Describe a facial expression, a gesture, and the specific lines you will be saying as you use the expression and gesture.

Expression: _____

Gesture: _____

What I will be saying: _____

The Cask of Amontillado
Edgar Allan Poe

Summary Montresor feels that his friend Fortunato has insulted him. To get revenge, he tricks Fortunato and lures him to a hidden room. Then, he chains Fortunato to the wall. He bricks up the entrance and leaves Fortunato to die.

Writing About the Big Question

Can truth change? In "The Cask of Amontillado," a wronged man seeks revenge. Complete this sentence:

The truth about a person can be discovered when _____

_____.

Note-taking Guide
Use this chart to record the four most important events of the story.

Event 1	Event 2
Montresor meets Fortunato. He mentions the cask of Amontillado	

Event 3	Event 4

The Cask of Amontillado

1. **Analyze:** Which character traits make Fortunato easy prey for Montresor?

   _____

   _____

2. **Support:** Why does Montresor believe that he has the right to punish Fortunato?

   _____

   _____

3. **Literary Analysis:** Using this chart, identify two key events in the **rising action**, one event in the **falling action**, and the event that marks the **climax**.

   Climax:

   Rising Action   Falling Action

   Exposition: Resolution:

4. **Reading Skill:** What **prediction** did you make after reading about Montresor's and Fortunato's shared interest in wine?

   _____

   _____

Writing: Critique

Write a **critique** evaluating "The Cask of Amontillado" as a suspenseful story. Use the chart below to decide whether you think Poe's story is suspenseful.

- Think about points in the story when you were excited or scared, or wondered what was going to happen next. Fill in the first column with those parts from the story.

- Use the second column to think about why these parts of the story were suspenseful.

Suspenseful Parts of the Story	Reasons These Parts Were Suspenseful
1. when they go down into the caverns	1. scary setting
2. _____	2. _____
3. _____	3. _____
4. _____	4. _____
5. _____	5. _____

Use these notes to help you write your critique.

Listening and Speaking: Retelling the Story

Plan your retelling of the story by answering the following questions.

1. The story will change when it is told from Fortunato's point of view.

   For example: when will the story begin? _____

2. When will Fortunato first suspect what Montresor is up to?

   _____

3. What facial expressions and gestures, or body movements, will you use? Describe a facial expression, a gesture, and the specific lines you will be saying as you use the expression and gesture.

   Expression: _____

   Gesture: _____

   What I will be saying: _____

Expository Texts: Articles

About Expository Texts: Articles

Expository texts explain and provide information. An **article** is a type of expository text that explains or describes a particular subject. Articles usually include these elements:

- Information about a general topic
- Specific details
- Titles and headings that organize details
- An informal tone

Reading Skill

When you **make inferences** and **draw conclusions**, you make logical guesses and reach decisions about what you are reading. When you infer, you develop ideas not directly stated in a text.

As you read the article, notice how information is organized. Use this information and the ideas in the text to make inferences and draw conclusions.

Information or Organization in Text	Inference or Conclusion

Early Texas Cuisine

John Raven

Europeans came to Texas in the early sixteenth century. Some Spanish explorers were shipwrecked and lived with the Native Texans for a while, probably sharing the native diet. The Natives ate mostly what they could hunt and gather. There was some farming going on in the piney woods of East Texas. Native game of the time was American Bison, Whitetail Deer, Antelope and small critters. Wild fruit and nuts rounded out the fare.

It was only when the Spaniards started putting missions in Texas that European-style food began to be imported. The Spaniards had cattle, hogs and sheep. They probably imported corn and other small grains. This was pretty much the menu for about three hundred years.

When the Anglo-Celts started settling in Texas in the early eighteen hundreds, they brought their cattle, hogs, sheep and poultry. There was some wild cattle left over from the Spanish missions, and most of those could be found in deep South Texas. The settlers had to grow most of everything they consumed. Nearly every family had a kitchen garden that provided corn, white potatoes and sweet potatoes. There were a lot more sweet potatoes than white potatoes. Oats was about the only small grain that did well in the Texas climate. Some rye was also raised. Wheat came later.

Things like salt, coffee, sugar and wheat flour had to be imported. A lot of it was brought in from New Orleans and Galveston.

The early Texans ate a lot of corn—fresh corn in season, dried corn in the winter, cornmeal the year around after milling was available.

Lacking any other method of preserving food, drying and salting was used a lot. Salt pork is made by packing fresh pork in salt for several weeks, and then smoking it to impart some flavor. Beef was dried into jerky. Wild game supplemented the diet, mostly deer, turkey, squirrels, rabbits, raccoon, opossum and fowl. Buffalo probably did not figure into the Anglo diet until the middle eighteen hundreds when the frontier moved out to the Llano Estacado.

You can connect the details in these two paragraphs. **Using these ideas along with prior knowledge you may have, what inference can you make about the reliability of the early Texans' food supply?**

Corn Cookery:

This subhead indicates that the author is moving from discussing general cuisine to a specific food—corn. By analyzing this organizational pattern, what complex conclusion can you draw about the importance of corn to early Texan cuisine?

The simplest method of eating corn is just to pull back the husk and take a bite, that is providing it's early in the season and the corn is still tender. Dried corn could be boiled and eaten that way, or it could be ground into meal and made into corn mush or corn cakes or corn bread.

Corn mush is simple food. Just stir some cornmeal into boiling water and cook it down until it thickens, add some butter, sugar or honey and a little milk, and you have a delicious hot breakfast. Omit the butter, sugar and milk and cut back on the water enough to make a thick batter, and you can fry it into Johnny cakes or bake it on a clean garden implement for hoe cakes.

For corn bread, you have to have a leavening agent, like baking powder or baking soda and buttermilk, to make it rise.

The Native Texans learned to soak dried corn in lime water to make hominy which can be ground into *masa,* a type of corn flour, a staple of Tex-Mex cooking.

Cornmeal comes in white or yellow. Either is acceptable. You can find some blue cornmeal in New Mexico and Arizona, and it's really blue. No matter the color, if you can find cornmeal that's been stone ground, it just seems to be better.

The recipes that follow go back quite a few years. As with many old recipes, it is assumed that the cook knows his or her way around a kitchen of the day. They don't exactly waste words with step-by-step directions.

Cornmeal Mush (from 1830)

½ cup Cornmeal
2-¾ cups Water
¾ teaspoon Salt

Sprinkle cornmeal into boiling water, stirring constantly. Add salt and cook for about half an hour. Serve with sugar and cream.

Indian Cornmeal Cake (from 1830)

1-½ cups Yellow Cornmeal
1 teaspoon Salt
½ cup Flour
3 teaspoons Rosewater (Vanilla)
1-⅔ cups Sugar
1 teaspoon Cinnamon
1 cup Butter
8 Eggs

Mix the sugar, butter and eggs. Mix the cornmeal and salt together, and combine with the sugar, butter and egg mixture. Add vanilla and cinnamon and mix well. Pour into a floured cake pan and bake in a moderate oven.

THE BIG ?

Can truth change?
How did immigration affect the essence of Texan cuisine?

Thinking About the Article

1. Where did early Texans get most of their food?

   _____

2. Why do the recipes not include detailed, step-by-step instructions?

   _____

(TALK)(ABOUT IT) **Reading Skill**

3. What inference can you make about why early Texans may have needed to preserve food through drying and salting? Explain your response.

   _____

4. You might draw the conclusion that early Texans did not eat much sugar or salt. What detail in the text might lead you to draw this conclusion?

   _____

5. The last section of the article is titled "Corn Cookery." Consider this subheading. What inference can you make about the importance of corn to early Texan cooking? Explain your response.

   _____

WRITE ABOUT IT > **Timed Writing: Essay (30 minutes)**

Write an essay about two main ingredients used in early Texan cuisine. Explain the reasons each ingredient was a big part of the early settlers' diet.

   To get started, review the article. Make a list of the foods mentioned as being typical of an early Texan's diet.

   _____

Choose the two foods that the article gives the most information about and use these as the focus of your essay.

from A White House Diary • My English

Literary Analysis

Voice is the way a writer sounds on the page. For example, the writer's voice in a work can be *smooth and sophisticated, choppy and blunt,* or *breathless and full of wonder.* Voice is a result of several elements:

- *Word Choice*: the kinds of words the writer uses
- *Attitude*: what the writer thinks or feels about his or her subject
- *Sentence Structure*: the arrangement of words in sentences

In **autobiographical writing**, the author tells all or part of his or her own life story. The details included show what the writer notices, thinks, and feels about events. The voice of autobiographical writing usually reflects the writer's personality and way of speaking.

Reading Skill

An **author's purpose** is his or her main reason for writing. An author writes for a general purpose, such as to inform, to entertain, or to persuade. He or she also writes for a specific purpose, such as to expose a particular problem in society. Before you read, **preview to look for an author's purpose**.

- Notice information or ideas conveyed in the title.
- Look for any organizing features, such as subheads.
- Identify the subject of photos, illustrations, or diagrams.

As you preview, use this chart to jot down ideas about the author's specific purpose. Later, as you read the full text, confirm whether your ideas are correct.

Text Feature	Insight About Purpose

from A White House Diary
Lady Bird Johnson

Summary Lady Bird Johnson remembers the day that President John F. Kennedy was shot. She reports the events of the day. She also talks about Mrs. Kennedy's courage and strength.

 Writing About the Big Question

Can truth change? In this passage from A White House Diary, Lady Bird Johnson recalls details about the day President John F. Kennedy was assassinated. Complete this sentence:

Abrupt changes in circumstances can _____.

Note-taking Guide

Fill in the diagram below to recall the range of feelings Mrs. Johnson experiences as the events of the day unfold.

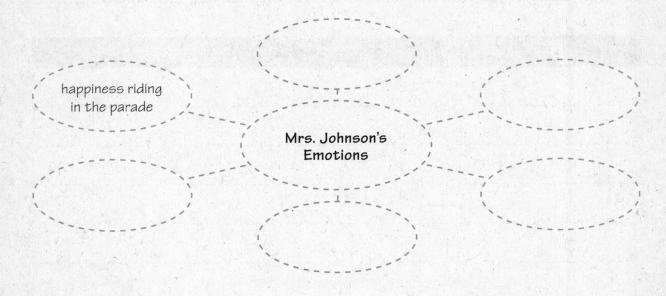

happiness riding in the parade

Mrs. Johnson's Emotions

from A White House Diary
Lady Bird Johnson

DALLAS, FRIDAY, NOVEMBER 22, 1963

It all began so beautifully. After a drizzle in the morning, the sun came out bright and clear. We were driving into Dallas. In the lead car were President and Mrs. Kennedy, John and Nellie Connally,[1] a Secret Service[2] car full of men, and then our car with Lyndon and me and Senator Ralph Yarborough.

The streets were lined with people—lots and lots of people—the children all smiling, placards, confetti, people waving from windows. One last happy moment I had was looking up and seeing Mary Griffith leaning out of a window waving at me. (Mary for many years had been in charge of altering the clothes which I purchased at Neiman-Marcus.)

Then, almost at the edge of town, on our way to the Trade Mart for the Presidential luncheon, we were rounding a curve, going down a hill, and suddenly there was a sharp, loud report. It sounded like a shot. The sound seemed to me to come from a building on the right above my shoulder. A moment passed, and then two more shots rang out in rapid succession. There had been such a gala air about the day that I thought the noise must come from firecrackers—part of the celebration. Then the Secret Service men were suddenly down in the lead car. Over the car radio system, I heard "Let's get out of here!" and our Secret Service man, Rufus Youngblood, vaulted over the front seat on top of Lyndon, threw him to the floor, and said, "Get down."

Senator Yarborough and I ducked our heads. The car accelerated terrifically—faster and faster. Then, suddenly, the brakes were put on so hard that I wondered if we were going to make it as we wheeled left and went around the corner. We pulled up to a building. I looked up and saw a sign, "HOSPITAL." Only then did I believe that this might be what it was. Senator Yarborough kept saying in an excited voice, "Have they shot the President? Have they shot the President?" I said something like, "No, it can't be."

Vocabulary Development

gala (GAL uh) *adj.* celebratory; festive

© Pearson Education

1. **John and Nellie Connally** John Connally, then Governor of Texas, and his wife, Nellie.
2. **Secret Service** division of the U.S. Treasury Department, responsible for protecting the President.

Activate Prior Knowledge

Why do some people keep diaries? Why might a diary be a good way for a person to deal with a tragic event?

_____

_____

_____

Reading Skill

Before you read, **preview to look for an author's purpose**, or main reason for writing. Preview the subhead. What does it suggest to you about the author's purpose in this part of her diary?

_____

_____

Literary Analysis 🔍

Attitude is the way that a writer thinks or feels about a subject. Read the bracketed passage. What do the details about firecrackers tell you about the writer's attitude toward the events she describes?

_____

_____

_____

Reading Check ✏️

Where are the Johnsons taken after shots are fired? Underline the word that tells you.

Voice is the way a writer sounds on the page. Read the first bracketed passage. How does the first sentence help you "hear" Mrs. Johnson's confusion and fear? Explain.

_____

_____

_____

Reading Skill

In the third paragraph, the author includes the names of several individuals. What might be the **author's purpose** for including these names?

_____

_____

_____

Literary Analysis ✎

Read the second bracketed passage. Underline the details about Lyndon Johnson that the author emphasizes. Why would Lady Bird Johnson notice these details more than someone else might?

_____

_____

_____

As we ground to a halt—we were still the third car—Secret Service men began to pull, lead, guide, and hustle us out. I cast one last look over my shoulder and saw in the President's car a bundle of pink, just like a <u>drift</u> of blossoms, lying on the back seat. It was Mrs. Kennedy lying over the President's body.

The Secret Service men rushed us to the right, then to the left, and then onward into a quiet room in the hospital—a very small room. It was lined with white sheets, I believe.

People came and went—Kenny O'Donnell, the President's top aide, Congressman Homer Thornberry, Congressman Jack Brooks. Always there was Rufe right there and other Secret Service agents—Emory Roberts, Jerry Kivett, Lem Johns, and Woody Taylor. People spoke of how widespread this might be. There was talk about where we would go—to the plane, to our house, back to Washington.

Through it all Lyndon was remarkably calm and quiet. He suggested that the Presidential plane ought to be moved to another part of the field. He spoke of going back out to the plane in unmarked black cars. Every face that came in, you searched for the answer. I think the face I kept seeing the answer on was the face of Kenny O'Donnell, who loved President Kennedy so much.

It was Lyndon who spoke of it first, although I knew I would not leave without doing it. He said, "You had better try to see Jackie and Nellie." We didn't know what had happened to John.

I asked the Secret Service if I could be taken to them. They began to lead me up one corridor and down another. Suddenly I found myself face to face with Jackie in a small hallway. I believe it was right outside the operating room. You always think of someone like her as being <u>insulated</u>, protected. She was quite alone. I don't think I ever saw anyone so much alone in my life. I went up to her, put my arms around her, and said something to her. I'm sure it was something like "God, help us all," because my feelings for her were too <u>tumultuous</u> to put into words.

And then I went to see Nellie. There it was different, because Nellie and I have gone through so many things together since 1938. I hugged her tight and we both cried and I said, "Nellie, John's going to be all right." And Nellie

Vocabulary Development

drift (drift) _n._ pile

insulated (IN suh layt id) _adj._ covered or protected from hardships

tumultuous (too MUL choo uhs) _adj._ greatly disturbed; in an uproar

said, "Yes, John's going to be all right." Among her many other fine qualities, she is also strong.

I turned and went back to the small white room where Lyndon was. Mac Kilduff, the President's press man on this trip, and Kenny O'Donnell were coming and going. I think it was from Kenny's face that I first knew the truth and from Kenny's voice that I first heard the words "The President is dead." Mr. Kilduff entered and said to Lyndon, "Mr. President."

It was decided that we would go immediately to the airport. Hurried plans were made about how we should get to the cars and who was to ride in which car. Our departure from the hospital and approach to the cars was one of the swiftest walks I have ever made.

We got in. Lyndon told the agents to stop the sirens. We drove along as fast as we could. I looked up at a building and there, already, was a flag at half-mast. I think that was when the enormity of what had happened first struck me.

When we got to the field, we entered *Air Force One*[3] for the first time. There was a TV set on and the commentator was saying, "Lyndon B. Johnson, now President of the United States." The news commentator was saying the President had been shot with a 30-30 rifle. The police had a suspect. They were not sure he was the assassin.

On the plane, all the shades were lowered. We heard that we were going to wait for Mrs. Kennedy and the coffin. There was a telephone call to Washington—I believe to the Attorney General.[4]

It was decided that Lyndon should be sworn in here as quickly as possible, because of national and world <u>implications</u>, and because we did not know how widespread this was as to intended victims. Judge Sarah Hughes, a Federal Judge in Dallas—and I am glad it was she—was called and asked to come in a hurry to administer the oath.

Mrs. Kennedy had arrived by this time, as had the coffin. There, in the very narrow confines of the plane— with Jackie standing by Lyndon, her hair falling in her face but very composed, with me beside him, Judge Hughes in front of him, and a cluster of Secret Service

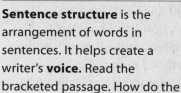

TAKE NOTES

Literary Analysis

Sentence structure is the arrangement of words in sentences. It helps create a writer's **voice.** Read the bracketed passage. How do the choppy sentences make the writer sound?

_____

_____

_____

Reading Skill

What is the **author's purpose** in mentioning the TV news report?

_____

_____

_____

Reading Check ✎

How did Mrs. Johnson first know that the president was dead? Underline the answer to the question.

© Pearson Education

Vocabulary Development

implications (im pli KAY shuhnz) *n.* indirect results

3. **Air Force One** name of the airplane officially assigned to transport the President of the United States.

4. **Attorney General** chief law officer of the nation, head of the U.S. Department of Justice; at the time, the position was held by Robert Kennedy, the President's brother.

Reading Skill

Underline Mrs. Johnson's descriptions of how Mrs. Kennedy looked. What was the **author's purpose** in telling readers about Mrs. Kennedy's clothes?

_____

_____

_____

Literary Analysis

A writer's **attitude** is the way he or she thinks or feels about the subject. Read the bracketed section. How does Mrs. Johnson feel about Mrs. Kennedy?

_____

_____

_____

_____

Reading Check

Mrs. Kennedy tells Mrs. Johnson that she does not want to change her bloody clothes. What reason does Mrs. Kennedy give? Circle the answer in the text.

people, staff, and Congressmen we had known for a long time around him—Lyndon took the oath of office.

It's odd the little things that come to your mind at times of utmost stress, the flashes of deep compassion you feel for people who are really not at the center of the tragedy. I heard a Secret Service man say in the most desolate voice—and I hurt for him: "We never lost a President in the Service." Then, Police Chief Curry of Dallas came on the plane and said, "Mrs. Kennedy, believe me, we did everything we possibly could." That must have been an <u>agonizing</u> moment for him.

We all sat around the plane. The casket was in the corridor. I went in the small private room to see Mrs. Kennedy, and though it was a very hard thing to do, she made it as easy as possible. She said things like, "Oh, Lady Bird, we've liked you two so much. . . . Oh, what if I had not been there. I'm so glad I was there."

I looked at her. Mrs. Kennedy's dress was stained with blood. One leg was almost entirely covered with it and her right glove was caked, it was caked with blood—her husband's blood. Somehow that was one of the most <u>poignant</u> sights—that <u>immaculate</u> woman exquisitely dressed, and caked in blood.

I asked her if I couldn't get someone in to help her change and she said, "Oh, no. Perhaps later I'll ask Mary Gallagher but not right now." And then with almost an element of fierceness—if a person that gentle, that dignified, can be said to have such a quality—she said, "I want them to see what they have done to Jack."

I tried to express how we felt. I said, "Oh, Mrs. Kennedy, you know we never even wanted to be Vice President and now, dear God, it's come to this." I would have done anything to help her, but there was nothing I could do, so rather quickly I left and went back to the main part of the airplane where everyone was seated.

The flight to Washington was silent, each sitting with his own thoughts. One of mine was a recollection of what I had said about Lyndon a long time ago—he's a good man in a tight spot. I remembered one little thing he had said in that hospital room—"Tell the children to get a Secret Service man with them."

Vocabulary Development

agonizing (AG uh nyz ing) *adj.* very difficult
poignant (POYN yuhnt) *adj.* emotionally touching
immaculate (i MAK yuh lit) *adj.* perfectly clean and neat

Finally we got to Washington, with a cluster of people waiting and many bright lights. The casket went off first, then Mrs. Kennedy, and then we followed. The family had come to join her. Lyndon made a very simple, very brief, and, I think, strong statement to the people there. Only about four sentences. We got in helicopters, dropped him off at the White House, and I came home in a car with Liz Carpenter.[5]

> Reader's Response: Lady Bird Johnson uses her diary to reflect on important events. What purpose does reflection serve in your life?
>
> _____
>
> _____
>
> _____
>
> _____
>
> _____
>
> _____

© Pearson Education

5. **Liz Carpenter** Mrs. Johnson's press secretary.

TAKE NOTES

Stop to Reflect

Mrs. Johnson remembers something she once said about her husband. She said he was "good in a tight spot." What does that comment mean?

_____

_____

Why would this be a good quality for Lyndon Johnson to have?

_____

_____

_____

_____

from A White House Diary

1. **Interpret:** Mrs. Johnson offers to get someone to help Mrs. Kennedy change her blood-stained clothes. However, Mrs. Kennedy refuses to change. Mrs. Kennedy replies, "I want them to see what they have done to Jack." What does she mean?

_____

_____

_____

2. **Analyze:** Why do you think Mrs. Johnson reported this detail?

_____

_____

_____

3. **Literary Analysis:** Use the chart shown to write examples of Johnson's **word choice**, **attitude**, and **sentence structure**.

VOICE		
Word Choice	Attitude	Sentence Structure

4. **Reading Skill:** What general purpose do you think Mrs. Johnson had in writing this part of *A White House Diary*? Explain.

_____

_____

_____

Writing: Essay or Poem

Write about an event that is important to you. First, choose the format you will use—essay or poem. Then, answer the following questions. Use your answers to write your text.

- What words and images, or pictures, does the event make you think of?

  _____

  _____

- Has this event always been important to you? Why or why not?

  _____

  _____

- Has this event changed how you see the world? Explain.

  _____

  _____

Research and Technology: Multimedia Presentation

Before you begin writing your script, jot down some ideas for your multimedia presentation.

Topic: _____

Purpose: _____

Ideas for introduction: _____

_____

Main Points: _____

_____

_____

Visual elements and where to put them: _____

_____

My English
Julia Alvarez

Summary As a young child, Julia Alvarez lived in the Dominican Republic. She began to study English at school. Then, her family moved to New York. There a teacher sparked Alvarez's love for the English language.

 Writing About the Big Question

Can truth change? In "My English," Alvarez describes how her view of her place in the world changes as she learns English. Complete this sentence:

Learning a language can affect our perspective because _____

_____.

Note-taking Guide

Use this chart to list quotations from the story that show what Alvarez remembers about speaking different languages.

Language	Positive Memory	Negative Memory
Spanish	"This campuno was my true mother tongue...."	
Spanglish		
English		"What I first recognized was not a language, but a tone of voice, serious, urgent, something important and top secret being said...."

My English

1. **Compare and Contrast:** Think about the method that Sister Maria Generosa used to teach English. How does this method differ from the way Alvarez was taught at the Carol Morgan School?

   _____

   _____

2. **Infer:** When Alvarez's parents spoke English at home, they did so to keep secrets. Why does Alvarez say that English was the "sound of being left out"?

   _____

   _____

3. **Literary Analysis: Voice** is the way a writer sounds on the page. An author's voice is the result of word choice, attitude, and sentence structure. Use the chart below to find examples of these elements that make up voice.

VOICE		
Word Choice	Attitude	Sentence Structure

4. **Reading Skill:** What general **purpose** do you think Alvarez had in writing this essay? Explain.

   _____

   _____

Writing: Essay or Poem

Write about an event that is important to you. First, choose the format you will use—essay or poem. Then, answer the following questions. Use your answers to write your text.

- What words and images, or pictures, does the event make you think of?

  _____

  _____

- Has this event always been important to you? Why or why not?

  _____

  _____

- Has this event changed how you see the world? Explain.

  _____

  _____

Research and Technology: Multimedia Presentation

Before you begin writing your script, jot down some ideas for your multimedia presentation.

Topic: _____

Purpose: _____

Ideas for introduction: _____

_____

Main Points: _____

_____

_____

Visual elements and where to put them: _____

_____

The Secret Life of Walter Mitty • Uncle Marcos

Literary Analysis

A **character** is a person or an animal who takes part in the action of a literary work.

- A **round character** is complex, showing many different qualities and revealing faults as well as virtues. A **flat character** is one-dimensional, showing a single trait.

- A **dynamic character** develops, changes, and learns something during the course of a story—unlike a **static character**, who remains the same.

The main character of a story tends to be a round character and usually a dynamic one. The main character's development and growth are often central to a story's plot and theme. As you read, consider the traits that make characters seem round or flat, dynamic or static.

Reading Skill

An **author's purpose** is his or her main reason for writing. In fiction, the specific purpose is often conveyed through the story's theme, message, or insight. Pause periodically while reading and **reflect** on the story's details and events to determine the author's purpose. Ask questions. Organize your thoughts to understand what the author's purpose might be. Use this chart.

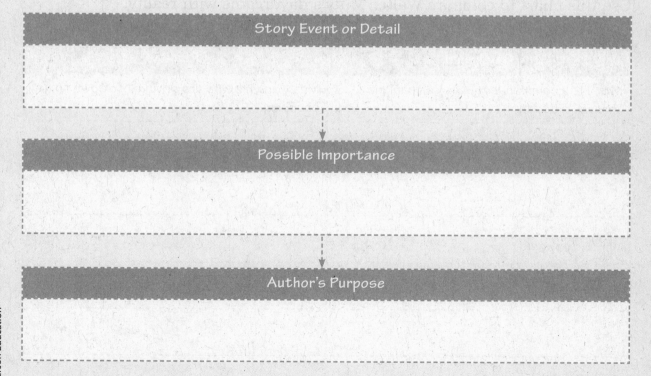

Story Event or Detail

↓

Possible Importance

↓

Author's Purpose

The Secret Life of Walter Mitty
James Thurber

Summary Walter Mitty is an ordinary man who escapes his boring life and nagging wife by daydreaming. Mitty's daydreams are caused by everyday events. These events happen during a shopping trip with his wife. Each time Mitty drifts off, real life pulls him back.

 Writing About the Big Question

Can truth change? In "The Secret Life of Walter Mitty," Mitty lives two lives: the life dominated by his wife and the life of his imagination. Complete this sentence:

Compared to our everyday life, the life of our imagination is

_____

Note-taking Guide
Use this chart to compare Walter Mitty's daydreams with reality.

Daydream	Reality
Mitty is a commander guiding a seaplane through a storm.	Mitty and his wife are driving into town to go shopping.

The Secret Life of Walter Mitty
James Thurber

"We're going through!" The Commander's voice was like thin ice breaking. He wore his full-dress uniform, with the heavily braided white cap pulled down <u>rakishly</u> over one cold gray eye. "We can't make it, sir. It's spoiling for a hurricane, if you ask me." "I'm not asking you, Lieutenant Berg," said the Commander. "Throw on the power lights! Rev her up to 8,500! We're going through!" The pounding of the cylinders increased: ta-pocketa-pocketa-pocketa-pocketa-pocketa. The Commander stared at the ice forming on the pilot window. He walked over and twisted a row of complicated dials. "Switch on No. 8 <u>auxiliary</u>!" he shouted. "Switch on No. 8 auxiliary!" repeated Lieutenant Berg. "Full strength in No. 3 turret!" shouted the Commander. "Full strength in No. 3 turret!" The crew, bending to their various tasks in the huge, hurtling eight-engined Navy hydroplane,[1] looked at each other and grinned. "The Old Man'll get us through," they said to one another. "The Old Man ain't afraid of Hell!" . . .

"Not so fast! You're driving too fast!" said Mrs. Mitty. "What are you driving so fast for?"

"Hmm?" said Walter Mitty. He looked at his wife, in the seat beside him, with shocked astonishment. She seemed <u>grossly</u> unfamiliar, like a strange woman who had yelled at him in a crowd. "You were up to fifty-five," she said. "You know I don't like to go more than forty. You were up to fifty-five." Walter Mitty drove on toward Waterbury in silence, the roaring of the SN202 through the worst storm in twenty years of Navy flying fading in the remote, intimate airways of his mind. "You're tensed up again," said Mrs. Mitty. "It's one of your days. I wish you'd let Dr. Renshaw look you over."

Walter Mitty stopped the car in front of the building where his wife went to have her hair done. "Remember to get those overshoes while I'm having my hair done," she said. "I don't need overshoes," said Mitty. She put her

Vocabulary Development

rakishly (RAYK ish lee) *adv.* in a happy, careless way

auxiliary (awg ZIL uh ree) *n.* something extra to be used in case of an emergency

grossly (GROHS lee) *adv.* greatly and unpleasantly

1. **hydroplane** (HY druh playn) *n.* seaplane.

Activate Prior Knowledge

When you find yourself daydreaming, what role do you like to imagine for yourself?

_____

_____

_____

Literary Analysis

A **character** is a person or an animal who takes part in the action of a literary work. A **round character** shows many different qualities. A **flat character** shows a single trait. Read the first bracketed passage. Is the Commander a round or a flat character? Underline the details that support your answer.

_____

_____

_____

Reading Skill

It is often helpful to **reflect** on a story's details to determine the **author's purpose**, or main reason for writing. In the second bracketed passage, what does the phrase "intimate airways of his mind" suggest about the author's purpose in writing the story?

_____

_____

_____

Literary Analysis 🔍

At this point in the story, would you describe Mrs. Mitty as a **round character** or a **flat character**? Explain.

_____

_____

_____

_____

Reading Skill 📖

The surgeons all praise Mitty and want his help. What is the **author's purpose** in adding these details?

_____

_____

_____

_____

Stop to Reflect 📖

Mitty uses a fountain pen to fix the machine in his daydream. What does this heroic quality say about Mitty?

_____

_____

_____

_____

mirror back into her bag. "We've been all through that," she said, getting out of the car. "You're not a young man any longer." He raced the engine a little. "Why don't you wear your gloves? Have you lost your gloves?" Walter Mitty reached in a pocket and brought out the gloves. He put them on, but after she had turned and gone into the building and he had driven on to a red light, he took them off again. "Pick it up, brother!" snapped a cop as the light changed, and Mitty hastily pulled on his gloves and lurched ahead. He drove around the streets aimlessly for a time, and then he drove past the hospital on his way to the parking lot.

. . . "It's the millionaire banker, Wellington McMillan," said the pretty nurse. "Yes?" said Walter Mitty, removing his gloves slowly. "Who has the case?" "Dr. Renshaw and Dr. Benbow, but there are two specialists here, Dr. Remington from New York and Mr. Pritchard-Mitford from London. He flew over." A door opened down a long, cool corridor and Dr. Renshaw came out. He looked <u>distraught</u> and haggard. "Hello, Mitty," he said. "We're having the devil's own time with McMillan, the millionaire banker and close personal friend of Roosevelt. Obstreosis of the ductal tract.[2] Tertiary. Wish you'd take a look at him." "Glad to," said Mitty.

In the operating room there were whispered introductions: "Dr. Remington, Dr. Mitty. Mr. Pritchard-Mitford, Dr. Mitty." "I've read your book on streptothricosis," said Pritchard-Mitford, shaking hands. "A brilliant performance, sir." "Thank you," said Walter Mitty. "Didn't know you were in the States, Mitty," grumbled Remington. "Coals to Newcastle,[3] bringing Mitford and me up here for tertiary." "You are very kind," said Mitty. A huge, complicated machine, connected to the operating table, with many tubes and wires, began at this moment to go pocketa-pocketa-pocketa. "The new anesthetizer is giving way!" shouted an intern. "There is no one in the East who knows how to fix it!" "Quiet, man!" said Mitty, in a low, cool voice. He sprang to the machine, which was now going pocketa-pocketa-queep-pocketa-queep. He began fingering delicately a row of glistening dials. "Give me a fountain pen!" he snapped. Someone handed him a fountain pen. He pulled a faulty piston out of the machine and inserted the pen in its place. "That will hold for ten minutes," he said. "Get on with the operation." A nurse

Vocabulary Development

distraught (di STRAWT) *adj.* troubled or confused

2. **obstreosis of the ductal tract** Thurber has invented this and other medical terms.

3. **coals to Newcastle** The proverb "bringing coals to Newcastle" means bringing things to a place unnecessarily—Newcastle, England, was a coal center and so did not need coal brought to it.

hurried over and whispered to Renshaw, and Mitty saw the man turn pale. "Coreopsis has set in," said Renshaw nervously. "If you would take over, Mitty?" Mitty looked at him and at the <u>craven</u> figure of Benbow, who drank, and at the grave, uncertain faces of the two great specialists. "If you wish," he said. They slipped a white gown on him; he adjusted a mask and drew on thin gloves; nurses handed him shining . . .

"Back it up, Mac! Look out for that Buick!" Walter Mitty jammed on the brakes. "Wrong lane, Mac," said the parking-lot attendant, looking at Mitty closely. "Gee. Yeh," muttered Mitty. He began cautiously to back out of the lane marked "Exit Only." "Leave her sit there," said the attendant. "I'll put her away." Mitty got out of the car. "Hey, better leave the key." "Oh," said Mitty, handing the man the ignition key. The attendant <u>vaulted</u> into the car, backed it up with <u>insolent</u> skill, and put it where it belonged.

They're so cocky, thought Walter Mitty, walking along Main Street; they think they know everything. Once he had tried to take his chains off, outside New Milford, and he had got them wound around the axles. A man had had to come out in a wrecking car and unwind them, a young, grinning garageman. Since then Mrs. Mitty always made him drive to a garage to have the chains taken off. The next time, he thought, I'll wear my right arm in a sling; they won't grin at me then. I'll have my right arm in a sling and they'll see I couldn't possibly take the chains off myself. He kicked at the slush on the sidewalk. "Overshoes," he said to himself, and he began looking for a shoe store.

When he came out into the street again, with the overshoes in a box under his arm, Walter Mitty began to wonder what the other thing was his wife had told him to get. She had told him, twice, before they set out from their house for Waterbury. In a way he hated these weekly trips to town—he was always getting something wrong. Kleenex, he thought, Squibb's, razor blades? No. Toothpaste, toothbrush, bicarbonate, carborundum, initiative and referendum?[4] He gave it up. But she would

TAKE NOTES

Literary Analysis

Read the first bracketed paragraph. Circle the text that describes the way Mitty feels about garagemen. What might these statements reveal about Mitty's type of **character**?

_____

_____

_____

Reading Skill

Read the second bracketed section. As Mitty comes out of the shoe store, he tries to remember his next task. What **purpose** might the author have for revealing Mitty's thoughts?

_____

_____

_____

_____

Reading Check

What stops Mitty's surgeon daydream? Underline the text that tells you.

Vocabulary Development

craven (CRAY vuhn) *adj.* fearful; cowardly

vaulted (VAWL tid) *v.* jumped

insolent (IN suh luhnt) *adj.* boldly disrespectful

---

4. **carborundum** (cahr buh RUN dum), **initiative** (i NISH uh tiv) and **referendum** Thurber is purposely making a nonsense list; carborundum is a hard substance used for scraping, initiative is a process by which citizens may introduce ideas for laws, and referendum is the process by which citizens may vote on laws.

Stop to Reflect

Why do you think timid Walter Mitty might daydream about being an expert shot on trial for murder?

_____

_____

_____

_____

Reading Skill

What might the **author's purpose** be for including the daydream about the court trial?

_____

_____

_____

Reading Check

What item does Mitty remember that he has to buy? Circle the text that tells you.

remember it. "Where's the what's-its-name?" she would ask. "Don't tell me you forgot the what's-its-name." A newsboy went by shouting something about the Waterbury trial.

. . . "Perhaps this will refresh your memory." The District Attorney suddenly thrust a heavy automatic at the quiet figure on the witness stand. "Have you ever seen this before?" Walter Mitty took the gun and examined it expertly. "This is my Webley-Vickers 50.80," he said calmly. An excited buzz ran around the courtroom. The Judge rapped for order. "You are a crack shot with any sort of firearms, I believe?" said the District Attorney, insinuatingly. "Objection!" shouted Mitty's attorney. "We have shown that the defendant could not have fired the shot. We have shown that he wore his right arm in a sling on the night of the fourteenth of July." Walter Mitty raised his hand briefly and the bickering attorneys were stilled. "With any known make of gun," he said evenly, "I could have killed Gregory Fitzhurst at three hundred *feet with my left hand*." <u>Pandemonium</u> broke loose in the courtroom. A woman's scream rose above the <u>bedlam</u> and suddenly a lovely, dark-haired girl was in Walter Mitty's arms. The District Attorney struck at her savagely. Without rising from his chair, Mitty let the man have it on the point of the chin. "You miserable <u>cur</u>!" . . .

"Puppy biscuit," said Walter Mitty. He stopped walking and the buildings of Waterbury rose up out of the misty courtroom and surrounded him again. A woman who was passing laughed. "He said 'Puppy biscuit,'" she said to her companion. "That man said 'Puppy biscuit' to himself." Walter Mitty hurried on. He went into an A. & P., not the first one he came to but a smaller one farther up the street. "I want some biscuit for small, young dogs," he said to the clerk. "Any special brand, sir?" The greatest pistol shot in the world thought a moment. "It says 'Puppies Bark for It' on the box," said Walter Mitty.

His wife would be through at the hairdresser's in fifteen minutes, Mitty saw in looking at his watch, unless they had trouble drying it; sometimes they had trouble drying it. She didn't like to get to the hotel first; she would want him to be there waiting for her as usual. He found a big leather chair in the lobby, facing a window, and he put the overshoes and the puppy biscuit on the floor beside it. He picked up an old copy of *Liberty* and sank down into

Vocabulary Development

pandemonium (PAN duh MOH nee uhm) *n.* chaos; loud and excited confusion
bedlam (BED luhm) *n.* loud activity
cur (ker) *n.* uncivilized person

the chair. "Can Germany Conquer the World Through the Air?" Walter Mitty looked at the pictures of bombing planes and of ruined streets.

. . . "The cannonading has got the wind up in young Raleigh,[5] sir," said the sergeant. Captain Mitty looked up at him through tousled hair. "Get him to bed," he said wearily. "With the others. I'll fly alone." "But you can't, sir," said the sergeant anxiously. "It takes two men to handle that bomber and the Archies[6] are pounding hell out of the air. Von Richtman's circus[7] is between here and Saulier." "Somebody's got to get that ammunition dump," said Mitty. "I'm going over. Spot of brandy?" He poured a drink for the sergeant and one for himself. War thundered and whined around the dugout and battered at the door. There was a rending of wood and splinters flew through the room. "A bit of a near thing," said Captain Mitty carelessly. "The box barrage is closing in," said the sergeant. "We only live once, Sergeant," said Mitty, with his faint, fleeting smile. "Or do we?" He poured another brandy and tossed it off. "I never see a man could hold his brandy like you, sir," said the sergeant. "Begging your pardon, sir." Captain Mitty stood up and strapped on his huge Webley-Vickers automatic. "It's forty kilometers through hell, sir," said the sergeant. Mitty finished one last brandy. "After all," he said softly, "what isn't?" The pounding of the cannon increased; there was the rat-tat-tatting of machine guns, and from somewhere came the menacing pocketa-pocketa-pocketa of the new flame-throwers. Walter Mitty walked to the door of the dugout humming "Aupres de Ma Blonde."[8] He turned and waved to the sergeant. "Cheerio!" he said. . . .

Something struck his shoulder. "I've been looking all over this hotel for you," said Mrs. Mitty. "Why do you have to hide in this old chair? How did you expect me to find you?" "Things close in," said Walter Mitty vaguely. "What?" Mrs. Mitty said. "Did you get the what's-its-name? The puppy biscuit? What's in that box?" "Overshoes," said Mitty. "Couldn't you have put them on in the store?" "I was thinking," said Walter Mitty. "Does it ever occur to you that I am sometimes thinking?" She looked at him. "I'm going to take your temperature when I get you home," she said.

Reading Skill

Reflect on the daydreams that Mitty has. What are they like? What do his daydreams reveal about the **author's purpose** in telling this story?

_____

_____

_____

Stop to Reflect

Why do you think Mitty always imagines himself as brave and bold characters?

_____

_____

_____

_____

Literary Analysis

Read the bracketed passage. How do Mitty's responses show that he is a **round character**? Explain.

_____

_____

_____

_____

Vocabulary Development

rending (REND ing) *v.* tearing into pieces

5. **has got the wind up in young Raleigh** has made young Raleigh nervous.

6. **Archies** slang term for antiaircraft guns.

7. **Von Richtman's circus** German airplane squadron.

8. **"Auprès de Ma Blonde"** "Next to My Blonde," a popular French song.

Stop to Reflect

In the last daydream, Mitty stands without fear before a firing squad. Why do people imagine doing things in daydreams that they would never do in real life?

_____

_____

_____

_____

_____

They went out through the revolving doors that made a faintly <u>derisive</u> whistling sound when you pushed them. It was two blocks to the parking lot. At the drugstore on the corner she said, "Wait here for me. I forgot something. I won't be a minute." She was more than a minute. Walter Mitty lighted a cigarette. It began to rain, rain with sleet in it. He stood up against the wall of the drugstore, smoking. . . . He put his shoulders back and his heels together. "To hell with the handkerchief," said Walter Mitty scornfully. He took one last drag on his cigarette and snapped it away. Then, with that faint, fleeting smile playing about his lips, he faced the firing squad; erect and motionless, proud and disdainful, Walter Mitty the Undefeated, <u>inscrutable</u> to the last.

Reader's Response: Did you laugh at Walter Mitty's daydreams or did they make you feel sorry for him? Why do you think you felt as you did?

_____

_____

_____

_____

_____

Vocabulary Development

derisive (di RY siv) *adj.* scornful; thinking something unworthy

inscrutable (in SKROO tuh buhl) *adj.* baffling; mysterious

The Secret Life of Walter Mitty

1. **Infer:** In the "real world," Walter Mitty and his wife are on a shopping trip. What deeds is Walter Mitty trying to accomplish in his fantasy life?

   _____

   _____

2. **Compare and Contrast:** How do the tasks of Mitty's daily life compare with those of his fantasy life?

   _____

   _____

3. **Literary Analysis:** Mitty wants to be like the heroes in his daydreams. Find one detail in each of Mitty's daydreams that shows a character trait Mitty wishes that he had. Write the detail and the character trait it reveals in the chart below.

Detail from Daydream	Desired Character Trait
1. Naval commander daydream: "The Old Man'll get us through."	Leadership
2. Surgeon daydream:	
3. Man on trial daydream:	
4. Bomber captain daydream:	
5. Condemned man daydream:	

4. **Reading Skill:** What **purpose** might James Thurber have had for creating the character of Walter Mitty?

   _____

   _____

Writing: Character Profile

Write a **character profile** of one of the personalities in Walter Mitty's daydreams. Use the following questions to create your profile.

- What single impression do you want to get across about the personality?

  _____

  _____

- What details from the story support this impression?

  _____

  _____

- How would you present these details in your profile?

  _____

  _____

Use your notes to write your character profile.

Research and Technology: Learning Log

Keep a **learning log** of the information that you gather about daydreams. Identify and give facts from each source you explore. Enclose quoted information in large quotation marks.

1. **Source:** _____

   What I learned: _____

2. **Source:** _____

   What I learned: _____

3. **Source:** _____

   What I learned: _____

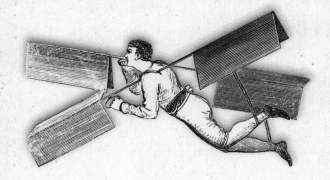

Uncle Marcos
Isabel Allende

Summary A young girl named Clara remembers her Uncle Marcos. He is a world traveler with a bold, courageous personality. Clara feels very close to him. Uncle Marcos lives life on his own terms, even up to his death.

Writing About the Big Question

Can truth change? In "Uncle Marcos," the narrator describes the fantastic escapades of an uncle who's not satisfied with the ordinary. Complete this sentence:

A person who believes strongly in impractical and impossible things, may

_____ .

Note-taking Guide

Use this chart to recall the four most important events in the story.

Clara remembers her Uncle Marcos. → → →

Uncle Marcos

1. **Interpret:** Uncle Marcos disappears. Clara refuses to believe that he is dead. What does Clara's reaction show about her personality and about her relationship with Uncle Marcos? Explain.

_____

_____

2. **Draw Conclusions:** What lessons about life do you think people can learn from the character of Uncle Marcos?

_____

_____

3. **Literary Analysis:** List three of Uncle Marcos's projects or adventures. Then, identify what **character** traits each project or adventure shows about Uncle Marcos. Use this chart.

Project or Adventure	Character Traits
shoots tiger	courage

4. **Reading Skill:** What specific **purpose** might the author have had for creating the character of Uncle Marcos?

_____

_____

_____

Writing: Character Profile

Write a **character profile** of Uncle Marcos. Use the following questions to create your profile.

- What single impression do you want to get across about the character?

  _____

  _____

- What details from the story support this impression?

  _____

  _____

  _____

- How would you present these details in your profile?

  _____

  _____

Use your notes to write your character profile.

Research and Technology: Learning Log

Keep a **learning log** of the information that you gather about the history of human flight. Identify and give facts from each source you explore. Enclose quoted information in large quotation marks.

1. **Source:** _____

   What I learned: _____

2. **Source:** _____

   What I learned: _____

3. **Source:** _____

   What I learned: _____

Procedural Text: Schedule

About Schedules

Schedules help people get where they want to go by listing the arrival and departure times of trains, planes, buses, and other forms of transportation. Schedules are a type of consumer document. Consumer documents help people buy or use a product or service. Other consumer documents include brochures, labels, loan applications, assembly instructions, and warranties.

Reading Skill

Reading a schedule is different from reading other materials. You must **analyze the data, or information, presented in graphical sources** in the schedule to find the information that you need. Graphical sources include charts, graphs, maps, and pictures. To analyze charts and graphs in a schedule, note the text's features. A schedule uses headings to show where to find departure and arrival times. Rows and columns show the arrival and departure times in a way that is easy to scan.

Look at the chart below. It describes other common features of charts and graphs in schedules.

Text Features	Descriptions
Subheads	Boldface words that identify the main idea of each section
Highlighted text	Bold faced, italicized, and uppercase words that emphasize important information
Charts, Graphs, Maps	Graphic organizers that order information in a clear easy-to-understand form
Illustrations and Diagrams	Graphic organizers that show ideas described in the text
Captions	Brief information that describes an illustration, diagram, or other graphic organizer

Pascack Valley Line Train Schedule

NJTRANSIT
The Way To Go.

AVOID THE $5 SURCHARGE
Buy before you board

Features:
- graphical sources
- quantitative data, such as departure and arrival times
- factual data, such as days of the week and locations
- headings and sub-headings

By analyzing this heading, you can determine that the data in this graphical source does not apply to weekends.

Analyze the quantitative and factual data in this graphical source. To go to the World Financial Center, what must you do when the train arrives at Hoboken? Explain.

To Hoboken Monday – Friday

TRAINS Departing from:	AM		Off-peak roundtrip fares are not valid to New York, Secaucus or Hoboken					
	1600	1602	1604	1606	1608	1610	1612	1614
METRO-NORTH STATION **PEARL RIVER**	5 15	5 38	6 04	6 35	6 45	7 05	7 24	7 38
Montvale	5 18	5 41	6 07		6 48	7 08	7 28	7 41
Park Ridge	5 20	5 43	6 09		6 50	7 11	7 30	7 44

Arriving at:								
HOBOKEN	6 14	6 37	7 07	7 18	7 49	8 07	8 19	8 41
via PATH	6 24	6 44	7 14	7 32	8 01	8 19	8 31	8 49
arrive World Trade Center	6 34	6 54	7 25	7 43	8 12	8 30	8 42	9 00
via FERRY	6 30	6 50	7 16	7 32	7 56	8 20	8 28	8 52
arrive World Financial Center	6 40	7 00	7 26	7 42	8 06	8 30	8 38	9 02

FARE OPTIONS saving you time and money

We want to make your travel convenient and economical, so we offer lots of options:

Monthly Passes Unlimited trips within a calendar month; can be purchased beginning the 20th of the month prior and are valid until noon on the first commuting weekday of the following month.

Weekly Passes Unlimited trips from 12:01 a.m. Saturday to 6:00 a.m. on the following Saturday.

10-Trip Tickets Ten one-way trips.

One-Way Tickets One continuous trip.

Off-Peak Roundtrip Tickets (ORT) One-way travel in the direction indicated on the ticket. Not valid for AM peak travel to/via, or PM peak travel from/via New York, Secaucus, Newark or Hoboken.

One-Way Reduced Tickets One-way travel valid for senior citizens, passengers with disabilities, and children.

Student Monthly Passes A good reason to stay in school. Ask a ticket agent for details.

Group Rates Travel cheaper together.

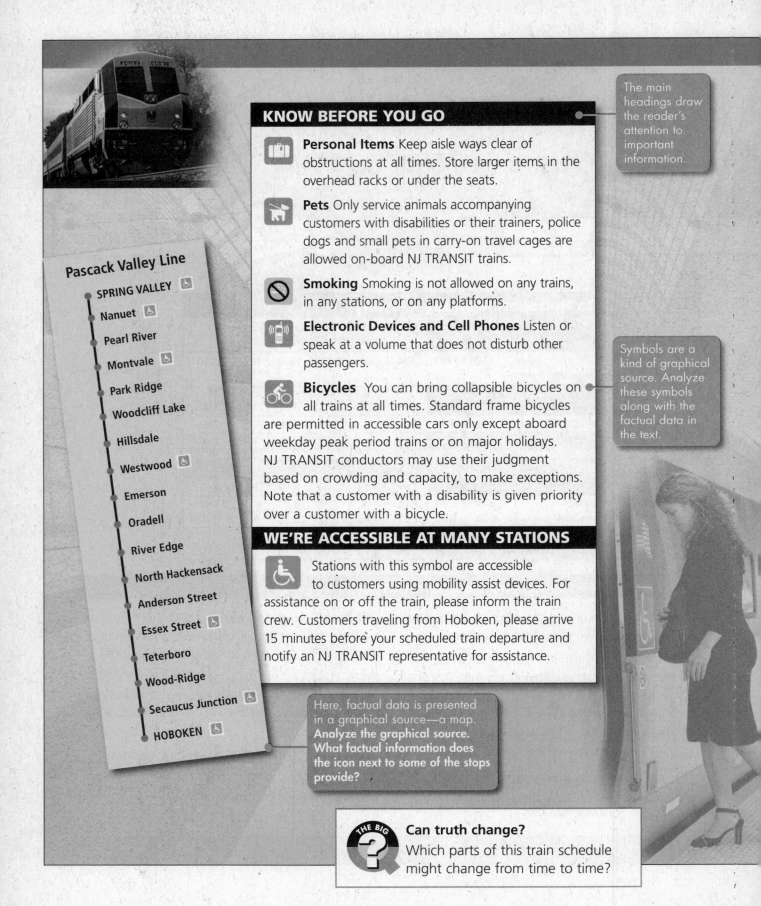

KNOW BEFORE YOU GO

Personal Items Keep aisle ways clear of obstructions at all times. Store larger items in the overhead racks or under the seats.

Pets Only service animals accompanying customers with disabilities or their trainers, police dogs and small pets in carry-on travel cages are allowed on-board NJ TRANSIT trains.

Smoking Smoking is not allowed on any trains, in any stations, or on any platforms.

Electronic Devices and Cell Phones Listen or speak at a volume that does not disturb other passengers.

Bicycles You can bring collapsible bicycles on all trains at all times. Standard frame bicycles are permitted in accessible cars only except aboard weekday peak period trains or on major holidays. NJ TRANSIT conductors may use their judgment based on crowding and capacity, to make exceptions. Note that a customer with a disability is given priority over a customer with a bicycle.

WE'RE ACCESSIBLE AT MANY STATIONS

Stations with this symbol are accessible to customers using mobility assist devices. For assistance on or off the train, please inform the train crew. Customers traveling from Hoboken, please arrive 15 minutes before your scheduled train departure and notify an NJ TRANSIT representative for assistance.

Pascack Valley Line

- SPRING VALLEY
- Nanuet
- Pearl River
- Montvale
- Park Ridge
- Woodcliff Lake
- Hillsdale
- Westwood
- Emerson
- Oradell
- River Edge
- North Hackensack
- Anderson Street
- Essex Street
- Teterboro
- Wood-Ridge
- Secaucus Junction
- HOBOKEN

THE BIG ?
Can truth change?
Which parts of this train schedule might change from time to time?

Thinking About the Schedule

1. In what situation would this schedule be useful?

   _____

   _____

2. Explain how you can learn what time a train will arrive at the Hoboken station.

   _____

   _____

TALK ABOUT IT **Reading Skill**

3. At what time does the 1600 train depart from the Montvale station?

   _____

4. How many train stations would you pass through before you reached Hoboken if you left from the Oradell station?

   _____

WRITE ABOUT IT **Timed Writing: Itinerary (20 minutes)**

An **itinerary** is a written document that includes dates, times, and locations for a trip. Plan an itinerary. Use the Pascack Valley Line Train Schedule to plan three trips to Hoboken from another train station. Use this chart to help you make plans.

Station from which you will leave	Train number	Departure time	Arrival time

Elements of Short Stories

A **short story** is a brief work of fiction. In most short stories, a character faces a problem. The problem is worked out in the plot of the story. Unlike the novel, the short story has to accomplish its purpose in very few words. In a story, all of the elements work closely together. This chart will help you understand the elements of the short story.

Element	Definition	Characteristics
Plot	the series of related events that happen in the story	• The events unfold until they reach the high point of the action, called the climax. • The end of the story is called the resolution. • In **linear plot development,** events are revealed in the order in which they occur. • In **non-linear plot development,** the series of events is interrupted.
Conflict	the problem that the characters try to solve during the plot	• In an **external conflict,** the main character struggles against an outside force. It may be another character, nature, or society in general. • In an **internal conflict,** the main character struggles with forces within—opposing feelings or thoughts.
Characters	the people or animals that take part in the action	Readers get to know **characters** by looking at • their physical appearance • their words and actions • their thoughts and feelings • other characters' reactions to them

The **setting** of a story is the time **(historical setting)** and place **(cultural setting)** of the action.

- **Time:** The time of the setting could be the past, present, or future. It could also be a certain year, season, or hour of the day.

- **Place:** The place could be the social, economic, or cultural environment. It could also be a certain location in a country, town, or community.

A **symbol** is a person, a place, or an object that has a literal meaning. However, a symbol also stands for something larger. It could stand for an idea or emotion. Symbols can be particular to a specific story, or they can be universal. An example of a universal symbol is a heart. Everyone knows that a heart stands for love.

The **theme** of a short story is its main message. It can also be an insight into life. This message can be told to you directly. It could also be implied.

- **Stated Theme:** The author tells you the theme.

- **Implied Theme:** The theme is suggested through the experiences of the characters. It could also be suggested through the actions and setting of the story.

The Jade Peony
Wayson Choy

Summary Eight-year-old Sek-Lung tells the story of his grandmother. Grandmama believes she will die soon. She wants to leave behind a windchime. With Sek-Lung, she searches garbage cans for materials. The rest of the family is embarrassed by this. They want to be modern Canadians, not old-fashioned Chinese. When Grandmama dies, she leaves Sek-Lung the item that she values the most. It is a carved jade peony from her childhood.

Note-taking Guide
Use this chart to help you identify the story elements of "The Jade Peony."

Plot	Conflict	Characters	Setting
Grandmama promises proof that her life has ended well.	Grandmama does not want to go into the hospital.	Sek-Lung, 8-year-old narrator	Vancouver, Canada

The Jade Peony[1]
Wayson Choy

When Grandmama died at 83 our whole household held its breath. She had promised us a sign of her leaving, final proof that her present life had ended well. My parents knew that without any clear sign, our own family fortunes could be altered, threatened. My stepmother looked endlessly into the small cluttered room the ancient lady had occupied. Nothing was touched; nothing changed. My father, thinking that a sign should appear in Grandmama's garden, looked at the frost-killed shoots and cringed: *no, that could not be it.*

My two older teenage brothers and my sister, Liang, age 14, were embarrassed by my parents' behavior. What would all the white people in Vancouver[2] think of us? We were Canadians now, *Chinese-Canadians*, a hyphenated reality that my parents could never accept. So it seemed, for different reasons, we all held our breath waiting for *something.*

I was eight when she died. For days she had resisted going into the hospital . . . *a cold, just a cold* . . . and instead gave constant instruction to my stepmother and sister on the boiling of ginseng roots mixed with bitter extract.[3] At night, between <u>wracking</u> coughs and deadly silences, Grandmama had her back and chest rubbed with heated camphor[4] oil and sipped a bluish decoction[5] of an herb called Peacock's Tail. When all these failed to <u>abate</u> her fever, she began to arrange the details of her will. This she did with my father, confessing finally: "I am too stubborn. The only cure for old age is to die."

My father wept to hear this. I stood beside her bed; she turned to me. Her round face looked darker, and the gentleness of her eyes, the thin, arching eyebrows, seemed weary. I brushed the few strands of gray, brittle hair from her face; she managed to smile at me. Being

Activate Prior Knowledge

How might an older adult, such as a grandparent or neighbor, play an important role in a young person's life?

_____

_____

_____

Short Story ✏

The **setting** of a story is its time and place. Circle the words in the first bracketed paragraph that tell you about the story's setting.

Short Story

Plot is the series of related events that happen in a story. A **conflict** is the problem characters try to solve in the plot. What is the conflict in the second bracketed passage?

_____

_____

_____

There are two kinds of conflicts. A character fights with an outside force in an **external conflict.** A character fights with opposing emotions in his or her self in an **internal conflict.** Is the conflict above external or internal? Explain.

_____

_____

_____

Vocabulary Development

wracking (RAK ing) *adj.* violent
abate (uh BAYT) *v.* help make less painful

---

1. **Jade Peony** (jayd PEE uh nee) jade is a hard, dense gemstone; a peony is a common garden flower, the Chinese variety of which produces large, single blossoms in early summer.

2. **Vancouver** (van KOO ver) large city in the province of British Columbia, Canada.

3. **ginseng** (JIN seng) **roots...bitter extract** ginseng is a Chinese herb known for its healing properties; bitter extract is a liquid made from bitter plants or herbs.

4. **camphor** (KAM fer) *n.* thick substance made from the bark and wood of the camphor tree.

5. **decoction** (dee KAHK shuhn) *n.* substance extracted by boiling.

A **character** is a person or an animal who takes part in the action. One way that readers get to know a character is by looking at his or her physical appearance. Read the bracketed text. Circle details that describe Grandmama's physical appearance.

Stop to Reflect

Why do you think Grandmama keeps the jade pendant in her pocket?

_____

_____

_____

_____

Reading Check

What does the juggler promise Grandmama? Underline the text that tells you.

the youngest, I had spent nearly all my time with her and could not imagine that we would ever be parted. Yet when she spoke, and her voice hesitated, cracked, the somber shadows of her room chilled me. Her wrinkled brow grew wet with fever, and her small body seemed even more diminutive.

"I—I am going to the hospital, Grandson." Her hand reached out for mine. "You know, Little Son, whatever happens I will never leave you." Her palm felt plush and warm, the slender, old fingers boney and firm, so magically strong was her grip that I could not imagine how she could ever part from me. Ever.

Her hands _were_ magical. My most vivid memories are of her hands: long, elegant fingers, with <u>impeccable</u> nails, a skein[6] of fine, barely-seen veins, and wrinkled skin like light pine. Those hands were quick when she taught me, at six, simple tricks of juggling, learnt when she was a village girl in Southern Canton;[7] a troupe of actors had stayed on her father's farm. One of them, "tall and pale as the whiteness of petals," fell in love with her, promising to return. In her last years his image came back like a third being in our two lives. He had been magician, acrobat, juggler, and some of the things he taught her she had absorbed and passed on to me through her stories and games. But above all, without realizing it then, her hands conveyed to me the quality of their love.

Most marvelous for me was the quick-witted skill her hands revealed in making windchimes for our birthdays: windchimes in the likeness of her lost friend's only present to her, made of bits of string and scraps, in the center of which once hung a precious jade peony. This wondrous gift to her broke apart years ago, in China, but Grandmama kept the jade pendant[8] in a tiny red silk envelope, and kept it always in her pocket, until her death.

These were not ordinary, carelessly made chimes, such as those you now find in our Chinatown[9] stores, whose rattling noises drive you mad. But making her special ones caused <u>dissension</u> in our family, and some shame.

Vocabulary Development

diminutive (di MIN yuh tiv) _adj._ small

impeccable (im PEK uh buhl) _adj._ perfect

dissension (di SEN shuhn) _n._ difference of opinion; disagreement

6. **skein** (skayn) n. something that resembles coiled yarn or thread.

7. **Canton** (kan TAHN) major port city in southeastern China.

8. **pendant** (PEN duhnt) _n._ hanging ornament, as on a necklace.

9. **Chinatown** (CHY nuh town) _n._ Chinese quarter of any city outside China; in this case, of Vancouver.

Each one that she made was created from a treasure trove of glass fragments and castaway costume jewelry, in the same way that her first windchime had been made. The problem for the rest of the family was in the fact that Grandmama looked for these treasures wandering the back alleys of Keefer and Pender Streets,[10] peering into our neighbors' garbage cans, chasing away hungry, nervous cats and shouting curses at them.

"All our friends are laughing at us!" Older Brother Jung said at last to my father, when Grandmama was away having tea at Mrs. Lim's.

"We are not poor," Oldest Brother Kiam declared, "Yet she and Sek-Lung poke through those awful things as if —" he shoved me in frustration and I stumbled against my sister, "—they were beggars!"

"She will make Little Brother crazy!" Sister Liang said. Without warning, she punched me sharply in the back; I jumped. "You see, look how *nervous* he is!"

I lifted my foot slightly, enough to swing it back and kick Liang in the shin. She yelled and pulled back her fist to punch me again. Jung made a menacing move towards me.

"Stop this, all of you!" My father shook his head in exasperation. How could he dare tell the Grand Old One, his aging mother, that what was somehow appropriate in a poor village in China, was an <u>abomination</u> here. How could he prevent me, his youngest, from accompanying her? If she went walking into those alleyways alone she could well be attacked by hoodlums. "She is not a beggar looking for food. She is searching for— for. . . ."

My stepmother attempted to speak, then fell silent. She, too, seemed perplexed and somewhat ashamed. They all loved Grandmama, but she was *inconvenient*, unsettling.

As for our neighbors, most understood Grandmama to be harmlessly crazy, others that she did indeed make lovely toys but for what purpose? *Why?* they asked, and the stories she told me, of the juggler who smiled at her, flashed in my head.

Finally, by their cutting remarks, the family did exert enough pressure so that Grandmama and I no longer openly announced our expeditions. Instead, she took me with her on "shopping trips," <u>ostensibly</u> for clothes or groceries, while in fact we spent most of our time exploring stranger and more distant neighborhoods, searching for splendid junk: jangling

Short Story

Another way to get to know a **character** is by looking at what other characters feel about him or her. What does Grandmama's family feel about her?

_____

_____

_____

Short Story

An **internal conflict** takes place within a character's own mind. What internal conflict is the father experiencing?

_____

_____

Reading Check

Where does Grandmama look for glass fragments and costume jewelry? Underline the the text that tells you.

Vocabulary Development

abomination (uh bahm uh NAY shuhn) *n.* anything hateful and disgusting

ostensibly (ah STEN suh blee) *adv.* supposedly

---

10. **Keefer and Pender Streets** principal streets of Vancouver's Chinatown.

Short Story

One way to learn about **characters'** personalities is by looking at their relationships with other characters. Underline words or sentences in the bracketed passage that describe the relationship between Sek-Lung and his grandmother. What does the relationship between the grandmother and grandson reveal about their characters?

_____

_____

_____

_____

Stop to Reflect

Why are Grandmama and Sek-Lung so happy about the pieces they find in the Chinese Presbyterian Church?

_____

_____

_____

Reading Check

Did Grandmama's juggler return to her? Circle the text that tells you.

_____

pieces of a vase, cranberry glass fragments <u>embossed</u> with leaves, discarded glass beads from Woolworth[11] necklaces. . . . . We would sneak them all home in brown rice sacks, folded into small parcels, and put them under her bed. During the day when the family was away at school or work, we brought them out and washed every item in a large black pot of boiling lye[12] and water, dried them quickly, carefully, and returned them, sparkling, under her bed.

Our greatest excitement occurred when a fire gutted the large Chinese Presbyterian Church, three blocks from our house. Over the still-smoking ruins the next day, Grandmama and I rushed precariously over the blackened beams to pick out the stained glass that glittered in the sunlight. Small figure bent over, wrapped against the autumn cold in a dark blue quilted coat, happily gathering each piece like gold, she became my spiritual playmate: "There's a good one! *There!*"

Hours later, soot-covered and smelling of smoke, we came home with a carton full of delicate fragments, still early enough to steal them all into the house and put the small box under her bed. "These are special pieces," she said, giving the box a last push, "because they come from a sacred place." She slowly got up and I saw, for the first time, her hand begin to shake. But then, in her joy, she embraced me. Both of our hearts were racing, as if we were two dreamers. I buried my face in her blue quilt, and for a moment, the whole world seemed silent.

"My juggler," she said, "he never came back to me from Honan[13] . . . perhaps the famine. . . ." Her voice began to quake. "But I shall have my sacred windchime . . . I shall have it again."

One evening, when the family was gathered in their usual places in the parlor, Grandmama gave me her secret nod: a slight wink of her eye and a flaring of her nostrils. There was *trouble* in the air. Supper had gone badly, school examinations were due, father had failed to meet an editorial deadline at the *Vancouver Chinese Times*. A huge sigh came from Sister Liang.

"But it is useless this Chinese they teach you!" she lamented, turning to Stepmother for support. Silence.

Vocabulary Development

embossed (im BAHST) *adj.* decorated with a raised pattern

11. **Woolworth** variety store belonging to the chain founded by Frank Woolworth in 1879.

12. **lye** (ly) *n.* substance derived from wood ashes, commonly used in making soap or for washing.

13. **Honan** (HOH NAN) province of east central China.

Liang frowned, <u>dejected</u>, and went back to her Chinese book, bending the covers back.

"Father," Oldest Brother Kiam began, waving his bamboo brush in the air, "you must realize that this Mandarin only confuses us. We are Cantonese[14] speakers. . . ."

"And you do not complain about Latin, French or German in your English school?" Father rattled his newspaper, a signal that his patience was ending.

"But, Father, those languages are *scientific*," Kiam jabbed his brush in the air. "We are now in a scientific, logical world."

Father was silent. We could all hear Grandmama's rocker.

"What about Sek-Lung?" Older Brother Jung pointed angrily at me. "He was sick last year, but this year he should have at least started Chinese school, instead of picking over garbage cans!"

"He starts next year," Father said, in a hard tone that immediately warned everyone to be silent. Liang slammed her book.

Grandmama went on rocking quietly in her chair. She complimented my mother on her knitting, made a remark about the "strong beauty" of Kiam's brushstrokes which, in spite of himself, immensely pleased him. All this babbling noise was her family torn and confused in a strange land: everything here was so very foreign and scientific.

The truth was, I was sorry not to have started school the year before. In my innocence I had imagined going to school meant certain privileges worthy of all my brothers' and sister's complaints. The fact that my lung infection in my fifth and sixth years, mistakenly diagnosed as TB,[15] earned me some <u>reprieve</u>, only made me long for school the more. Each member of the family took turns on Sunday, teaching me or annoying me. <u>But it was the countless hours I spent with Grandmama that were my real education</u>. Tapping me on my head she would say, "Come, Sek-Lung, we have *our* work," and we would walk up the stairs to her small crowded room. There, in the

© Pearson Education

Vocabulary Development

dejected (di JEK tid) *adj.* sad and disappointed

reprieve (ri PREEV) *n.* temporary relief; postponement of a penalty

14. **Mandarin** (MAN duh rin) . . . **Cantonese** (kan tuhn EEZ) Mandarin is the most commonly spoken form of Chinese; Cantonese is a variety of Chinese spoken in some parts of China, including the cities of Canton and Hong Kong, and by most Chinese emigrants.

15. **TB** (tee bee) *n.* abbreviation for tuberculosis, a contagious disease that begins in the lungs.

TAKE NOTES

Short Story

Summarize the **conflict** that the older children in the family experience.

_____

_____

_____

_____

Stop to Reflect

Read the underlined sentence. What do you think Sek-Lung means by his comment about his real education?

_____

_____

_____

Reading Check

How does Grandmama react to the family arguing? Circle the text that tells you.

Short Story

Read the first bracketed passage. Why is the windchime important in relation to Grandmama's death?

_____

_____

_____

Stop to Reflect

Read the second bracketed passage. Why do you think the narrator becomes "lost in the magic of her task"?

_____

_____

_____

Reading Check

Why does Grandmama say her hand shakes? Circle the text that tells you.

---

midst of her antique shawls, the old ancestral <u>calligraphy</u> and multi-colored embroidered hangings, beneath the mysterious shelves of sweet herbs and bitter potions, we would continue doing what we had started that morning: the elaborate windchime for her death.

"I can't last forever," she declared, when she let me in on the secret of this one. "It will sing and dance and glitter," her long fingers stretched into the air, <u>pantomiming</u> the waving motion of her ghost chimes; "My spirit will hear its sounds and see its light and return to this house and say goodbye to you."

Deftly she reached into the carton she had placed on the chair beside me. She picked out a fish-shape amber piece, and with a long needle-like tool and a steel ruler, she scored[16] it. Pressing the blade of a cleaver against the line, with the fingers of her other hand, she lifted up the glass until it cleanly *snapped* into the exact shape she required. Her hand began to tremble, the tips of her fingers to shiver, like rippling water.

"You see that, Little One?" She held her hand up. "That is my body fighting with Death. He is in this room now."

My eyes darted in panic, but Grandmama remained calm, undisturbed, and went on with her work. Then I remembered the glue and uncorked the jar for her. Soon the graceful ritual movements of her hand returned to her, and I became lost in the magic of her task: she dabbed a cabalistic[17] mixture of glue on one end and skillfully dropped the braided end of a silk thread into it. This part always amazed me: the braiding would slowly, *very* slowly, *unknot*, fanning out like a prized fishtail. In a few seconds the clear, homemade glue began to harden as I blew lightly over it, welding to itself each separate silk strand.

Each jam-sized pot of glue was precious; each large cork had been wrapped with a fragment of pink silk. I remember this part vividly, because each cork was treated to a special rite. First we went shopping in the best silk stores in Chinatown for the perfect square of silk she required. It had to be a deep pink, a shade of color blushing toward red. And the tone had to match—as closely as possible—her precious jade carving, the small peony of white and light-red jade, her most lucky

---

Vocabulary Development

calligraphy (kuh LIG ruh fee) *n.* beautiful writing produced with pens and brushes

pantomiming (PAN tuh my ming) *v.* acting without using words

---

16. **scored** (skawrd) *v.* put a notch or groove in.

17. **cabalistic** (kab uh LIS tik) *adj.* relating to a secret or mystical belief or practice.

possession. In the center of this semi-translucent carving, no more than an inch wide, was a pool of pink light, its veins swirling out into the petals of the flower.

"This color is the color of my spirit," she said, holding it up to the window so I could see the delicate pastel against the broad strokes of sunlight. She dropped her voice, and I held my breath at the wonder of the color. "This was given to me by the young actor who taught me how to juggle. He had four of them, and each one had a center of this rare color, the color of Good Fortune." The pendant seemed to pulse as she turned it: "Oh, Sek-Lung! He had white hair and white skin *to his toes*! It's *true*, I saw him bathing." She laughed and blushed, her eyes softened at the memory. The silk had to match the pink heart of her pendant: the color was magical for her, to hold the unraveling strands of her memory. . . .

It was just six months before she died that we really began to work on her last windchime. Three thin bamboo sticks were steamed and bent into circlets; 30 exact lengths of silk thread, the strongest kind, were cut and braided at both ends and glued to stained glass. Her hands worked on their own command, each hand racing with a life of its own: cutting, snapping, braiding, knotting. . . . Sometimes she breathed heavily and her small body, growing thinner, sagged against me. <u>*Death,* I thought, *He is in this room,* and I would work harder alongside her.</u> For months Grandmama and I did this every other evening, a half dozen pieces each time. The shaking in her hand grew worse, but we said nothing. Finally, after discarding hundreds, she told me she had the necessary 30 pieces. But this time, because it was a sacred chime, I would not be permitted to help her tie it up or have the joy of raising it. "Once tied," she said, holding me against my disappointment, "not even I can raise it. Not a sound must it make until I have died."

"What will happen?"

"Your father will then take the center braided strand and raise it. He will hang it against my bedroom window so that my ghost may see it, and hear it, and return. I must say goodbye to this world properly or wander in this foreign land forever."

"You can take the streetcar!" I blurted, suddenly shocked that she actually meant to leave me. I thought I could hear the clear-<u>chromatic</u> chimes, see the

TAKE NOTES

Short Story

A **symbol** is a person, a place, or an object that stands for something larger. In the first bracketed passage, Choy connects the windchime with Grandmama's spirit. How are the windchimes a symbol of Grandmama's spirit?

_____

_____

_____

Short Story

Read the second bracketed passage. What does it reveal about Sek-Lung's character?

_____

_____

_____

Stop to Reflect 📖

Read the underlined sentence. Why does Sek-Lung work harder?

_____

_____

_____

Vocabulary Development

translucent (tranz LOO suhnt) *adj.* clear enough for some light to pass through

chromatic (kroh MAT ik) *adj.* referring to all of the tones of the musical scale

Stop to Reflect 📖

How will Grandmama always be
with Sek-Lung?

_____

_____

_____

_____

Short Story 📖

What does the white cat
symbolize to Grandmama?

_____

_____

_____

Stop to Reflect 📖

How do you think Sek-Lung feels
when Grandmama is not there
when he wakes up?

_____

_____

_____

_____

shimmering colors on the wall: I fell against her and cried, and there in my crying I knew that she would die. I can still remember the touch of her hand on my head, and the smell of her thick woolen sweater pressed against my face. "I will always be with you, Little Sek-Lung, but in a different way . . . you'll see."

Months went by, and nothing happened. Then one late September evening, when I had just come home from Chinese School, Grandmama was preparing supper when she looked out our kitchen window and saw a cat—a long, lean white cat—jump into our garbage pail and knock it over. She ran out to chase it away, shouting curses at it. She did not have her thick sweater on and when she came back into the house, a chill gripped her. She leaned against the door: "That was not a cat," she said, and the odd tone of her voice caused my father to look with alarm at her. "I can not take back my curses. It is too late." She took hold of my father's arm: "It was all white and had pink eyes like sacred fire."

My father started at this, and they both looked pale. My brothers and sister, clearing the table, froze in their gestures.

"The fog has confused you," Stepmother said. "It was just a cat."

But Grandmama shook her head, for she knew it was a sign. "I will not live forever," she said. "I am prepared."

The next morning she was confined to her bed with a severe cold. Sitting by her, playing with some of my toys, I asked her about the cat: "Why did father jump at the cat with the pink eyes? He didn't see it, you did."

"But he and your mother know what it means."

"What?"

"My friend, the juggler, the magician, was as pale as white jade, and he had pink eyes." I thought she would begin to tell me one of her stories, a tale of enchantment or of a wondrous adventure, but she only paused to swallow; her eyes glittered, lost in memory. She took my hand, gently opening and closing her fingers over it. "Sek-Lung," she sighed, "*he* has come back to me."

Then Grandmama sank back into her pillow and the embroidered flowers lifted to frame her wrinkled face. I saw her hand over my own, and my own began to tremble. I fell fitfully asleep by her side. When I woke up it was dark and her bed was empty. She had been taken to the hospital and I was not permitted to visit.

Vocabulary Development

fitfully (FIT ful lee) *adv.* always starting and stopping, not continuous

A few days after that she died of the complications of pneumonia.[18] Immediately after her death my father came home and said nothing to us, but walked up the stairs to her room, pulled aside the drawn lace curtains of her window and lifted the windchimes to the sky.

I began to cry and quickly put my hand in my pocket for a handkerchief. Instead, caught between my fingers, was the small, round firmness of the jade peony. In my mind's eye I saw Grandmama smile and heard, softly, the pink center beat like a beautiful, cramped heart.

Reader's Response: Do you agree or disagree with the author's ideas about family? Explain.

_____

_____

_____

_____

_____

Short Story

The **theme** of a story is its main message. It can also be an insight into life. What do you think is the theme of this story?

_____

_____

_____

There are two kinds of themes. A theme is a **stated theme** if the author directly tells you what it is. A theme is an **implied theme** if it is suggested through the experiences of the characters. Do you think the theme is stated or implied? Explain.

_____

_____

_____

Reading Check

What does the narrator find in his pocket? Circle the answer in the text.

18. pneumonia (nuh MOH nyuh) *n.* a serious illness that affects your lungs and makes it difficult to breathe.

The Jade Peony

1. **Infer:** The plot of the story revolves around the process of making windchimes. Why was this activity important to Grandmama?

_____

_____

_____

_____

2. **Compare and Contrast:** How do Sek-Lung's reactions to Grandmama's activities differ from those of the other family members?

_____

_____

_____

_____

3. **Short Story:** Use this chart to record details in the story. In the first column, list events, actions, statements, or descriptions that you think are important to the story. Then, fill in the rest of the chart.

What It Says	What It Means	Why It Is Important

4. **Short Story:** What did you think was the **theme**, or main message of the story? Did filling in the chart change your interpretation of the story's theme? Explain.

_____

_____

_____

_____

Oral Report

Create an **oral report** to discuss Choy's insights into his Chinese-Canadian heritage. The following bullets will help you find information for your report.

- Read some of the author's other works. *All That Matters* and *Paper Shadows: A Memoir of a Past Lost and Found* are two other works by Choy.

What I learned from Choy's fiction and nonfiction:

_____

_____

_____

- Search the Internet.

What I learned about Choy:

_____

_____

_____

- Watch the video interview with Wayson Choy. Use it and your source material to answer these questions.

1. What did you learn about Choy's cultural background? How did his background affect his writing?

_____

_____

_____

_____

2. What did you learn about Choy's interest in family history?

_____

_____

_____

_____

The Most Dangerous Game • American History

Literary Analysis

Conflict is a struggle between opposing forces.

- With **external conflict**, a character struggles against an outside force, such as another character, society, or nature.
- With **internal conflict**, a character grapples with his or her own opposing feelings, beliefs, needs, or desires.

In narrative literature, conflict and the search for a solution drives the plot. The solution usually occurs near the end of a story, during the **resolution**.

In some stories, however, the conflict is not truly solved. Instead, the character has an **epiphany**, or sudden flash of insight. The conflict remains, but the character's feelings about it change.

Reading Skill

Inferences are logical assumptions based on details in a story. To make inferences as you read, **ask questions** such as these:

- *What does this detail show about the reasons for a character's actions or words?*
- *What does this passage say about the character's unspoken feelings?*

Use this chart to make inferences as you read.

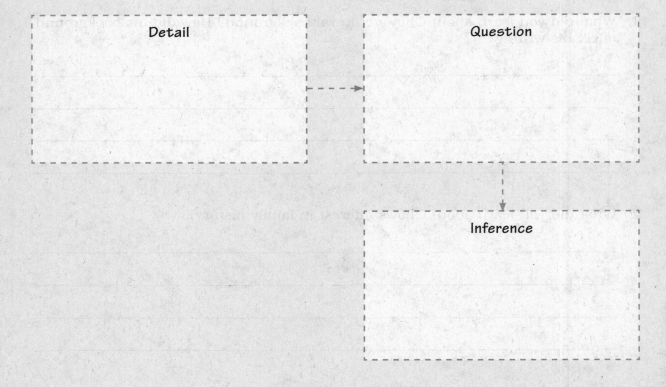

Detail

Question

Inference

The Most Dangerous Game
Richard Connell

Summary Rainsford is an expert hunter. While on a boat trip he falls overboard and swims to an island. There, he meets General Zaroff. Zaroff stocks the island with shipwrecked sailors. He hunts these men instead of animals. Rainsford refuses to join the hunt. As a result, Zaroff hunts Rainsford. Rainsford escapes and then returns to confront Zaroff.

Writing About the Big Question

Is conflict necessary? In "The Most Dangerous Game," a hunter faces a life-threatening conflict. Complete this sentence:

To succeed in a fight for survival, a person needs to _____

_____.

Note-taking Guide

Use this chart to recall the main events in the story.

Beginning Event			Final Event
Rainsford falls overboard			

Activate Prior Knowledge

Describe a time when someone else had different rules for playing a game. What happened?

_____

_____

_____

Reading Skill

When you make an **inference** you use information in the story to make a logical guess. What can you infer from the name Ship-Trap Island?

_____

_____

Literary Analysis

Underline details that show how Rainsford and Whitney feel about hunting. How is Rainsford's attitude in **conflict** with Whitney's?

_____

_____

Reading Check

What two classes does Rainsford believe make up the world? Underline your answer.

The Most Dangerous Game
Richard Connell

"Off there to the right—somewhere—is a large island," said Whitney. "It's rather a mystery—"

"What island is it?" Rainsford asked.

"The old charts call it 'Ship-Trap Island,'" Whitney replied. "A suggestive name, isn't it? Sailors have a curious dread of the place. I don't know why. Some superstition—"

"Can't see it," remarked Rainsford, trying to peer through the dank tropical night that was <u>palpable</u> as it pressed its thick warm blackness in upon the yacht.

"You've good eyes," said Whitney, with a laugh, "and I've seen you pick off a moose moving in the brown fall bush at four hundred yards, but even you can't see four miles or so through a moonless Caribbean[1] night."

"Not four yards," admitted Rainsford. "Ugh! It's like moist black velvet."

"It will be light in Rio," promised Whitney. "We should make it in a few days. I hope the jaguar guns have come from Purdey's. We should have some good hunting up the Amazon. Great sport, hunting."

"The best sport in the world," agreed Rainsford.

"For the hunter," amended Whitney. "Not for the jaguar."

"Don't talk rot, Whitney," said Rainsford. "You're a big-game hunter, not a philosopher. Who cares how a jaguar feels?"

"Perhaps the jaguar does," observed Whitney.

"Bah! They've no understanding."

"Even so, I rather think they understand one thing—fear. The fear of pain and the fear of death."

"Nonsense," laughed Rainsford. "This hot weather is making you soft, Whitney. Be a realist. The world is made up of two classes—the hunters and the huntees. Luckily, you and I are the hunters. Do you think we've passed that island yet?"

"I can't tell in the dark. I hope so."

"Why?" asked Rainsford.

"The place has a reputation—a bad one."

"Cannibals?" suggested Rainsford.

"Hardly. Even cannibals wouldn't live in such a God-forsaken place. But it's gotten into sailor lore, somehow.

Vocabulary Development

palpable (PAL puh buhl) *adj.* able to be felt; easily perceived

---

1. **Caribbean** (kar uh BEE uhn) the Caribbean Sea, a part of the Atlantic Ocean, bounded by the north coast of South America, Central America, and the West Indies.

Didn't you notice that the crew's nerves seemed a bit jumpy today?"

"They were a bit strange, now you mention it. Even Captain Nielsen—"

"Yes, even that tough-minded old Swede, who'd go up to the devil himself and ask him for a light. Those fishy blue eyes held a look I never saw there before. All I could get out of him was: 'This place has an evil name among seafaring men, sir.' Then he said to me, very gravely: 'Don't you feel anything?'—as if the air about us was actually poisonous. Now, you mustn't laugh when I tell you this—I did feel something like a sudden chill.

"There was no breeze. The sea was as flat as a plate-glass window. We were drawing near the island then. What I felt was a—a mental chill; a sort of sudden dread."

"Pure imagination," said Rainsford. "One superstitious sailor can taint the whole ship's company with his fear."

"Maybe. But sometimes I think sailors have an extra sense that tells them when they are in danger. Sometimes I think evil is a <u>tangible</u> thing—with wave lengths, just as sound and light have. An evil place can, so to speak, broadcast vibrations of evil. Anyhow, I'm glad we're getting out of this zone. Well, I think I'll turn in now, Rainsford."

"I'm not sleepy," said Rainsford. "I'm going to smoke another pipe on the afterdeck."

"Good night, then, Rainsford. See you at breakfast."

"Right. Good night, Whitney."

There was no sound in the night as Rainsford sat there, but the muffled throb of the engine that drove the yacht swiftly through the darkness, and the swish and ripple of the wash of the propeller.

Rainsford, reclining in a steamer chair, <u>indolently</u> puffed on his favorite brier. The <u>sensuous</u> drowsiness of the night was on him. "It's so dark," he thought, "that I could sleep without closing my eyes; the night would be my eyelids—"

An abrupt sound startled him. Off to the right he heard it, and his ears, expert in such matters, could not be mistaken. Again he heard the sound, and again. Somewhere, off in the blackness, someone had fired a gun three times.

Rainsford sprang up and moved quickly to the rail, mystified. He strained his eyes in the direction from which

Vocabulary Development

tangible (TAN juh buhl) *adj.* real; able to be touched

indolently (IN duh lunt lee) *adv.* lazily; idly

sensuous (SEN shoo uhs) *adj.* pleasing to the senses

Stop to Reflect

Rainsford says that superstitions are "pure imagination." Whitney believes superstitions may be true. Are you ever superstitious? For example, some people think that 13 is an unlucky number. How might a superstition change the way you act? Explain.

_____

_____

_____

_____

_____

_____

Reading Check

What sound startles Rainsford out of his drowsiness? Circle the sentence that tells you.

Reading Skill

What can you **infer** from the sound that Rainsford hears?

_____

_____

_____

_____

Literary Analysis

An **external conflict** occurs when a character fights with an outside force. With what external conflict is Rainsford suddenly confronted?

_____

_____

_____

_____

Reading Skill

Rainsford reacts calmly to his situation when he falls overboard. What can you **infer** about him based on how he handles himself in a crisis?

_____

_____

_____

Reading Check

As Rainsford swims for shore, what sounds does he hear coming out of the darkness? Underline the words that tell you.

---

the reports had come, but it was like trying to see through a blanket. He leaped upon the rail and balanced himself there, to get greater elevation; his pipe, striking a rope, was knocked from his mouth. He lunged for it; a short, hoarse cry came from his lips as he realized he had reached too far and had lost his balance. The cry was pinched off short as the blood-warm waters of the Caribbean Sea closed over his head.

He struggled up to the surface and tried to cry out, but the wash from the speeding yacht slapped him in the face and the salt water in his open mouth made him gag and strangle. Desperately he struck out with strong strokes after the receding lights of the yacht, but he stopped before he had swum fifty feet. A certain cool-headedness had come to him; it was not the first time he had been in a tight place. There was a chance that his cries could be heard by someone aboard the yacht, but that chance was slender, and grew more slender as the yacht raced on. He wrestled himself out of his clothes, and shouted with all his power. The lights of the yacht became faint and ever-vanishing fireflies; then they were blotted out entirely by the night.

Rainsford remembered the shots. They had come from the right, and doggedly he swam in that direction, swimming with slow, deliberate strokes, conserving his strength. For a seemingly endless time he fought the sea. He began to count his strokes; he could do possibly a hundred more and then—

Rainsford heard a sound. It came out of the darkness, a high screaming sound, the sound of an animal in an extremity of anguish and terror.

He did not recognize the animal that made the sound; he did not try to; with fresh vitality he swam toward the sound. He heard it again; then it was cut short by another noise, crisp, staccato.

"Pistol shot," muttered Rainsford, swimming on.

Ten minutes of determined effort brought another sound to his ears—the most welcome he had ever heard— the muttering and growling of the sea breaking on a rocky shore. He was almost on the rocks before he saw them; on a night less calm he would have been shattered against them. With his remaining strength he dragged himself from the swirling waters. Jagged crags appeared to jut

---

Vocabulary Development

extremity (ik STREM uh tee) *n.* highest degree
vitality (vy TAL uh tee) *n.* life and energy
staccato (stuh KAHT oh) *adj.* short and sharp

into the opaqueness, he forced himself upward, hand over hand. Gasping, his hands raw, he reached a flat place at the top. Dense jungle came down to the very edge of the cliffs. What perils that tangle of trees and underbrush might hold for him did not concern Rainsford just then. All he knew was that he was safe from his enemy, the sea, and that utter weariness was on him. He flung himself down at the jungle edge and tumbled headlong into the deepest sleep of his life.

When he opened his eyes he knew from the position of the sun that it was late in the afternoon. Sleep had given him new vigor; a sharp hunger was picking at him. He looked about him, almost cheerfully.

"Where there are pistol shots, there are men. Where there are men, there is food," he thought. But what kind of men, he wondered, in so forbidding a place? An unbroken front of snarled and ragged jungle fringed the shore.

He saw no sign of a trail through the closely knit web of weeds and trees; it was easier to go along the shore, and Rainsford floundered along by the water. Not far from where he had landed, he stopped.

Some wounded thing, by the evidence a large animal, had thrashed about in the underbrush; the jungle weeds were crushed down and the moss was lacerated; one patch of weeds was stained crimson. A small, glittering object not far away caught Rainsford's eye and he picked it up. It was an empty cartridge.

"A twenty-two," he remarked. "That's odd. It must have been a fairly large animal too. The hunter had his nerve with him to tackle it with a light gun. It's clear that the brute put up a fight. I suppose the first three shots I heard was when the hunter flushed his quarry and wounded it. The last shot was when he trailed it here and finished it."

He examined the ground closely and found what he had hoped to find—the print of hunting boots. They pointed along the cliff in the direction he had been going. Eagerly he hurried along, now slipping on a rotten log or a loose stone, but making headway; night was beginning to settle down on the island.

Bleak darkness was blacking out the sea and jungle when Rainsford sighted the lights. He came upon them as he turned a crook in the coast line, and his first thought was that he had come upon a village, for there were many lights. But as he forged along he saw to his great astonishment that all the lights were in one enormous

Reading Skill

Rainsford knows from the position of the sun that it is late in the afternoon. What can you **infer** about him from this information?

_____

_____

_____

Literary Analysis

What evidence of recent **conflict** does Rainsford see on his way through the jungle? List three examples.

_____

_____

_____

_____

Reading Check

Does Rainsford make it safely to land? Circle the text that tells you.

Vocabulary Development

opaqueness (oh PAYK nuhs) *adj.* lack of transparence

lacerated (LAS uh ray tid) *adj.* cut or torn

Reading Skill

When Rainsford lifts the door knocker, it creaks as if it had never before been used. What do you **infer** from this detail?

_____

_____

_____

_____

Reading Check

The building he sees amazes Rainsford. Circle words in the bracketed text that describe the building.

Reading Skill

Underline details that describe Ivan's appearance and behavior. What do you **infer** about Ivan's past from these details? Explain.

_____

_____

_____

_____

_____

Literary Analysis

How is the tension between Rainsford and the giant man resolved?

_____

_____

_____

_____

building—a lofty structure with pointed towers plunging upward into the gloom. His eyes made out the shadowy outlines of a palatial chateau;[2] it was set on a high bluff, and on three sides of it cliffs dived down to where the sea licked greedy lips in the shadows.

"Mirage," thought Rainsford. But it was no mirage, he found, when he opened the tall spiked iron gate. The stone steps were real enough; the massive door with a leering gargoyle[3] for a knocker was real enough; yet about it all hung an air of unreality.

He lifted the knocker, and it creaked up stiffly, as if it had never before been used. He let it fall, and it startled him with its booming loudness. He thought he heard steps within; the door remained closed. Again Rainsford lifted the heavy knocker, and let it fall. The door opened then, opened as suddenly as if it were on a spring, and Rainsford stood blinking in the river of glaring gold light that poured out. The first thing Rainsford's eyes discerned was the largest man Rainsford had ever seen—a gigantic creature, solidly made and black-bearded to the waist. In his hand the man held a long-barreled revolver, and he was pointing it straight at Rainsford's heart.

Out of the snarl of beard two small eyes regarded Rainsford.

"Don't be alarmed," said Rainsford, with a smile which he hoped was disarming. "I'm no robber. I fell off a yacht. My name is Sanger Rainsford of New York City."

The menacing look in the eyes did not change. The revolver pointed as rigidly as if the giant were a statue. He gave no sign that he understood Rainsford's words, or that he had even heard them. He was dressed in uniform, a black uniform trimmed with gray astrakhan.[4]

"I'm Sanger Rainsford of New York," Rainsford began again. "I fell off a yacht. I am hungry."

The man's only answer was to raise with his thumb the hammer of his revolver. Then Rainsford saw the man's free hand go to his forehead in a military salute, and he saw him click his heels together and stand at attention. Another man was coming down the broad marble steps, an erect, slender man in evening clothes. He advanced to Rainsford and held out his hand.

Vocabulary Development

leering (LEER ing) *v.* looking unpleasantly

2. **palatial** (puh LAY shuhl) **chateau** (sha TOH) a mansion as luxurious as a palace.
3. **gargoyle** (GAHR goyl) *n.* strange and distorted animal form projecting from a building.
4. **astrakhan** (AS truh kuhn) *n.* loosely curled fur made from the skins of very young lambs.

In a cultivated voice marked by a slight accent that gave it added precision and <u>deliberateness</u>, he said: "It is a very great pleasure and honor to welcome Mr. Sanger Rainsford, the celebrated hunter, to my home."

Automatically Rainsford shook the man's hand.

"I've read your book about hunting snow leopards in Tibet, you see," explained the man. "I am General Zaroff."

Rainsford's first impression was that the man was <u>singularly</u> handsome; his second was that there was an original, almost <u>bizarre</u> quality about the general's face. He was a tall man past middle age, for his hair was a vivid white; but his thick eyebrows and pointed military mustache were as black as the night from which Rainsford had come. His eyes, too, were black and very bright. He had high cheek bones, a sharp-cut nose, a spare, dark face, the face of a man used to giving orders, the face of an aristocrat. Turning to the giant in uniform, the general made a sign. The giant put away his pistol, saluted, withdrew.

"Ivan is an incredibly strong fellow," remarked the general, "but he has the misfortune to be deaf and dumb. A simple fellow, but, I'm afraid, like all his race, a bit of a savage."

"Is he Russian?"

"He is a Cossack," said the general, and his smile showed red lips and pointed teeth. "So am I."

"Come," he said, "we shouldn't be chatting here. We can talk later. Now you want clothes, food, rest. You shall have them. This is a most restful spot."

Ivan had reappeared, and the general spoke to him with lips that moved but gave forth no sound.

"Follow Ivan, if you please, Mr. Rainsford," said the general. "I was about to have my dinner when you came. I'll wait for you. You'll find that my clothes will fit you, I think."

It was to a huge, beam-ceilinged bedroom with a canopied bed big enough for six men that Rainsford followed the silent giant. Ivan laid out an evening suit, and Rainsford, as he put it on, noticed that it came from a London tailor who ordinarily cut and sewed for none below the rank of duke.

The dining room to which Ivan conducted him was in many ways remarkable. There was a medieval magnificence about it; it suggested a baronial hall of

Vocabulary Development

deliberateness (di LIB uh rit nis) *n.* carefulness

singularly (SING gyuh ler lee) *adj.* very noticeably

bizarre (bi ZAHR) *adj.* very strange

TAKE NOTES

Stop to Reflect

What is your opinion of General Zaroff? Support your answer with details from the story.

_____

_____

_____

_____

_____

Reading Skill

What might Rainsford **infer** about General Zaroff from the way the general treats him? Support your answer with details or dialogue from the story.

_____

_____

_____

_____

_____

Reading Check

How does Zaroff recognize Rainsford? Underline the words that tell you.

Literary Analysis

Was the general's encounter with the buffalo an **internal** or **external conflict**? Explain.

_____

_____

_____

_____

Reading Skill

Zaroff killed the Cape buffalo in spite of the general's fractured skull. What can you **infer** about his character from this action?

_____

_____

_____

_____

Reading Check

What about Zaroff makes Rainsford uncomfortable? Circle the text that tells you.

feudal times with its oaken panels, its high ceiling, its vast refectory table where twoscore men could sit down to eat. About the hall were the mounted heads of many animals—lions, tigers, elephants, moose, bears; larger or more perfect specimens Rainsford had never seen. At the great table the general was sitting, alone.

"You'll have a cocktail, Mr. Rainsford," he suggested. The cocktail was surpassingly good; and, Rainsford noted, the table appointments were of the finest—the linen, the crystal, the silver, the china.

They were eating *borsch*, the rich, red soup with whipped cream so dear to Russian palates. Half apologetically General Zaroff said: "We do our best to preserve the amenities of civilization here. Please forgive any lapses. We are well off the beaten track, you know. Do you think the champagne has suffered from its long ocean trip?"

"Not in the least," declared Rainsford. He was finding the general a most thoughtful and affable host, a true cosmopolite.[5] But there was one small trait of the general's that made Rainsford uncomfortable. Whenever he looked up from his plate he found the general studying him, appraising him narrowly.

"Perhaps," said General Zaroff, "you were surprised that I recognized your name. You see, I read all books on hunting published in English, French, and Russian. I have but one passion in my life, Mr. Rainsford, and it is the hunt."

"You have some wonderful heads here," said Rainsford as he ate a particularly well cooked filet mignon. "That Cape buffalo is the largest I ever saw."

"Oh, that fellow. Yes, he was a monster."

"Did he charge you?"

"Hurled me against a tree," said the general. "Fractured my skull. But I got the brute."

"I've always thought," said Rainsford, "that the Cape buffalo is the most dangerous of all big game."

For a moment the general did not reply; he was smiling his curious red-lipped smile. Then he said slowly: "No. You are wrong, sir. The Cape buffalo is not the most dangerous big game." He sipped his wine. "Here in my preserve on this island," he said in the same slow tone, "I hunt more dangerous game."

Vocabulary Development

feudal (FYOO dl) *adj.* of the Middle Ages

refectory (ri FEK tuhr ee) *n.* dining room

appraising (uh PRAYZ ing) *v.* judging

Rainsford expressed his surprise. "Is there big game on this island?"

The general nodded. "The biggest."

"Really?"

"Oh, it isn't here naturally, of course. I have to stock the island."

"What have you imported, general?" Rainsford asked. "Tigers?"

The general smiled. "No," he said. "Hunting tigers ceased to interest me some years ago. I exhausted their possibilities, you see. No thrill left in tigers, no real danger. I live for danger, Mr. Rainsford."

The general took from his pocket a gold cigarette case and offered his guest a long black cigarette with a silver tip; it was perfumed and gave off a smell like incense.

"We will have some <u>capital</u> hunting, you and I," said the general. "I shall be most glad to have your society."

"But what game—" began Rainsford.

"I'll tell you," said the general. "You will be amused, I know. I think I may say, in all modesty, that I have done a rare thing. I have invented a new sensation. May I pour you another glass of <u>port</u>, Mr. Rainsford?"

"Thank you, general."

The general filled both glasses, and said: "God makes some men poets. Some He makes kings, some beggars. Me He made a hunter. My hand was made for the trigger, my father said. He was a very rich man with a quarter of a million acres in the Crimea,[6] and he was an ardent sportsman. When I was only five years old he gave me a little gun, specially made in Moscow for me, to shoot sparrows with. When I shot some of his prize turkeys with it, he did not punish me; he complimented me on my marksmanship. I killed my first bear in the Caucasus[7] when I was ten. My whole life has been one prolonged hunt. I went into the army—it was expected of noblemen's sons—and for a time commanded a division of Cossack cavalry, but my real interest was always the hunt. I have hunted every kind of game in every land. It would be impossible for me to tell you how many animals I have killed."

The general puffed at his cigarette.

"After the debacle[8] in Russia I left the country, for it was imprudent for an officer of the Czar to stay there. Many

Vocabulary Development

capital (KAP uh tuhl) *adj.* outstanding

port (pawrt) *n.* type of wine

6. **Crimea** (kry MEE uh) region in southwestern Ukraine extending into the Black Sea.

7. **Caucasus** (KAW kuh suhs) mountain range between the Black and Caspian Seas.

8. **debacle** (di BAH kuhl) *n.* bad defeat (Zaroff is referring to the Russian Revolution of 1917, a defeat for upper-class Russians like himself).

 TAKE NOTES

Reading Skill

Zaroff is secretive about the game he hunts. What do you **infer** from his secretive behavior?

_____

_____

_____

_____

_____

Reading Check

Why did Zaroff leave Russia? Underline the text that tells you.

Reading Skill

Read the bracketed passage. What can you **infer** about Zaroff from the information in the passage?

_____

_____

_____

_____

_____

Stop to Reflect

Have you ever become bored with something that you were good at doing? Did you have the same feelings as Zaroff?

_____

_____

_____

_____

Literary Analysis

How is the "tragic moment" Zaroff refers to the sign of an **internal conflict**?

_____

_____

_____

_____

_____

Reading Check ✎

What "terrible thought" does Zaroff have one night after hunting jaguar? Underline the sentence that tells you.

noble Russians lost everything. I, luckily, had invested heavily in American securities, so I shall never have to open a tea room in Monte Carlo or drive a taxi in Paris. Naturally, I continued to hunt—grizzlies in your Rockies, crocodiles in the Ganges, rhinoceroses in East Africa. It was in Africa that the Cape buffalo hit me and laid me up for six months. As soon as I recovered I started for the Amazon to hunt jaguars, for I had heard they were unusually cunning. They weren't." The Cossack sighed. "They were no match at all for a hunter with his wits about him, and a high-powered rifle. I was bitterly disappointed. I was lying in my tent with a splitting headache one night when a terrible thought pushed its way into my mind. Hunting was beginning to bore me! And hunting, remember, had been my life. I have heard that in America business men often go to pieces when they give up the business that has been their life."

"Yes, that's so," said Rainsford.

The general smiled. "I had no wish to go to pieces," he said. "I must do something. Now, mine is an <u>analytical</u> mind, Mr. Rainsford. Doubtless that is why I enjoy the problems of the chase."

"No doubt, General Zaroff."

"So," continued the general, "I asked myself why the hunt no longer fascinated me. You are much younger than I am, Mr. Rainsford, and have not hunted as much, but you perhaps can guess the answer."

"What was it?"

"Simply this: hunting had ceased to be what you call 'a sporting proposition.' It had become too easy. I always got my <u>quarry</u>. Always. There is no greater bore than perfection."

The general lit a fresh cigarette.

"No animal had a chance with me any more. That is no boast; it is a mathematical certainty. The animal had nothing but his legs and his instinct. Instinct is no match for reason. When I thought of this it was a tragic moment for me, I can tell you."

Rainsford leaned across the table, absorbed in what his host was saying.

"It came to me as an inspiration what I must do," the general went on.

"And that was?"

The general smiled the quiet smile of one who has faced an obstacle and <u>surmounted</u> it with success. "I had to invent a new animal to hunt," he said.

Vocabulary Development

analytical (an uh LIT i kuhl) _adj._ having a tendency to examine carefully

quarry (KWAW ree) _n._ animal or person being hunted

surmounted (ser MOWN tid) _v._ dealt with a difficulty

"A new animal? You're joking."

"Not at all," said the general. "I never joke about hunting. I needed a new animal. I found one. So I bought this island, built this house, and here I do my hunting. The island is perfect for my purpose—there are jungles with a maze of trails in them, hills, swamps—"

"But the animal, General Zaroff?"

"Oh," said the general, "it supplies me with the most exciting hunting in the world. No other hunting compares with it for an instant. Every day I hunt, and I never grow bored now, for I have a quarry with which I can match my wits."

Rainsford's bewilderment showed in his face.

"I wanted the ideal animal to hunt," explained the general. "So I said: 'What are the attributes of an ideal quarry?' And the answer was, of course: 'It must have courage, cunning, and, above all, it must be able to reason.'"

"But no animal can reason," objected Rainsford.

"My dear fellow," said the general, "there is one that can."

"But you can't mean—" gasped Rainsford.

"And why not?"

"I can't believe you are serious, General Zaroff. This is a grisly joke."

"Why should I not be serious? I am speaking of hunting."

"Hunting? General Zaroff, what you speak of is murder."

The general laughed with entire good nature. He regarded Rainsford quizzically. "I refuse to believe that so modern and civilized a young man as you seem to be harbors romantic ideas about the value of human life. Surely your experiences in the war—"

"Did not make me condone cold-blooded murder," finished Rainsford stiffly.

Laughter shook the general. "How extraordinarily droll you are!" he said. "One does not expect nowadays to find a young man of the educated class, even in America, with such a naive, and, if I may say so, mid-Victorian point of view.[9] It's like finding a snuff-box in a limousine. Ah, well, doubtless you had Puritan ancestors. So many Americans

Vocabulary Development

condone (kuhn DOHN) *v.* approve of something most people disapprove of

droll (drohl) *adj.* funny

naive (nah EEV) *adj.* innocent and easily fooled

9. **mid-Victorian point of view** a point of view emphasizing proper behavior and associated with the time of Queen Victoria of England (1819–1901).

Reading Skill

The general is trying to build suspense. Can you **infer** what the animal is? If you have not guessed, pay close attention as you read the rest of this page. Circle the sentence at the point that you figure out what the animal is.

_____

_____

Literary Analysis

Rainsford suddenly understands what new animal Zaroff hunts. What **conflict** grows between Rainsford and Zaroff as a result?

_____

_____

_____

Reading Check

The general names three traits that the perfect prey should have. Circle the three traits Zaroff identifies.

Stop to Reflect

Do you agree with Zaroff's philosophy as it is expressed in the first bracketed paragraph? Explain.

_____

_____

_____

_____

Reading Skill

Read the description in the second bracketed passage. What can you **infer** about the way Zaroff brings sailors to the island?

_____

_____

_____

_____

_____

Reading Check

Underline the passage that explains why Zaroff delights in hunting men.

_____

appear to have had. I'll wager you'll forget your notions when you go hunting with me. You've a genuine new thrill in store for you, Mr. Rainsford."

"Thank you, I'm a hunter, not a murderer."

"Dear me," said the general, quite unruffled, "again that unpleasant word. But I think I can show you that your scruples are quite ill founded."

"Yes?"

"Life is for the strong, to be lived by the strong, and, if need be, taken by the strong. The weak of the world were put here to give the strong pleasure. I am strong. Why should I not use my gift? If I wish to hunt, why should I not? I hunt the scum of the earth—sailors from tramp ships—lascars,[10] blacks, Chinese, whites, mongrels—a thoroughbred horse or hound is worth more than a score of them."

"But they are men," said Rainsford hotly.

"Precisely," said the general. "That is why I use them. It gives me pleasure. They can reason, after a fashion. So they are dangerous."

"But where do you get them?"

The general's left eyelid fluttered down in a wink. "This island is called Ship-Trap," he answered. "Sometimes an angry god of the high seas sends them to me. Sometimes, when Providence is not so kind, I help Providence a bit. Come to the window with me."

Rainsford went to the window and looked out toward the sea.

"Watch! Out there!" exclaimed the general, pointing into the night. Rainsford's eyes saw only blackness, and then, as the general pressed a button, far out to sea Rainsford saw the flash of lights.

The general chuckled. "They indicate a channel," he said, "where there's none: giant rocks with razor edges crouch like a sea monster with wide-open jaws. They can crush a ship as easily as I crush this nut." He dropped a walnut on the hardwood floor and brought his heel grinding down on it. "Oh, yes," he said, casually, as if in answer to a question, "I have electricity. We try to be civilized here."

"Civilized? And you shoot down men?"

A trace of anger was in the general's black eyes, but it was there for but a second, and he said, in his most

Vocabulary Development

scruples (SKROO puhlz) *n.* beliefs that keep a person from doing something that he or she thinks is wrong

10. **lascars** (LAS kuhrz) *n.* Indian and East Indian sailors, employed on European ships.

pleasant manner: "Dear me, what a righteous young man you are! I assure you I do not do the thing you suggest. That would be barbarous. I treat these visitors with every consideration. They get plenty of good food and exercise. They get into splendid physical condition. You shall see for yourself tomorrow."

"What do you mean?"

"We'll visit my training school," smiled the general. "It's in the cellar. I have about a dozen pupils down there now. They're from the Spanish bark San Lucar that had the bad luck to go on the rocks out there. A very inferior lot, I regret to say. Poor specimens and more accustomed to the deck than to the jungle."

He raised his hand, and Ivan, who served as waiter, brought thick Turkish coffee. Rainsford, with an effort, held his tongue in check.

"It's a game, you see," pursued the general blandly. "I suggest to one of them that we go hunting. I give him a supply of food and an excellent hunting knife. I give him three hours' start. I am to follow, armed only with a pistol of the smallest caliber and range. If my quarry eludes me for three whole days, he wins the game. If I find him"—the general smiled—"he loses."

"Suppose he refuses to be hunted?"

"Oh," said the general, "I give him his option, of course. He need not play the game if he doesn't wish to. If he does not wish to hunt, I turn him over to Ivan. Ivan once had the honor of serving as official knouter[11] to the Great White Czar, and he has his own ideas of sport. Invariably, Mr. Rainsford, invariably they choose the hunt."

"And if they win?"

The smile on the general's face widened. "To date I have not lost," he said.

Then he added, hastily: "I don't wish you to think me a braggart, Mr. Rainsford. Many of them afford only the most elementary sort of problem. Occasionally I strike a tartar.[12] One almost did win. I eventually had to use the dogs."

"The dogs?"

"This way, please. I'll show you."

The general steered Rainsford to a window. The lights from the windows sent a flickering illumination that made

Vocabulary Development

righteous (RY chuhs) *adj.* angry because a situation is not right or fair

invariably (in VAR ee uh blee) *adv.* always

11. **knouter** (NOWT er) *n.* someone who beats criminals with a leather whip.

12. **tartar** (TAHRT er) *n.* stubborn, violent person.

TAKE NOTES

Stop to Reflect

Why would Zaroff refer to shipwrecked sailors as "specimens"?

_____

_____

_____

_____

_____

Literary Analysis

Zaroff's captives must decide whether to hunt or to face Ivan. Explain how making this decision would present an **internal conflict**.

_____

_____

_____

_____

Reading Check

Who are the "pupils" in Zaroff's cellar? Underline the sentence that gives the answer.

What kinds of heads are likely to be in Zaroff's "new collection" in the library? Explain how you arrived at your **inference**.

_____

_____

_____

_____

_____

Stop to Reflect 📖

Has your impression of Zaroff changed since you first met him in the story? Explain.

_____

_____

_____

_____

Literary Analysis 🔍

Describe the **conflict** that keeps Rainsford awake. Is it **internal**, **external**, or both? Explain.

_____

_____

_____

_____

_____

grotesque patterns on the courtyard below, and Rainsford could see moving about there a dozen or so huge black shapes; as they turned toward him, their eyes glittered greenly.

"A rather good lot, I think," observed the general. "They are let out at seven every night. If anyone should try to get into my house—or out of it—something extremely regrettable would occur to him." He hummed a snatch of song from the Folies Bergère.[13]

"And now," said the general, "I want to show you my new collection of heads. Will you come with me to the library?"

"I hope," said Rainsford, "that you will excuse me tonight, General Zaroff. I'm really not feeling at all well."

"Ah, indeed?" the general inquired solicitously. "Well, I suppose that's only natural, after your long swim. You need a good, restful night's sleep. Tomorrow you'll feel like a new man, I'll wager. Then we'll hunt, eh? I've one rather promising prospect—"

Rainsford was hurrying from the room.

"Sorry you can't go with me tonight," called the general. "I expect rather fair sport—a big, strong black. He looks resourceful—Well good night, Mr. Rainsford; I hope you have a good night's rest."

The bed was good, and the pajamas of the softest silk, and he was tired in every fiber of his being, but nevertheless Rainsford could not quiet his brain with the opiate of sleep. He lay, eyes wide open. Once he thought he heard stealthy steps in the corridor outside his room. He sought to throw open the door; it would not open. He went to the window and looked out. His room was high up in one of the towers. The lights of the chateau were out now, and it was dark and silent, but there was a fragment of sallow moon, and by its wan light he could see, dimly, the courtyard; there, weaving in and out in the pattern of shadow, were black, noiseless forms; the hounds heard him at the window and looked up, expectantly, with their green eyes. Rainsford went back to the bed and lay down. By many methods he tried to put himself to sleep. He had achieved a doze when, just as morning began to come, he heard, far off in the jungle, the faint report of a pistol.

Vocabulary Development

grotesque (groh TESK) *adj.* uncomfortably ugly and strange
solicitously (suh LI suh tuhs lee) *adv.* accomodatingly
opiate (OH pee it) *n.* drug

13. **Folies Bergère** (faw LEE ber ZHER) musical theater in Paris.

General Zaroff did not appear until luncheon. He was dressed faultlessly in the tweeds of a country squire. He was solicitous about the state of Rainsford's health.

"As for me," sighed the general, "I do not feel so well. I am worried, Mr. Rainsford. Last night I detected traces of my old complaint."

To Rainsford's questioning glance the general said: "Ennui. Boredom."

Then, taking a second helping of crépes suzette, the general explained: "The hunting was not good last night. The fellow lost his head. He made a straight trail that offered no problems at all. That's the trouble with these sailors; they have dull brains to begin with, and they do not know how to get about in the woods. They do excessively stupid and obvious things. It's most annoying. Will you have another glass of Chablis, Mr. Rainsford?"

"General," said Rainsford firmly, "I wish to leave this island at once."

The general raised his thickets of eyebrows; he seemed hurt. "But, my dear fellow," the general protested, "you've only just come. You've had no hunting—"

"I wish to go today," said Rainsford. He saw the dead black eyes of the general on him, studying him. General Zaroff's face suddenly brightened.

He filled Rainsford's glass with <u>venerable</u> Chablis from a dusty bottle.

"Tonight," said the general, "we will hunt—you and I."

Rainsford shook his head. "No, general," he said. "I will not hunt."

The general shrugged his shoulders and delicately ate a hothouse grape. "As you wish, my friend," he said. "The choice rests entirely with you. But may I not venture to suggest that you will find my idea of sport more diverting than Ivan's?"

He nodded toward the corner to where the giant stood, scowling, his thick arms crossed on his hogshead of chest.

"You don't mean—" cried Rainsford.

"My dear fellow," said the general, "have I not told you I always mean what I say about hunting? This is really an inspiration. I drink to a foeman worthy of my steel—at last."

The general raised his glass, but Rainsford sat staring at him.

"You'll find this game worth playing," the general said enthusiastically. "Your brain against mine. Your woodcraft against mine. Your strength and stamina against mine. Outdoor chess! And the stake is not without value, eh?"

"And if I win—" began Rainsford huskily.

Vocabulary Development

venerable (VEN uhr uh buhl) *adj.* respected because of its quality

Literary Analysis

Circle details that show how Zaroff reacts when Rainsford says that he wishes to leave. How does Rainsford's statement about leaving make his **internal conflict** an **external** one?

_____

_____

_____

_____

Reading Skill

Rainsford figures out that Zaroff plans to hunt him. What can you **infer** about Rainsford's feelings when he hears this?

_____

_____

_____

Reading Check

Why is Zaroff not feeling well in the morning? Underline the sentences that tell you the answer.

Reading Skill

What can you **infer** happened to Zaroff's dog, Lazarus?

_____

_____

Stop to Reflect

Why do you think Zaroff gives Rainsford advice even though Zaroff wants to hunt and kill him?

_____

_____

_____

Reading Skill

When Ivan gives Rainsford a "long-bladed hunting knife," what **inference** do you make?

_____

_____

_____

Reading Check

Zaroff says he will announce his defeat if Rainsford can last a certain number of days. Underline the text that tells you the number of days.

"I'll cheerfully acknowledge myself defeated if I do not find you by midnight of the third day," said General Zaroff. "My sloop will place you on the mainland near a town."

The general read what Rainsford was thinking.

"Oh, you can trust me," said the Cossack. "I will give you my word as a gentleman and a sportsman. Of course you, in turn, must agree to say nothing of your visit here."

"I'll agree to nothing of the kind," said Rainsford.

"Oh," said the general, "in that case— But why discuss that now? Three days hence we can discuss it over a bottle of Veuve Cliquot, unless—"

The general sipped his wine.

Then a businesslike air animated him. "Ivan," he said to Rainsford, "will supply you with hunting clothes, food, a knife. I suggest you wear moccasins; they leave a poorer trail. I suggest too that you avoid the big swamp in the southeast corner of the island. We call it Death Swamp. There's quicksand there. One foolish fellow tried it. The deplorable part of it was that Lazarus followed him. You can imagine my feelings, Mr. Rainsford. I loved Lazarus; he was the finest hound in my pack. Well, I must beg you to excuse me now. I always take a siesta after lunch. You'll hardly have time for a nap, I fear. You'll want to start, no doubt. I shall not follow till dusk. Hunting at night is so much more exciting than by day, don't you think? Au revoir,[14] Mr. Rainsford, au revoir."

General Zaroff, with a deep, courtly bow, strolled from the room.

From another door came Ivan. Under one arm he carried khaki hunting clothes, a haversack of food, a leather sheath containing a long-bladed hunting knife; his right hand rested on a cocked revolver thrust in the crimson sash about his waist. . . .

Rainsford had fought his way through the bush for two hours. "I must keep my nerve. I must keep my nerve," he said through tight teeth.

He had not been entirely clear-headed when the chateau gates snapped shut behind him.

His whole idea at first was to put distance between himself and General Zaroff, and, to this end, he had plunged along, spurred on by the sharp rowels of something very like panic. Now he had got a grip on himself, had stopped, and was taking stock of himself and the situation.

Vocabulary Development
sloop (sloop) *n.* boat
animated (AN uh mayt id) *v.* gave energy or life

14. **Au revoir** (oh re VWAHR) French for "until we meet again."

He saw that straight flight was <u>futile</u>; inevitably it would bring him face to face with the sea. He was in a picture with a frame of water, and his operations, clearly, must take place within that frame.

"I'll give him a trail to follow," muttered Rainsford, and he struck off from the rude paths he had been following into the trackless wilderness. He executed a series of intricate loops; he doubled on his trail again and again, recalling all the lore of the fox hunt, and all the dodges of the fox. Night found him leg-weary, with his hands and face lashed by the branches, on a thickly wooded ridge. He knew it would be insane to blunder on through the dark, even if he had the strength. His need for rest was <u>imperative</u> and he thought: "I have played the fox, now I must play the cat of the fable." A big tree with a thick trunk and outspread branches was nearby, and, taking care to leave not the slightest mark, he climbed up into the crotch, and stretching out on one of the broad limbs, after a fashion, rested. Rest brought him new confidence and almost a feeling of security. Even so zealous a hunter as General Zaroff could not trace him there, he told himself; only the devil himself could follow that complicated trail through the jungle after dark. But, perhaps, the general was a devil—

An <u>apprehensive</u> night crawled slowly by like a wounded snake, and sleep did not visit Rainsford, although the silence of a dead world was on the jungle. Toward morning when a dingy gray was varnishing the sky, the cry of some startled bird focused Rainsford's attention in that direction. Something was coming through the bush, coming slowly, carefully, coming by the same winding way Rainsford had come. He flattened himself down on the limb, and through a screen of leaves almost as thick as tapestry, he watched. The thing that was approaching was a man.

It was General Zaroff. He made his way along with his eyes fixed in utmost concentration on the ground before him. He paused, almost beneath the tree, dropped to his knees and studied the ground. Rainsford's impulse was to hurl himself down like a panther, but he saw the general's right hand held something metallic—a small automatic pistol.

© Pearson Education

TAKE NOTES

Literary Analysis

What **external conflict** does Rainsford experience in the bracketed passage?

_____

_____

_____

Reading Skill

Rainsford says that Zaroff would not be able to trace him. What can you **infer** about Rainsford from his assumption?

_____

_____

_____

Stop to Reflect

Why do you think Rainsford is unable to fall asleep?

_____

_____

_____

Reading Check

What two animals does Rainsford compare himself to? Circle the words in the text.

Vocabulary Development

futile (FYOO tl) *adj.* useless; hopeless

imperative (im PER uh tiv) *adj.* extremely important

apprehensive (ap ri HEN siv) *adj.* anxious; concerned

Reading Skill

Which details suggest that Zaroff knows Rainsford is in the tree? Circle the details in the bracketed passage that tell you.

Stop to Reflect

Why do you think Zaroff walks away, leaving Rainsford safely in the tree?

_____

_____

_____

_____

Literary Analysis

Rainsford tells himself, "I will not lose my nerve. I will not." What **internal conflict** is Rainsford experiencing?

_____

_____

_____

_____

_____

The hunter shook his head several times, as if he were puzzled. Then he straightened up and took from his case one of his black cigarettes; its <u>pungent</u> incense-like smoke floated up to Rainsford's nostrils.

Rainsford held his breath. The general's eyes had left the ground and were traveling inch by inch up the tree. Rainsford froze there, every muscle tensed for a spring. But the sharp eyes of the hunter stopped before they reached the limb where Rainsford lay; a smile spread over his brown face. Very deliberately he blew a smoke ring into the air; then he turned his back on the tree and walked carelessly away, back along the trail he had come. The swish of the underbrush against his hunting boots grew fainter and fainter.

The pent-up air burst hotly from Rainsford's lungs. His first thought made him feel sick and numb. The general could follow a trail through the woods at night; he could follow an extremely difficult trail; he must have <u>uncanny</u> powers; only by the merest chance had the Cossack failed to see his quarry.

Rainsford's second thought was even more terrible. It sent a shudder of cold horror through his whole being. Why had the general smiled? Why had he turned back?

Rainsford did not want to believe what his reason told him was true, but the truth was as evident as the sun that had by now pushed through the morning mists. The general was playing with him! The general was saving him for another day's sport! The Cossack was the cat; he was the mouse. Then it was that Rainsford knew the full meaning of terror.

"I will not lose my nerve. I will not."

He slid down from the tree, and struck off again into the woods. His face was set and he forced the machinery of his mind to function. Three hundred yards from his hiding place he stopped where a huge dead tree leaned precariously on a smaller, living one. Throwing off his sack of food, Rainsford took his knife from its sheath and began to work with all his energy.

The job was finished at last, and he threw himself down behind a fallen log a hundred feet away. He did not have to wait long. The cat was coming again to play with the mouse.

Following the trail with the sureness of a bloodhound, came General Zaroff. Nothing escaped those searching black eyes, no crushed blade of grass, no bent twig, no mark, no matter how faint, in the moss. So intent was the Cossack on his stalking that he was upon the thing Rainsford had made before he saw it. His foot touched the

© Pearson Education

Vocabulary Development
pungent (PUN juhnt) *adj.* strong-smelling
uncanny (un KAN ee) *adj.* very strange

protruding bough that was the trigger. Even as he touched it, the general sensed his danger and leaped back with the agility of an ape. But he was not quite quick enough; the dead tree, delicately adjusted to rest on the cut living one, crashed down and struck the general a glancing blow on the shoulder as it fell; but for his alertness, he must have been smashed beneath it. He staggered, but he did not fall; nor did he drop his revolver. He stood there, rubbing his injured shoulder, and Rainsford, with fear again gripping his heart, heard the general's mocking laugh ring through the jungle.

"Rainsford," called the general, "if you are within the sound of my voice, as I suppose you are, let me congratulate you. Not many men know how to make a Malay mancatcher. Luckily, for me, I too have hunted in Malacca. You are proving interesting, Mr. Rainsford. I am going now to have my wound dressed; it's only a slight one. But I shall be back. I shall be back."

When the general, nursing his bruised shoulder, had gone, Rainsford took up his flight again. It was flight now, a desperate, hopeless flight, that carried him on for some hours. Dusk came, then darkness, and still he pressed on. The ground grew softer under his moccasins; the vegetation grew ranker, denser; insects bit him savagely. Then, as he stepped forward, his foot sank into the ooze. He tried to wrench it back, but the muck sucked viciously at his foot as if it were a giant leech. With a violent effort, he tore his foot loose. He knew where he was now. Death Swamp and its quicksand.

His hands were tight closed as if his nerve were something tangible that someone in the darkness was trying to tear from his grip. The softness of the earth had given him an idea. He stepped back from the quicksand a dozen feet or so, and, like some huge prehistoric beaver, he began to dig.

Rainsford had dug himself in[15] in France when a second's delay meant death. That had been a <u>placid</u> pastime compared to his digging now. The pit grew deeper; when it was above his shoulders, he climbed out and from some hard saplings cut stakes and sharpened them to a fine point. These stakes he planted in the bottom of the pit with the points sticking up. With flying fingers he wove a rough carpet of weeds and branches and with it he covered the mouth of the pit. Then, wet with sweat and aching with tiredness, he crouched behind the stump of a lightning-charred tree.

© Pearson Education

Vocabulary Development

placid (PLA sid) *adj.* calm

15. **dug himself in** dug a foxhole for himself during a war.

Stop to Reflect

Why do you think Zaroff congratulates Rainsford?

_____

_____

_____

_____

Literary Analysis

Who seems to be winning the **conflict** at this point in the story? Explain.

_____

_____

_____

_____

_____

Reading Check

Where does Rainsford go after he wounds the general? Underline the name of the place.

Reading Skill

When Rainsford hears the sharp scream of pain from the Burmese tiger pit, what does he **infer**?

_____

_____

_____

Is his **inference** correct? Explain.

_____

_____

_____

_____

Literary Analysis

New "hunters" join Zaroff in the chase. What additional **external conflict** does Rainsford now face?

_____

_____

_____

_____

_____

Reading Check

What sound awakens Rainsford at daybreak and gives him new fear? Underline the words that tell you.

He knew his pursuer was coming; he heard the padding sound of feet on the soft earth, and the night breeze brought him the perfume of the general's cigarette. It seemed to Rainsford that the general was coming with unusual swiftness; he was not feeling his way along, foot by foot. Rainsford, crouching there, could not see the general, nor could he see the pit. He lived a year in a minute. Then he felt an impulse to cry aloud with joy, for he heard the sharp crackle of the breaking branches as the cover of the pit gave way; he heard the sharp scream of pain as the pointed stakes found their mark. He leaped up from his place of concealment. Then he cowered back. Three feet from the pit a man was standing, with an electric torch in his hand.

"You've done well, Rainsford," the voice of the general called. "Your Burmese tiger pit has claimed one of my best dogs. Again you score. I think, Mr. Rainsford, I'll see what you can do against my whole pack. I'm going home for a rest now. Thank you for a most amusing evening."

At daybreak Rainsford, lying near the swamp, was awakened by a sound that made him know that he had new things to learn about fear. It was a distant sound, faint and wavering, but he knew it. It was the baying of a pack of hounds.

Rainsford knew he could do one of two things. He could stay where he was and wait. That was suicide. He could flee. That was postponing the <u>inevitable</u>. For a moment he stood there, thinking. An idea that held a wild chance came to him, and, tightening his belt, he headed away from the swamp.

The baying of the hounds drew nearer, then still nearer, nearer, ever nearer. On a ridge Rainsford climbed a tree. Down a watercourse, not a quarter of a mile away, he could see the bush moving. Straining his eyes, he saw the lean figure of General Zaroff; just ahead of him Rainsford made out another figure whose wide shoulders surged through the tall jungle weeds; it was the giant Ivan, and he seemed pulled forward by some unseen force; Rainsford knew that Ivan must be holding the pack in leash.

They would be on him any minute now. His mind worked frantically. He thought of a native trick he had learned in Uganda. He slid down the tree. He caught hold of a springy young sapling and to it he fastened his hunting knife, with the blade pointing down the trail; with a bit of wild grapevine he tied back the sapling. Then he ran for his life. The hounds raised their voices as they hit the fresh scent. Rainsford knew now how an animal at bay feels.

He had to stop to get his breath. The baying of the hounds stopped abruptly, and Rainsford's heart stopped too. They must have reached the knife.

He <u>shinnied</u> excitedly up a tree and looked back. His pursuers had stopped. But the hope that was in Rainsford's brain when he climbed died, for he saw in the shallow valley that General Zaroff was still on his feet. But Ivan was not. The knife, driven by the recoil of the springing tree, had not wholly failed.

"Nerve, nerve, nerve!" he panted, as he dashed along. A blue gap showed between the trees dead ahead. Ever nearer drew the hounds. Rainsford forced himself on toward that gap. He reached it. It was the shore of the sea. Across a cove he could see the gloomy gray stone of the chateau. Twenty feet below him the sea rumbled and hissed. Rainsford hesitated. He heard the hounds. Then he leaped far out into the sea. . . .

When the general and his pack reached the place by the sea, the Cossack stopped. For some minutes he stood regarding the blue-green expanse of water. He shrugged his shoulders. Then he sat down, took a drink of brandy from a silver flask, lit a perfumed cigarette, and hummed a bit from *Madame Butterfly*.[16]

General Zaroff had an exceedingly good dinner in his great paneled dining hall that evening. With it he had a bottle of Pol Roger and half a bottle of Chambertin. Two slight annoyances kept him from perfect enjoyment. One was the thought that it would be difficult to replace Ivan; the other was that his quarry had escaped him; of course the American hadn't played the game—so thought the general as he tasted his after-dinner liqueur. In his library he read, to soothe himself, from the works of Marcus Aurelius.[17] At ten he went up to his bedroom. He was deliciously tired, he said to himself, as he locked himself in. There was a little moonlight, so, before turning on his light, he went to the window and looked down at the courtyard. He could see the great hounds, and he called: "Better luck another time," to them. Then he switched on the light.

A man, who had been hiding in the curtain of the bed, was standing there.

TAKE NOTES

Literary Analysis

Rainsford hesitates before leaping into the sea. He experiences an **internal conflict**. Describe this conflict.

_____

_____

_____

_____

_____

Reading Skill

When Rainsford leaps into the sea, what **inference** do you think the author wants you to make?

_____

_____

_____

_____

Reading Check

Who is injured by the knife? Circle the text that tells you.

Vocabulary Development

shinnied (SHI need) *v.* climbed quickly

---

16. *Madame Butterfly* an opera by Giacomo Puccini.

17. *Marcus Aurelius* (MAHR kus aw REE lee uhs) Roman emperor and philosopher (A.D. 121–180).

© Pearson Education

Literary Analysis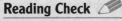

How is the **conflict** between Rainsford and Zaroff finally **resolved**?

_____

_____

_____

Reading Skill

What can you **infer** about Rainsford's state of mind in the underlined sentence?

_____

_____

_____

Reading Check

Zaroff congratulates Rainsford on winning the game. Circle the sentence that tells you Rainsford does not agree he has won.

"Rainsford!" screamed the general. "How in God's name did you get here?"

"Swam," said Rainsford. "I found it quicker than walking through the jungle."

The general sucked in his breath and smiled. "I congratulate you," he said. "You have won the game."

Rainsford did not smile. "I am still a beast at bay," he said, in a low, hoarse voice. "Get ready, General Zaroff."

The general made one of his deepest bows. "I see," he said. "Splendid! One of us is to furnish a <u>repast</u> for the hounds. The other will sleep in this very excellent bed. On guard, Rainsford. . . ."

<u>He had never slept in a better bed, Rainsford decided.</u>

Reader's Response: Were you satisfied with the outcome of this story? Why or why not?

_____

_____

_____

_____

_____

Vocabulary Development

repast (ri PAST) *n.* meal; food

The Most Dangerous Game

1. **Respond:** What do you like or dislike about Rainsford? Explain.

   _____

   _____

   _____

2. **Speculate:** How might Rainsford's experience on the island change him? Use evidence from the text to support your answer.

   _____

   _____

   _____

   _____

3. **Literary Analysis:** Use this chart to record details that reveal **conflicts** in the story.

Rainsford vs. nature	Rainsford vs. himself

4. **Reading Skill:** Write down one **inference** you made about Whitney.

   _____

   _____

   _____

   _____

Writing: Alternative Ending

Write an **alternative ending** to "The Most Dangerous Game." Use your notes from the following questions to help create your ending.

- If the general, rather than his dog, had fallen into the trap, how might the story have ended?

_____

_____

_____

- If Rainsford had not jumped into the sea, how might the story have ended?

_____

_____

_____

Listening and Speaking: Oral Presentation

Use the following lines to create an oral presentation about two or three-big game species mentioned in the story "The Most Dangerous Game."

Species #1: _____

Facts about this species: _____

Species #2: _____

Facts about this species: _____

Species #3: _____

Facts about this species: _____

Sources used: _____

_____

American History
Judith Ortiz Cofer

Summary Elena lives with her parents in Paterson, New Jersey. Her family is from Puerto Rico. She experiences discrimination on the day of President Kennedy's death. Elena tries to be sad for President Kennedy. However, she is too worried about her own problems.

Writing About the Big Question

Is conflict necessary? In "American History," a teenage girl wrestles with personal feelings while the adults around her try to grasp a historic but tragic event. Complete this sentence:

For both individuals and countries, important events often involve

because _____.

Note-taking Guide
Use this chart to recall the conflicts in the story.

Story Detail	What conflict does this story detail show?
Elena lives in El Building; Eugene lives in a house with a backyard.	Elena and Eugene come from different backgrounds.

American History

1. **Compare and Contrast:** How are Elena's feelings for her home different from her feelings for Eugene's house?

_____

_____

2. **Analyze:** At the end of the story, why does Elena say that her tears are just for herself?

_____

_____

3. **Literary Analysis:** Use the chart to write details that show both **external** and **internal conflict** in the story.

Elena vs. another person	Elena vs. herself

4. **Reading Skill:** Write three **inferences** you made while reading the story. What details did you use to make your inferences?

_____

_____

_____

_____

_____

Writing: Alternative Ending

Write an **alternative ending** to "American History." Write four possible events that could happen in your alternative ending. Then, write how the characters feel about the events. Write some dialogue to show what the characters think about the events. Your notes will help you write your alternative ending.

Event	How Characters Feel	Possible Dialogue

Listening and Speaking: Oral Presentation

Use the following lines to create an oral presentation on the effect of President Kennedy's assassination upon the American public.

Audience: _____

Tone: _____

How the public reacted to Kennedy's assassination: _____
_____
_____

Print sources used: _____
_____

Non-print sources used: _____
_____

The Gift of the Magi • The Interlopers

Literary Analysis

Irony is a difference or a contradiction between appearance and reality. It can also be a difference between what is expected and what actually happens.

- **Situational irony** occurs when something happens in the story that contradicts what a character or a reader thinks will happen. For example, if a runner trains hard for a race, she should run well in it. However, she could train so hard that she oversleeps and misses the race. That situation is ironic.

- A **surprise ending** often helps create situational irony. It has a turn of events that takes a reader by surprise. An author builds clues into the story to make a surprise ending believable. These clues make the ending logical.

Irony and a surprise ending help show the story's theme, or message.

Reading Skill

An **inference** is a logical guess. Base your inferences on details in the story. Also, **use your own prior knowledge and experience** to make inferences.

- You gather knowledge and experiences as you read, watch movies and plays, and observe the world every day.

- When you read something new, look for ways in which the characters and situations resemble ones you have seen before.

- Then, apply that knowledge and experience to make inferences.

Use this chart to record your inferences.

Detail	My Experience	Inference
	→	→

The Gift of the Magi
O. Henry

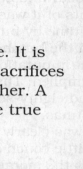

Summary Jim and Della are in love. It is Christmas Eve. Both people make sacrifices in order to buy presents for each other. A shocking twist at the end shows the true spirit of giving.

Writing About the Big Question

Is conflict necessary? In "The Gift of the Magi," Jim and Della want to exchange Christmas presents, but money is an issue. Complete this sentence:

When money is tight, it may be hard to show you appreciate others

because _____.

Note-taking Guide
Use this chart to record the events of the story.

Characters	Christmas Gift Idea	Action	Unexpected Result
Della	a watch chain		
Jim			

© Pearson Education

The Gift of the Magi

O. Henry

Activate Prior Knowledge

Think of a time when you wanted to buy something that you could not afford. What sacrifices did you make in order to save enough money to afford it?

_____

_____

Literary Analysis

Irony occurs when there is a difference between appearances and reality. Based on appearances so far, what kind of Christmas present will Della be able to buy for Jim? Underline the details that help you answer the question.

_____

_____

Reading Skill

When you make an **inference**, you draw a conclusion based on details in the story. Read the bracketed paragraph. What can you infer about Jim? What kind of person would he like to be?

_____

_____

Reading Check

Why is Della crying? Circle the text that tells you.

One dollar and eighty-seven cents. That was all. And sixty cents of it was in pennies. Pennies saved one and two at a time by bulldozing the grocer and the vegetable man and the butcher until one's cheeks burned with the silent imputation of parsimony[1] that such close dealing implied. Three times Della counted it. One dollar and eighty-seven cents. And the next day would be Christmas.

There was clearly nothing to do but flop down on the shabby little couch and howl. So Della did it. Which instigates the moral reflection that life is made up of sobs, sniffles, and smiles, with sniffles predominating.

While the mistress of the home is gradually subsiding from the first stage to the second, take a look at the home. A furnished flat[2] at $8 per week. It did not exactly beggar description,[3] but it certainly had that word on the lookout for the mendicancy squad.[4]

In the vestibule below was a letter-box into which no letter would go, and an electric button from which no mortal finger could coax a ring. Also appertaining thereunto was a card bearing the name "Mr. James Dillingham Young."

The "Dillingham" had been flung to the breeze during a former period of prosperity when its possessor was being paid $30 per week. Now, when the income was shrunk to $20, the letters of "Dillingham" looked blurred, as though they were thinking seriously of contracting to a modest and unassuming D. But whenever Mr. James Dillingham Young came home and reached his flat above he was called "Jim" and greatly hugged by Mrs. James Dillingham Young, already introduced to you as Della. Which is all very good.

Della finished her cry and attended to her cheeks with the powder rag. She stood by the window and looked out dully at a gray cat walking a gray fence in a gray backyard. Tomorrow would be Christmas Day, and she had only $1.87 with which to buy Jim a present. She had

---

Vocabulary Development

instigates (IN stuh gayts) _v._ urges on; stirs up

---

1. **imputation** (im pyoo TAY shuhn) **of parsimony** (PAHR suh moh nee) accusation of stinginess.
2. **flat** (flat) _n._ apartment.
3. **beggar description** make description seem inadequate or useless.
4. **it certainly...mendicancy** (MEN di kuhn see) **squad** It would have been noticed by the police who arrested beggars.

been saving every penny she could for months, with this result. Twenty dollars a week doesn't go far. Expenses had been greater than she had calculated. They always are. Only $1.87 to buy a present for Jim. Her Jim. Many a happy hour she had spent planning for something nice for him. Something fine and rare and sterling—something just a little bit near to being worthy of the honor of being owned by Jim.

There was a pier glass[5] between the windows of the room. Perhaps you have seen a pier glass in an $8 flat. A very thin and very agile person may, by observing his reflection in a rapid sequence of longitudinal strips, obtain a fairly accurate conception of his looks. Della, being slender, had mastered the art.

Suddenly she whirled from the window and stood before the glass. Her eyes were shining brilliantly, but her face had lost its color within twenty seconds. Rapidly she pulled down her hair and let it fall to its full length.

Now, there were two possessions of the James Dillingham Youngs in which they both took a mighty pride. One was Jim's gold watch that had been his father's and his grandfather's. The other was Della's hair. Had the Queen of Sheba[6] lived in the flat across the airshaft, Della would have let her hair hang out the window some day to dry just to <u>depreciate</u> Her Majesty's jewels and gifts. Had King Solomon been the janitor, with all his treasures piled up in the basement, Jim would have pulled out his watch every time he passed, just to see him pluck at his beard from envy.

So now Della's beautiful hair fell about her rippling and shining like a <u>cascade</u> of brown waters. It reached below her knee and made itself almost a garment for her. And then she did it up again nervously and quickly. Once she faltered for a minute and stood still while a tear or two splashed on the worn red carpet.

On went her old brown jacket; on went her old brown hat. With a whirl of skirts and with the brilliant sparkle still in her eyes, she fluttered out the door and down the stairs to the street.

Where she stopped the sign read: "Mme. Sofronie. Hair Goods of All Kinds." One flight up Della ran, and collected herself, panting. Madame, large, too white, chilly, hardly looked the "Sofronie."

© Pearson Education

Vocabulary Development

depreciate (di PREE shee ayt) v. to reduce in value

cascade (kas KAYD) n. waterfall

5. **pier glass** (peer glass) n. tall mirror between two windows.
6. **Queen of Sheba** the biblical queen who visited King Solomon to test his wisdom.

Stop to Reflect

Why do you think people want to give expensive gifts?

_____

_____

_____

Reading Skill ✏️

What can you **infer** about Della's thoughts and plans? Underline any details in the story that help you make your inference.

_____

_____

What **prior knowledge and experience** help you make this inference?

_____

_____

Reading Check

Why does Della have only $1.87 to spend on Jim's Christmas present? Circle the sentences that tell you.

Stop to Reflect

How do you think Della feels when she finds the perfect gift for Jim?

_____

_____

_____

How would you feel?

_____

_____

_____

Reading Skill ✏

How does Della feel as she waits for Jim to come home? **Use your own prior knowledge and experience**. Think about how you might feel after you have changed how you look and are waiting for someone's reaction. Then, underline sentences or phrases that help you **infer** Della's feelings.

_____

_____

_____

Reading Check ✏

How does Della get the money to buy Jim's present? Circle the text that tells you.

"Will you buy my hair?" asked Della.

"I buy hair," said Madame. "Take yer hat off and let's have a sight at the looks of it."

Down rippled the brown cascade.

"Twenty dollars," said Madame, lifting the mass with a practiced hand.

"Give it to me quick," said Della.

Oh, and the next two hours tripped by on rosy wings. Forget the hashed metaphor. She was ransacking the stores for Jim's present.

She found it at last. It surely had been made for Jim and no one else. There was no other like it in any of the stores, and she had turned all of them inside out. It was a platinum fob chain[7] simple and <u>chaste</u> in design, properly proclaiming its value by substance alone and not by <u>meretricious</u> ornamentation—as all good things should do. It was even worthy of The Watch. As soon as she saw it she knew that it must be Jim's. It was like him. Quietness and value—the description applied to both. Twenty-one dollars they took from her for it, and she hurried home with the 87 cents. With that chain on his watch Jim might be properly anxious about the time in any company. Grand as the watch was he sometimes looked at it on the sly on account of the old leather strap that he used in place of a chain.

When Della reached home her intoxication gave way a little to prudence and reason. She got out her curling irons and lighted the gas and went to work repairing the <u>ravages</u> made by generosity added to love. Which is always a tremendous task, dear friends—a mammoth task.

Within forty minutes her head was covered with tiny, close-lying curls that made her look wonderfully like a truant schoolboy. She looked at her reflection in the mirror long, carefully, and critically.

"If Jim doesn't kill me," she said to herself, "before he takes a second look at me, he'll say I look like a Coney Island[8] chorus girl. But what could I do—oh! what could I do with a dollar and eighty-seven cents?"

At 7 o'clock the coffee was made and the frying-pan was on the back of the stove hot and ready to cook the chops.

Jim was never late. Della doubled the fob chain in her hand and sat on the corner of the table near the door that

Vocabulary Development

chaste (CHAST) *adj.* pure or clean in style; not ornate

meretricious (mer uh TRISH uhs) *adj.* attractive in a cheap and flashy way

ravages (RA vij iz) *n.* ruins, devastating damages

7. **fob chain** (fahb chayn) small chain connecting a watch to its pocket.

8. **Coney** (KOH nee) **Island** beach and amusement park in New York City.

he always entered. Then she heard his step on the stair away down on the first flight, and she turned white for just a moment. She had a habit of saying little silent prayers about the simplest everyday things, and now she whispered: "Please God, make him think I am still pretty."

The door opened and Jim stepped in and closed it. He looked thin and very serious. Poor fellow, he was only twenty-two—and to be burdened with a family! He needed a new overcoat and he was without gloves.

Jim stopped inside the door, as immovable as a setter[9] at the scent of quail. His eyes were fixed upon Della, and there was an expression in them that she could not read, and it terrified her. It was not anger, nor surprise, nor disapproval, nor horror, nor any of the sentiments that she had been prepared for. He simply stared at her fixedly with that peculiar expression on his face.

Della wriggled off the table and went for him.

"Jim, darling," she cried, "don't look at me that way. I had my hair cut off and sold it because I couldn't have lived through Christmas without giving you a present. It'll grow out again—you won't mind, will you? I just had to do it. My hair grows awfully fast. Say 'Merry Christmas!' Jim, and let's be happy. You don't know what a nice—what a beautiful, nice gift I've got for you."

"You've cut off your hair?" asked Jim, <u>laboriously</u>, as if he had not arrived at that patent fact yet even after the hardest mental labor.

"Cut it off and sold it," said Della. "Don't you like me just as well, anyhow? I'm me without my hair, ain't I?"

Jim looked about the room curiously.

"You say your hair is gone?" he said, with an air almost of idiocy.

"You needn't look for it," said Della. "It's sold, I tell you—sold and gone, too. It's Christmas Eve, boy. Be good to me, for it went for you. Maybe the hairs of my head were numbered," she went on with a sudden serious sweetness, "but nobody could ever count my love for you. Shall I put the chops on, Jim?"

Out of his trance Jim seemed quickly to wake. He enfolded his Della. For ten seconds let us regard with <u>discreet</u> scrutiny some inconsequential object in the other direction. Eight dollars a week or a million a year—what is the difference? A mathematician or a wit would give you

Vocabulary Development

laboriously (luh BAWR ee uhs lee) *adv.* slowly and with a lot of effort

discreet (dis KREET) *adj.* careful about what one says or does

9. **setter** (SET uhr) *n.* hunting dog.

Reading Skill

Read the first bracketed passage. What can you **infer** about Jim's behavior when he sees Della?

_____

_____

_____

Reading Skill

Read the second bracketed passage. What might you **infer** about why Jim keeps asking Della whether her hair is gone?

_____

_____

_____

Reading Check

What does Della hope Jim will think when he sees her? Underline the sentence that tells you.

Literary Analysis

Irony is a difference between what is expected and what actually happens. In what way does Jim's gift to Della create an ironic situation?

_____

_____

_____

Reading Skill

Jim smiles when Della asks him for his watch. What can you **infer** about how Jim feels about the situation?

_____

_____

_____

Reading Check

Draw a circle around the paragraph that answers this question: Does Jim really mind that Della has cut her hair, as Della fears?

---

the wrong answer. The Magi brought valuable gifts, but that was not among them. This dark assertion will be illuminated later on.

Jim drew a package from his overcoat pocket and threw it upon the table.

"Don't make any mistake, Dell," he said, "about me. I don't think there's anything in the way of a haircut or a shave or a shampoo that could make me like my girl any less. But if you'll unwrap that package you may see why you had me going a while at first."

White fingers and nimble tore at the string and paper. And then an ecstatic scream of joy; and then, alas! a quick feminine change to hysterical tears and wails, necessitating the immediate employment of all the comforting powers of the lord of the flat.

For there lay The Combs—the set of combs, side and back, that Della had worshipped for long in a Broadway window. Beautiful combs, pure tortoise shell, with jeweled rims—just the shade to wear in the beautiful vanished hair. They were expensive combs, she knew, and her heart had simply craved and yearned over them without the least hope of possession. And now, they were hers, but the tresses that should have adorned the coveted adornments were gone.

But she hugged them to her bosom, and at length she was able to look up with dim eyes and a smile and say: "My hair grows so fast, Jim!"

And then Della leaped up like a little singed cat and cried, "Oh, oh!"

Jim had not yet seen his beautiful present. She held it out to him eagerly upon her open palm. The dull precious metal seemed to flash with a reflection of her bright and ardent spirit.

"Isn't it a dandy, Jim? I hunted all over town to find it. You'll have to look at the time a hundred times a day now. Give me your watch. I want to see how it looks on it."

Instead of obeying, Jim tumbled down on the couch and put his hands under the back of his head and smiled.

"Dell," said he, "let's put our Christmas presents away and keep 'em a while. They're too nice to use just at present. I sold the watch to get the money to buy your combs. And now suppose you put the chops on."

The Magi, as you know, were wise men—wonderfully wise men—who brought gifts to the Babe in the manger. They invented the art of giving Christmas presents. Being wise, their gifts were no doubt wise ones, possibly bearing

---

Vocabulary Development

necessitating (nuh SES uh tayt ing) *v.* making something necessary

the privilege of exchange in case of duplication. And here I have lamely related to you the uneventful <u>chronicle</u> of two foolish children in a flat who most <u>unwisely</u> sacrificed for each other the greatest treasures of their house. But in a last word to the wise of these days let it be said that of all who give gifts these two were the wisest. Of all who give and receive gifts, such as they are wisest. Everywhere they are wisest. They are the magi.

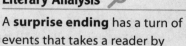
Reader's Response: Do you think that Jim and Della were foolish to spend money they did not have on gifts for each other? Why or why not?

_____

_____

_____

_____

_____

Literary Analysis

A **surprise ending** has a turn of events that takes a reader by surprise. Explain why the ending is a surprise to both the characters and the reader.

_____

_____

_____

Stop to Reflect

Why do you think the narrator describes the couple as "foolish"? Why does the narrator then describe them as "wise"?

_____

_____

_____

_____

_____

Vocabulary Development

chronicle (KRAH ni kuhl) *n.* a story telling the sequence of historical events

The Gift of the Magi

1. **Infer:** Della sells her hair to buy Jim's present. What does this action tell you about her character?

   _____

   _____

2. **Draw Conclusions:** O. Henry says of these "two foolish children" that they were "the wisest." How do you think he would define wisdom?

   _____

   _____

3. **Literary Analysis:** Read the chart below. What theme or message about life does this **situational irony** convey?

   _____

   _____

What Characters Expect	What Actually Happens
Della expects Jim to put the watch chain on his watch right away. Jim expects Della to be happy about the expensive combs for her hair.	Jim tells Della that he has sold his watch to buy her combs. He cannot use the watch chain. Della has cut her hair. She cannot use the combs.

4. **Reading Skill:** In what ways do your **prior knowledge and experience** of characters like Jim and Della help you make inferences about them? Explain.

   _____

   _____

   _____

Writing: News Story

Write a brief **news story** about Jim and Della's experience. The following questions will help you complete your news story:

- In your lead paragraph, did you use eye-catching details that will keep a reader interested? List two of these details.

  _____

  _____

  _____

- Did you elaborate on the details in the paragraphs following your lead paragraph? Name two of the details you elaborated on.

  _____

  _____

  _____

- Was your information clear to readers? Reread your news story. Rewrite sections or sentences that might be unclear to a reader.

  _____

  _____

  _____

Listening and Speaking: Debate

Look at each position for your debate about the lesson of "The Gift of the Magi." List some quotations from the story that support each position.

Position 1: The story's lesson is that sacrifice is the best expression of love.

Support for this position: _____

_____

Position 2: The story's lesson is that it is foolish to spend money on gifts instead of necessities.

Support for this position: _____

_____

The Interlopers
Saki

Summary Two men are involved in a long-standing family feud. One night, they meet in a forest. They are ready to kill each other, but then a tree falls on them. Waiting to be rescued, they overcome their differences. Unfortunately, an unexpected danger makes their efforts at peace useless.

Writing About the Big Question

Is conflict necessary? In "The Interlopers," men from feuding families face a situation that makes them rethink their grievance. Complete this sentence:

In a longtime feud, the people involved may struggle to resolve their

issues amicably because _____.

Note-taking Guide

Record details about the surprises in the story. Follow the example below.

Detail	What the Reader Expects	What Actually Happen
Ulrich and Georg meet in the woods. They are prepared to fight to the death.	The men will fight. One of them will kill the other.	The storm brings down a tree. It pins them to the ground.

The Interlopers

1. **Interpret:** Why does Georg not consider himself a poacher?

   _____

   _____

   _____

2. **Draw Conclusions:** Why do Ulrich and Georg decide to end their feud?

   _____

   _____

   _____

3. **Literary Analysis:** Read the chart below. What theme or message about life does this **situational irony** convey?

   _____

   _____

   _____

What Characters Expect	What Actually Happens
Ulrich and Georg expect to be friends and end their feud.	They will probably be attacked by wolves and will die.

4. **Reading Skill:** What **inferences** do you think Saki intended readers to make about Ulrich and Georg?

   _____

   _____

   _____

Writing: News Story

Write a brief **news story** about Ulrich and Georg's experience. Your lead paragraph should make your readers want to learn more. The following questions will help you write a strong lead.

- Tell what happened. Make sure you answer the questions *Who? What? When? Where?* and *Why?*

_____

_____

_____

_____

- Choose one fact to present as your lead.

_____

_____

_____

- Write your lead paragraph and read it aloud to a partner. Take out or change any part that is not clear or that does not make your partner curious.

Listening and Speaking: Debate

Look at each position for your debate about the disputed land in "The Interlopers." List some quotations from the story that support each position.

Position 1: Ulrich von Gradwitz is entitled to the disputed land.

Support for this position: _____

_____

Position 2: Georg Znaeym is entitled to the disputed land.

Support for this position: _____

_____

Procedural Texts

About Procedural Texts

Consumer guides, instructions, and how-to manuals are all **procedural texts**. The objective, or goal, of a procedural text is to give a reader instructions or important information about how to do something properly.

These features make **consumer guides** easy to understand:

- Simple words
- Pictures or symbols
- Colors and lettering that help words and pictures stand out

Instructions can have more words than consumer guides. However, these features make most instructions easy to understand:

- Easy-to-understand words
- Step-by-step guidance
- "Do this" statements with no extra information

Reading Skill

When you **analyze the objectives of a procedural text**, look at how clearly the text gives instructions or information. Ask yourself: *Are the instructions easy to understand and follow? Is the information clear and straightforward?* Some procedural texts use pictures, color, and letters to give information. You should look at these text features when you analyze the objectives of a procedural text. You can decide whether you think these features make the document easy to understand.

How to Analyze Procedural Texts

STOP
Do the graphics and text grab your attention?

READ
Can you easily understand the message?

ASK
Are the elements used effectively to emphasize the most important information?

Text Structure

The graphic is a warning. Circle the part of the picture that shows what could happen to you. Underline the words that tell you the same thing.

Vocabulary Builder

Parts of Speech As a noun, *surf* means "waves that come onto the beach." As a verb, it means "ride on ocean waves standing on a special board." Which meaning is used in the section labeled "Condition"?

_____

_____

Fluency Builder

With a partner, read aloud the section labeled "Instructions." Be sure to read the text with expression.

BEACH SAFETY: HIGH SURF SIGN

WARNING LEVEL: *DANGEROUS* . . . a potential for loss of life or limb exists.

CONDITION: Large powerful waves are generated by winds and storms at sea sometimes thousands of miles from the Hawaiian Islands. Seasonal high surf occurs on all shores of O'ahu. Typically, shorelines facing North, East and West receive high surf during Winter months. Shores facing Southeast and Southwest receive high surf during Summer months. Surf on the North shore may reach heights of twenty-five feet plus,—on the West shore, fifteen feet plus!

INSTRUCTIONS: If you're uncertain of your abilities, don't go into the ocean during high surf, heed all posted high surf warnings! Your life could depend on it!

BEACH SAFETY: STRONG CURRENT SIGN

WARNING LEVEL: *DANGEROUS* . . . a potential for loss of life or limb exists.

CONDITION: These are swift moving channels of water against which it is difficult to swim. Strong currents frequently accompany high surf and rapid tide changes and can be recognized as a turbulent channel of water between areas where waves are breaking.

INSTRUCTIONS: When caught in a strong current— Try to keep a level head, i.e., don't panic! Wave one or both hands in the air, and scream or call for help. Swim diagonally to the current, not against it.

OCEAN SAFETY TIPS:
- Swim in Lifeguarded Areas
- Never Swim Alone.
- Don't Dive Into Unknown Water or Into Shallow Breaking Waves.
- Ask a Lifeguard About Beach and Surf Conditions Before Swimming.
- If You Are Unable to Swim Out of a Strong Current, Signal for Help.
- Rely on Your Swimming Ability Rather Than a Flotation Device.
- Look For, Read and Obey All Beach Safety Signs and Symbols.
- If In Doubt, Just Stay Out!

Text Structure

The most important words on graphics are printed in large letters. This graphic has two areas of large text. Circle these two words or phrases. Write these words or phrases below the ideas that they match.

Tells people to be careful

_____

Tells people why they need to be careful

_____

Comprehension Builder

How should a person swim if he or she is caught in a current? Write your answer on the lines below.

_____

_____

_____

Cultural Understanding

In 1959, Hawaii became the 50th state in the United States. Hawaii is a group of volcanic islands located in the Pacific Ocean. It is a very popular state. The islands are busy with tourists and with the people who live there.

Thinking About Consumer Safety Guides

1. Consumer guides can be helpful to people who do not read English. Explain why.

   _____

2. The picture on the High Surf graphic shows what can happen. The instructions below the graphic suggest that some people might be safe. Who might be safe?

   _____

TALK ABOUT IT **Reading Skill**

3. What is the objective, or goal, of the consumer safety guide?

   _____

4. What text features help the guide make information clear?

   _____

   _____

WRITE ABOUT IT **Timed Writing: Speech (25 minutes)**

People can get hurt when they do not follow guides and instructions. Write a speech for your class. Urge your classmates to follow guides and instructions. Be sure to support your ideas. Begin by thinking of safety problems you have seen. List them below.

_____

_____

_____

_____

Rules of the Game • The Necklace

Literary Analysis

A **character** is a person, an animal, or even an object that participates in the action of a story. Writers tell what characters are like through **characterization:**

- **Direct characterization:** The writer explains a character.
- **Indirect characterization:** The writer gives clues about a character. The writer does this by describing the character's behavior, words and thoughts, physical appearance, or how others react to the character.

Use this chart to track characterization as you read.

Story Details	What They Show About the Character
Narrator's comments	
Character's thoughts and words	
Character's actions	
Character's appearance	
What others say or think about the character	

Reading Skill

A **cause** is an event, an action, or a feeling. It produces a result. An **effect** is the result it produces. As you read, **ask questions to analyze cause and effect.**

- What happened?
- Why did it happen?
- What happens as a result?

Sometimes a single cause produces more than one effect. For example, a character is a poor student. She starts to do well in school. Doing well makes her feel better about herself. Effects may, in turn, become causes. That same character's new confidence leads her to try out for a play.

Rules of the Game
Amy Tan

Summary Waverly Jong, a Chinese American girl, is fascinated with the game of chess. She becomes a national champion. She uses her knowledge of the game in her arguments with her mother.

❓ Writing About the Big Question

Is conflict necessary? In "The Rules of the Game," a girl learns some life lessons while learning to master chess. Complete this sentence:

Real-life conflicts resemble a game when _____

_____.

Note-taking Guide

Use this chart to record two events in the rising action, the climax, and the resolution of the story.

Event 1: Waverly learns that if she wants something, it is better to remain silent.	→	Event 2:	→	Event 3:

Climax:

Resolution:

Rules of the Game

1. **Connect:** Mrs. Jong teaches Waverly rules of behavior. How does Waverly translate these rules into strategies for winning at chess?

   _____

   _____

2. **Speculate:** Who do you think will "win" the game between Waverly and her mother? Explain.

   _____

   _____

   _____

3. **Literary Analysis:** Waverly and Mrs. Jong discuss Chinese torture. Is this conversation an example of **direct** or **indirect characterization**? Explain.

   _____

   _____

   _____

4. **Reading Skill:** Use this chart to **analyze cause and effect** in the story. Identify two causes for Waverly's success with chess. Then, identify three **effects** of her success.

Causes		Effects
_____	Waverly is successful at chess.	_____
_____		_____
_____		_____
_____		_____

Writing: Written Presentation

Think about a lesson you could teach Waverly and her mother to help them resolve their conflict. Use this chart to organize your ideas for the **written presentation**.

- In the left column, write an issue that Waverly and her mother face.

- In the center column, write what you would teach them.

- In the right column, write "story with a moral" or "essay" to show how you would write the lesson.

Issue	What I Would Teach	How I Would Write the Lesson
_____	_____	_____
_____	_____	_____

Use your notes to draft your presentation.

Research and Technology: Informative Brochure

Create an **informative brochure** on chess. Use the chart below to list the questions that you want to answer in your research. Use your notes to help you create your brochure.

What I Want to Know About Chess	
QUESTIONS	ANSWERS
What is chess?	
Where did chess start?	

The Necklace
Guy de Maupassant

Summary Madame Loisel dreams of being rich. When her husband receives an invitation to an important party, Madame Loisel borrows a diamond necklace to wear with her new dress. She loses the necklace. For ten years she works to pay for a replacement. Then, she learns a secret about the necklace.

 Writing About the Big Question

Is conflict necessary? In "The Necklace," a woman is jealous of people with greater wealth and social standing. Complete this sentence:

Jealously can lead to many conflicts because _____

_____ .

Note-taking Guide

Use this sequence-of-events chart to list the order of the four most important events in the story.

Beginning Event			Final Event
Madame Loisel borrows a diamond necklace.			

The Necklace
Guy de Maupassant

Activate Prior Knowledge

Have you ever lost or broken something that was valuable? Describe your feelings when you first realized the object was missing or broken.

_____

_____

_____

Literary Analysis

In **direct characterization**, the author simply tells you what a character is like. What does the author tell you about the young woman in the first two paragraphs?

_____

_____

_____

Reading Check

Why does Madame Loisel suffer constantly? Circle the details that tell you the answer.

Literary Analysis

In **indirect characterization,** the author gives clues about the character. What does the husband's comment in the bracketed passage show indirectly about his character?

_____

_____

_____

She was one of those pretty, charming young women who are born, as if by an error of Fate, into a petty official's family. She had no dowry,[1] no hopes, not the slightest chance of being appreciated, understood, loved, and married by a rich and distinguished man; so she slipped into marriage with a minor civil servant at the Ministry of Education.

Unable to afford jewelry, she dressed simply: but she was as wretched as a déclassé, for women have neither caste nor breeding—in them beauty, grace, and charm replace pride of birth. Innate refinement, instinctive elegance, and suppleness of wit give them their place on the only scale that counts, and these qualities make humble girls the peers of the grandest ladies.

She suffered constantly, feeling that all the attributes of a gracious life, every luxury, should rightly have been hers. The poverty of her rooms—the shabby walls, the worn furniture, the ugly upholstery—caused her pain. All these things that another woman of her class would not even have noticed, tormented her and made her angry. The very sight of the little Breton girl who cleaned for her awoke rueful thoughts and the wildest dreams in her mind. She dreamt of thick-carpeted reception rooms with Oriental hangings, lighted by tall, bronze torches, and with two huge footmen in knee breeches, made drowsy by the heat from the stove, asleep in the wide armchairs. She dreamt of great drawing rooms upholstered in old silks, with fragile little tables holding priceless knick-knacks, and of enchanting little sitting rooms redolent of perfume, designed for tea-time chats with intimate friends—famous, sought-after men whose attentions all women longed for.

When she sat down to dinner at her round table with its three-day-old cloth, and watched her husband opposite her lift the lid of the soup tureen and exclaim, delighted: "Ah, a good homemade beef stew! There's nothing better . . ." she would visualize elegant dinners with gleaming silver amid tapestried walls peopled by knights and ladies and exotic birds in a fairy forest; she would think of exquisite dishes

---

Vocabulary Development

caste (kast) *n.* social class

innate (i NAYT) *adj.* belonging to someone since birth

rueful (ROO fuhl) *adj.* feeling sorrow or regret

---

1. **dowry** (DOW ree) *n.* property that a woman brings to her husband at marriage.

served on gorgeous china, and of gallantries whispered and received with sphinx-like smiles[2] while eating the pink flesh of trout or wings of grouse.

She had no proper wardrobe, no jewels, nothing. And those were the only things that she loved—she felt she was made for them. She would have so loved to charm, to be envied, to be admired and sought after.

She had a rich friend, a schoolmate from the convent she had attended, but she didn't like to visit her because it always made her so miserable when she got home again. She would weep for whole days at a time from sorrow, regret, despair, and distress.

Then one evening her husband arrived home looking triumphant and waving a large envelope.

"There," he said, "there's something for you."

She tore it open eagerly and took out a printed card which said:

"The Minister of Education and Madame Georges Ramponneau[3] request the pleasure of the company of M. and Mme. Loisel[4] at an evening reception at the Ministry on Monday, January 18th."

Instead of being delighted, as her husband had hoped, she tossed the invitation on the table and muttered, annoyed:

"What do you expect me to do with that?"

"Why, I thought you'd be pleased, dear. You never go out and this would be an occasion for you, a great one! I had a lot of trouble getting it. Everyone wants an invitation; they're in great demand and there are only a few reserved for the employees. All the officials will be there."

She looked at him, irritated, and said impatiently:

"I haven't a thing to wear. How could I go?"

It had never even occurred to him. He stammered:

"But what about the dress you wear to the theater? I think it's lovely. . . ."

He fell silent, amazed and bewildered to see that his wife was crying. Two big tears escaped from the corners of her eyes and rolled slowly toward the corners of her mouth. He mumbled:

"What is it? What is it?"

But, with great effort, she had overcome her misery; and now she answered him calmly, wiping her tear-damp cheeks:

"It's nothing. It's just that I have no evening dress and so I can't go to the party. Give the invitation to one of your colleagues whose wife will be better dressed than I would be."

© Pearson Education

2. **gallantries whispered and received with sphinx-like smiles** flirtatious compliments whispered and received with mysterious smiles.

3. **Madame Georges Ramponneau** (muh DAHM zhorzh rahm puh NOH)

4. **Loisel** (lwah ZEL)

Reading Skill

A **cause** is an event, an action, or a feeling that produces a result. An **effect** is the result produced. Why do visits to her rich friend always cause the young woman to be upset?

_____

_____

Stop to Reflect

If you could speak to Madame Loisel at this point in the story, what advice would you give her?

_____

_____

_____

Reading Skill

What **causes** the husband to be surprised by his wife's reaction to the party invitation?

_____

_____

Reading Check

Why does Madame Loisel feel unable to go to the reception at the Ministry of Education? Draw a circle around the text that tells you the answer.

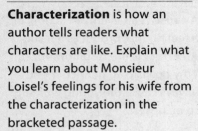
Literary Analysis

Characterization is how an author tells readers what characters are like. Explain what you learn about Monsieur Loisel's feelings for his wife from the characterization in the bracketed passage.

_____

_____

_____

Reading Skill

As you read, you should **ask questions to analyze cause and effect.** Underline a passage that shows an effect of the Loisels' invitation to the party. Then, ask a question about how this effect might become the cause of another event.

_____

_____

_____

_____

Reading Check

How does Madame Loisel feel when her husband suggests that she wear flowers to the party? Circle the sentence that tells the answer.

He was overcome. He said:

"Listen, Mathilde,[5] how much would an evening dress cost—a suitable one that you could wear again on other occasions, something very simple?"

She thought for several seconds, making her calculations and at the same time estimating how much she could ask for without <u>eliciting</u> an immediate refusal and an exclamation of horror from this economical government clerk.

At last, not too sure of herself, she said:

"It's hard to say exactly but I think I could manage with four hundred francs."

He went a little pale, for that was exactly the amount he had put aside to buy a rifle so that he could go hunting the following summer near Nanterre, with a few friends who went shooting larks around there on Sundays.

However, he said:

"Well, all right, then. I'll give you four hundred francs. But try to get something really nice."

As the day of the ball drew closer, Madame Loisel seemed depressed, disturbed, worried—despite the fact that her dress was ready. One evening her husband said:

"What's the matter? You've really been very strange these last few days."

And she answered:

"I hate not having a single jewel, not one stone, to wear. I shall look so dowdy.[6] I'd almost rather not go to the party."

He suggested:

"You can wear some fresh flowers. It's considered very chic[7] at this time of year. For ten francs you can get two or three beautiful roses."

That didn't satisfy her at all.

"No . . . there's nothing more humiliating than to look poverty-stricken among a lot of rich women."

Then her husband exclaimed:

"Wait—you silly thing! Why don't you go and see Madame Forestier[8] and ask her to lend you some jewelry. You certainly know her well enough for that, don't you think?"

She let out a joyful cry.

"You're right. It never occurred to me."

The next day she went to see her friend and related her tale of woe.

Vocabulary Development

eliciting (i LIS it ing) _v._ getting information from someone

5. **Mathilde** (muh TEELD)

6. **dowdy** (DOW dee) _adj._ shabby.

7. **chic** (sheek) _adj._ fashionable.

8. **Forestier** (foh ruh STYAY)

Madame Forestier went to her mirrored wardrobe, took out a big jewel case, brought it to Madame Loisel, opened it, and said:

"Take your pick, my dear."

Her eyes wandered from some bracelets to a pearl necklace, then to a gold Venetian cross set with stones, of very fine workmanship. She tried on the jewelry before the mirror, hesitating, unable to bring herself to take them off, to give them back. And she kept asking:

"Do you have anything else, by chance?"

"Why yes. Here, look for yourself. I don't know which ones you'll like."

All at once, in a box lined with black satin, she came upon a superb diamond necklace, and her heart started beating with overwhelming desire. Her hands trembled as she picked it up. She fastened it around her neck over her high-necked dress and stood there gazing at herself ecstatically.

Hesitantly, filled with terrible anguish, she asked:

"Could you lend me this one—just this and nothing else?"

"Yes, of course."

She threw her arms around her friend's neck, kissed her ardently, and fled with her treasure.

The day of the party arrived. Madame Loisel was a great success. She was the prettiest woman there—resplendent, graceful, beaming, and deliriously happy. All the men looked at her, asked who she was, tried to get themselves introduced to her. All the minister's aides wanted to waltz with her. The minister himself noticed her.

She danced enraptured—carried away, intoxicated with pleasure, forgetting everything in this triumph of her beauty and the glory of her success, floating in a cloud of happiness formed by all this homage, all this admiration, all the desires she had stirred up—by this victory so complete and so sweet to the heart of a woman.

When she left the party, it was almost four in the morning. Her husband had been sleeping since midnight in a small, deserted sitting room, with three other gentlemen whose wives were having a wonderful time.

He brought her wraps so that they could leave and put them around her shoulders—the plain wraps from her everyday life whose shabbiness jarred with the elegance of her evening dress. She felt this and wanted to escape quickly so that the other women, who were enveloping themselves in their rich furs, wouldn't see her.

© Pearson Education

Vocabulary Development

resplendent (ri SPLEN duhnt) *adj.* shining brightly

enraptured (in RAP chuhrd) *adv.* filled with delight

TAKE NOTES

Literary Analysis

Underline the phrases in the first bracketed paragraph that are examples of **indirect characterization**. What do you learn about Madame Loisel from this characterization?

_____

_____

_____

_____

Reading Skill

Read the second bracketed passage. What **question** might you ask about Madame Loisel's behavior?

_____

_____

_____

Reading Check

Why does Madame Loisel want to leave quickly when the party is over? Circle the sentence that gives you the answer.

Read the bracketed passage. Why do you think the Loisels are sad?

_____

_____

_____

_____

Reading Skill

What **question** might you ask about how Monsieur Loisel and Madame Loisel react to the loss of the necklace?

_____

_____

_____

Underline a sentence or phrase that shows the **effect** of the necklace's loss on Monsieur Loisel.

Reading Check

When does Madame Loisel discover the loss of the necklace? Circle the passage that tells you.

Loisel held her back.

"Wait a minute. You'll catch cold out there. I'm going to call a cab."

But she wouldn't listen to him and went hastily downstairs. Outside in the street, there was no cab to be found; they set out to look for one, calling to the drivers they saw passing in the distance.

They walked toward the Seine,[9] shivering and miserable. Finally, on the embankment, they found one of those ancient <u>nocturnal</u> broughams[10] which are only to be seen in Paris at night, as if they were ashamed to show their shabbiness in daylight.

It took them to their door in the Rue des Martyrs, and they went sadly upstairs to their apartment. For her, it was all over. And he was thinking that he had to be at the Ministry by ten.

She took off her wraps before the mirror so that she could see herself in all her glory once more. Then she cried out. The necklace was gone; there was nothing around her neck.

Her husband, already half undressed, asked:

"What's the matter?"

She turned toward him in a frenzy:

"The . . . the . . . necklace—it's gone."

He got up, thunderstruck.

"What did you say? . . . What! . . . Impossible!"

And they searched the folds of her dress, the folds of her wrap, the pockets, everywhere. They didn't find it.

He asked:

"Are you sure you still had it when we left the ball?"

"Yes. I remember touching it in the hallway of the Ministry."

"But if you had lost it in the street, we would have heard it fall. It must be in the cab."

"Yes, most likely. Do you remember the number?"

"No. What about you—did you notice it?"

"No."

They looked at each other in utter <u>dejection</u>. Finally Loisel got dressed again.

"I'm going to retrace the whole distance we covered on foot," he said, "and see if I can't find it."

Vocabulary Development

nocturnal (nahk TER nel) *adj.* active at night

dejection (di JEK shuhn) *n.* disappointment

9. **Seine** (SAYN) river flowing through Paris.
10. **broughams** (BROOMZ) *n.* horse-drawn carriages.

And he left the house. She remained in her evening dress, too weak to go to bed, sitting crushed on a chair, lifeless and blank.

Her husband returned at about seven o'clock. He had found nothing.

He went to the police station, to the newspapers to offer a reward, to the offices of the cab companies—in a word, wherever there seemed to be the slightest hope of tracing it.

She spent the whole day waiting, in a state of utter hopelessness before such an <u>appalling</u> catastrophe.

Loisel returned in the evening, his face lined and pale; he had learned nothing.

"You must write to your friend," he said, "and tell her that you've broken the clasp of the necklace and that you're getting it mended. That'll give us time to decide what to do."

She wrote the letter at his dictation.

By the end of the week, they had lost all hope.

Loisel, who had aged five years, declared:

"We'll have to replace the necklace."

The next day they took the case in which it had been kept and went to the jeweler whose name appeared inside it. He looked through his ledgers:

"I didn't sell this necklace, madame. I only supplied the case."

Then they went from one jeweler to the next, trying to find a necklace like the other, racking their memories, both of them sick with worry and distress.

In a fashionable shop near the Palais Royal, they found a diamond necklace which they decided was exactly like the other. It was worth 40,000 francs. They could have it for 36,000 francs.

They asked the jeweler to hold it for them for three days, and they stipulated that he should take it back for 34,000 francs if the other necklace was found before the end of February.

Loisel possessed 18,000 francs left him by his father. He would borrow the rest.

He borrowed, asking a thousand francs from one man, five hundred from another, a hundred here, fifty there. He signed promissory notes,[11] borrowed at <u>exorbitant</u> rates,

Vocabulary Development

appalling (uh PAWL ing) *adj.* greatly shocking

exorbitant (ig ZAWR buh tuhnt) *adj.* much higher or greater than is normal

11. **promissory** (PRAHM i sawr ee) **notes** written promises to pay back borrowed money.

TAKE NOTES

Literary Analysis

After the necklace is lost, what do the Loisels' actions reveal about their individual **characters?**

_____

_____

_____

_____

Reading Skill

The Loisels look for the necklace for a week, but they do not find it. What is one **effect** of their unsuccessful search?

_____

_____

_____

Reading Check

The Loisels do not have enough money to replace the necklace. What do they plan on doing to get more money? Circle the sentence that tells the answer.

Reading Skill

What **causes** the Loisels not to tell Madame Forestier that the necklace was lost? Underline the sentence that gives you the answer.

Literary Analysis

At the beginning of the story, Madame Loisel was ashamed of her modest lifestyle. How has Madame Loisel changed?

_____

_____

_____

Circle a passage in which the author shows the change in Madame Loisel through **indirect characterization**.

Reading Check

Why is Madame Loisel now responsible for doing all the heavy household chores? Underline the sentence that tells you the answer.

dealt with <u>usurers</u> and the entire race of moneylenders. He compromised his whole career, gave his signature even when he wasn't sure he would be able to honor it, and horrified by the anxieties with which his future would be filled, by the black misery about to descend upon him, by the prospect of physical <u>privation</u> and moral suffering, went to get the new necklace, placing on the jeweler's counter 36,000 francs.

When Madame Loisel went to return the necklace, Madame Forestier said in a faintly <u>waspish</u> tone:

"You could have brought it back a little sooner! I might have needed it."

She didn't open the case as her friend had feared she might. If she had noticed the substitution, what would she have thought? What would she have said? Mightn't she have taken Madame Loisel for a thief?

Madame Loisel came to know the awful life of the poverty-stricken. However, she resigned herself to it with unexpected fortitude. The crushing debt had to be paid. She would pay it. They dismissed the maid; they moved into an attic under the roof.

She came to know all the heavy household chores, the loathsome work of the kitchen. She washed the dishes, wearing down her pink nails on greasy casseroles and the bottoms of saucepans. She did the laundry, washing shirts and dishcloths which she hung on a line to dry; she took the garbage down to the street every morning, and carried water upstairs, stopping at every floor to get her breath. Dressed like a working-class woman, she went to the fruit store, the grocer, and the butcher with her basket on her arm, bargaining, outraged, contesting each sou[12] of her pitiful funds.

Every month some notes had to be honored and more time requested on others.

Her husband worked in the evenings, putting a shopkeeper's ledgers in order, and often at night as well, doing copying at twenty-five centimes a page.

And it went on like that for ten years.

After ten years, they had made good on everything, including the usurious[13] rates and the compound interest.

Vocabulary Development

usurers (YOO zhuhr erz) *n.* people who lend money at particularly high rates
privation (pry VAY shuhn) *n.* loss or absence of something
waspish (WAHS pish) *adj.* sharp, cross

12. **sou** (SOO) *n.* former French coin, worth very little; the centime (sahn TEEM), mentioned later, was also of little value.

13. **usurious** (yoo ZHOOR ee uhs) *adj.* extremely high.

Madame Loisel looked old now. She had become the sort of strong woman, hard and coarse, that one finds in poor families. <u>Disheveled</u>, her skirts <u>askew</u>, with reddened hands, she spoke in a loud voice, slopping water over the floors as she washed them. But sometimes, when her husband was at the office, she would sit down by the window and muse over that party long ago when she had been so beautiful, the belle of the ball.

How would things have turned out if she hadn't lost that necklace? Who could tell? How strange and fickle life is! How little it takes to make or break you!

Then one Sunday when she was strolling along the Champs Elysées[14] to forget the week's chores for a while, she suddenly caught sight of a woman taking a child for a walk. It was Madame Forestier, still young, still beautiful, still charming.

Madame Loisel started to tremble. Should she speak to her? Yes, certainly she should. And now that she had paid everything back, why shouldn't she tell her the whole story?

She went up to her.

"Hello, Jeanne."

The other didn't recognize her and was surprised that this plainly dressed woman should speak to her so familiarly. She murmured:

"But . . . madame! . . . I'm sure . . . You must be mistaken."

"No, I'm not. I am Mathilde Loisel."

Her friend gave a little cry.

"Oh! Oh, my poor Mathilde, how you've changed!"

"Yes, I've been through some pretty hard times since I last saw you and I've had plenty of trouble—and all because of you!"

"Because of me? What do you mean?"

"You remember the diamond necklace you lent me to wear to the party at the Ministry?"

"Yes. What about it?"

"Well, I lost it."

"What are you talking about? You returned it to me."

"What I gave back to you was another one just like it. And it took us ten years to pay for it. You can imagine it wasn't easy for us, since we were quite poor. . . Anyway, I'm glad it's over and done with."

Vocabulary Development

disheveled (di SHEV uhld) *adj.* untidy

askew (uh SKYOO) *adj.* not straight

14. **Champs Elysées** (shahn zay lee ZAY) fashionable street in Paris.

Literary Analysis

Read the bracketed passage. What does this passage tell you about Madame Loisel?

_____

_____

Is this passage an example of **direct** or **indirect characterization**? Explain your answer.

_____

_____

_____

Reading Skill

What **causes** Madame Loisel to tremble at the sight of Madame Forestier?

_____

_____

_____

_____

Stop to Reflect

Why do you think Madame Loisel decides to tell Madame Forestier the true story of the necklace?

_____

_____

_____

_____

Literary Analysis 🔍

How does the author **characterize** Madame Forestier at the end of the story?

_____

_____

_____

_____

Reading Check ✏️

Circle the passage in which Madame Loisel learns the true value of the necklace.

Stop to Reflect 📖

Madame Forestier now knows that the diamonds were real. Madame Loisel now knows that she has spent ten years of her life in poverty for no good reason. What do you think should happen now? Give reasons for your answer.

_____

_____

_____

_____

_____

_____

Madame Forestier stopped short.

"You say you bought a diamond necklace to replace that other one?"

"Yes. You didn't even notice then? They really were exactly alike."

And she smiled, full of a proud, simple joy.

Madame Forestier, <u>profoundly</u> moved, took Mathilde's hands in her own.

"Oh, my poor, poor Mathilde! Mine was false. It was worth five hundred francs at the most!"

Reader's Response: How did you react to the twist at the end? Why do you think you reacted in the way that you did?

_____

_____

_____

_____

Vocabulary Development

profoundly (proh FOWND lee) *adv.* deeply

The Necklace

1. **Compare and Contrast:** How is Monsieur Loisel different from his wife?

   _____

   _____

2. **Interpret:** How does Madame Loisel change over the ten years as she works to pay for the necklace?

   _____

   _____

3. **Literary Analysis:** A writer uses **indirect characterization** to give the reader clues about a character. These clues might be a character's words, thoughts, or actions. Describe Madame Loisel's **character**. Support your answer with an example of indirect characterization from the story.

   _____

   _____

   _____

4. **Reading Skill:** Use this chart to **analyze cause and effect** in this story. In the first box, note two causes for Madame Loisel's decision to borrow the necklace from Madame Forestier. In the third box, list three **effects** of her decision.

Causes		Effects
	She borrows the necklace.	

Writing: Written Presentation

Think about a lesson you could teach the Loisels to help them move on with their lives. Use this chart to organize ideas for the **written presentation**.

- In the left column, write an issue that the Loisels face.

- In the center column, write what you would teach them.

- In the right column, write "story with a moral" or "essay" to show how you would write the lesson.

Issue	What I Would Teach	How I Would Write the Lesson
_____	_____	_____
_____	_____	_____

Research and Technology: Informative Brochure

Create an **informative brochure** on diamonds. Use the chart below to list the questions that you want to answer in your research. Use your notes to help you create your brochure.

What I Want to Know About Diamonds	
QUESTIONS	ANSWERS
What is a diamond?	
Where are diamonds found?	

Blues Ain't No Mockin Bird • The Invalid's Story

Literary Analysis

Dialogue is a conversation between characters in a story. In prose, dialogue is usually set off by quotation marks. A new paragraph means a change in speaker. Writers use dialogue for these purposes:

- to tell readers about character traits and relationships
- to move forward the action of the plot and develop the conflict
- to add variety, color, and realism to stories

Authors may write dialogue reflecting characters' dialect. This type of dialogue makes the characters and settings more vivid. **Dialect** is a way of speaking. It is common to people of a region or group. A dialect's words, pronunciations, and grammar differ from those of the standard form of a language.

As you read, notice passages of dialogue and dialect. Determine what they show about the characters and the setting.

Reading Skill

A **cause** is an event, an action, or a feeling. It produces a result. An **effect** is the result produced. When reading a story, **visualize the action to analyze cause and effect**.

- Use story details to picture the setting, characters, and action.
- Use the details of your mental picture to help you identify the relationships between actions and events.

Organize your ideas in the chart shown.

Cause	Mental Picture	Effect

Blues Ain't No Mockin Bird
Toni Cade Bambara

Summary As children play in the front yard of their farm, Granny does chores on the porch. Two men approach. One carries a movie camera. They want to film the people and property to promote the county food-stamp program. Granny is offended. The narrator observes how both Granny and Granddaddy deal with the unwanted guests.

Writing About the Big Question

Is conflict necessary? In "Blues Ain't No Mockin Bird," an elderly woman finds it necessary to battle with people who threaten something important to her. Complete this sentence:

People will battle to protect _____

because _____.

Note-taking Guide

Use this sequence-of-events chart to write the order of the six most important events in the story.

1. Beginning Event	2.	3.

4.	5.	6. Final Event

Blues Ain't No Mockin Bird

Toni Cade Bambara

The puddle had frozen over, and me and Cathy went stompin in it. The twins from next door, Tyrone and Terry, were swingin so high out of sight we forgot we were waitin our turn on the tire. Cathy jumped up and came down hard on her heels and started tap-dancin. And the frozen patch splinterin every which way underneath kinda spooky. "Looks like a plastic spider web," she said. "A sort of weird spider, I guess, with many mental problems." But really it looked like the crystal paperweight Granny kept in the parlor. She was on the back porch, Granny was, making the cakes drunk. The old ladle dripping rum into the Christmas tins, like it used to drip maple syrup into the pails when we lived in the Judson's woods, like it poured cider into the vats when we were on the Cooper place, like it used to scoop buttermilk and soft cheese when we lived at the dairy.

"Go tell that man we ain't a bunch of trees."

"Ma'am?"

"I said to tell that man to get away from here with that camera." Me and Cathy look over toward the meadow where the men with the station wagon'd been roamin around all mornin. The tall man with a huge camera lassoed to his shoulder was buzzin our way.

"They're makin movie pictures," yelled Tyrone, stiffenin his legs and twistin so the tire'd come down slow so they could see.

"They're makin movie pictures," sang out Terry.

"That boy don't never have anything original to say," say Cathy grown-up.

By the time the man with the camera had cut across our neighbor's yard, the twins were out of the trees swingin low and Granny was onto the steps, the screen door bammin soft and scratchy against her palms. "We thought we'd get a shot or two of the house and everything and then—"

"Good mornin," Granny cut him off. And smiled that smile.

"Good mornin," he said, head all down the way Bingo does when you yell at him about the bones on the kitchen floor. "Nice place you got here, aunty. We thought we'd take a—"

"Did you?" said Granny with her eyebrows. Cathy pulled up her socks and giggled.

Activate Prior Knowledge

Think about an older person whom you know. What kind of facial expressions and gestures does that person make when he or she disapproves of something?

_____

_____

_____

Literary Analysis

Dialect is how people of a certain region speak. Words, grammar, and pronunciation in dialect are different from those of standard English. Which features of the title and first paragraph show that this story is written in dialect?

_____

_____

_____

Reading Skill

An **effect** is the result produced by a cause. **Visualizing** means picturing something in your mind. Which details in the bracketed passage help you visualize the effect that the camera crew has on Granny?

_____

_____

_____

Reading Check

Why are the men on the family's property? Underline the text that tells you.

Stop to Reflect

The narrator refers to the two men as "Camera man" and "Smilin man." How does this affect the way you think of these two men?

_____

_____

_____

_____

Literary Analysis 🔍

Dialogue is conversation between or among characters in a story. What does the dialogue between Granny and the film crew show about their attitudes toward each other?

_____

_____

_____

_____

Reading Check

What is Granny's response when Smilin man asks her to make a statement? Underline the text that tells you.

"Nice things here," said the man, buzzin his camera over the yard. The pecan barrels, the sled, me and Cathy, the flowers, the printed stones along the driveway, the trees, the twins, the toolshed.

"I don't know about the thing, the it, and the stuff," said Granny, still talkin with her eyebrows. "Just people here is what I tend to consider."

Camera man stopped buzzin. Cathy giggled into her collar.

"Mornin, ladies," a new man said. He had come up behind us when we weren't lookin. "And gents," discoverin the twins givin him a nasty look. "We're filmin for the county," he said with a smile. "Mind if we shoot a bit around here?"

"I do indeed," said Granny with no smile. Smilin man was smiling up a storm. So was Cathy. But he didn't seem to have another word to say, so he and the camera man backed on out the yard, but you could hear the camera buzzin still. "Suppose you just shut that machine off," said Granny real low through her teeth, and took a step down off the porch and then another.

"Now, aunty," Camera said, pointin the thing straight at her.

"Your mama and I are not related."

Smilin man got his notebook out and a chewed-up pencil. "Listen," he said movin back into our yard, "we'd like to have a statement from you . . . for the film. We're filmin for the county, see. Part of the food stamp campaign. You know about the food stamps?"

Granny said nuthin.

"Maybe there's somethin you want to say for the film. I see you grow your own vegetables," he smiled real nice. "If more folks did that, see, there'd be no need—"

Granny wasn't sayin nuthin. So they backed on out, buzzin at our clothesline and the twins' bicycles, then back on down to the meadow. The twins were danglin in the tire, lookin at Granny. Me and Cathy were waitin, too, cause Granny always got somethin to say. She teaches steady with no let-up.[1] "I was on this bridge one time," she started off. "Was a crowd cause this man was goin to jump, you understand. And a minister was there and the police and some other folks. His woman was there, too."

"What was they doin?" asked Tyrone.

Vocabulary Development

campaign (kam PAYN) *n.* a series of steps that are carried out in order to achieve something

---

1. **no let-up** (noh LET uhp) without stopping or slowing down.

154 Reader's Notebook

"Tryin to talk him out of it was what they was doin. The minister talkin about how it was a mortal sin, suicide. His woman takin bites out of her own hand and not even knowin it, so nervous and cryin and talkin fast."

"So what happened?" asked Tyrone.

"So here comes . . . this person . . . with a camera, takin pictures of the man and the minister and the woman. Takin pictures of the man in his misery about to jump, cause life so bad and people been messin with him so bad. This person takin up the whole roll of film practically. But savin a few, of course."

"Of course," said Cathy, hatin the person. Me standin there wonderin how Cathy knew it was "of course" when I didn't and it was my grandmother.

After a while Tyrone say, "Did he jump?"

"Yeh, did he jump?" say Terry all eager. And Granny just stared at the twins till their faces swallow up the eager and they don't even care any more about the man jumpin. Then she goes back onto the porch and lets the screen door go for itself. I'm lookin to Cathy to finish the story cause she knows Granny's whole story before me even. Like she knew how come we move so much and Cathy ain't but a third cousin we picked up on the way last Thanksgivin visitin. But she knew it was on account of people drivin Granny crazy till she'd get up in the night and start packin. Mumblin and packin and wakin everybody up sayin, "Let's get on away from here before I kill me somebody." Like people wouldn't pay her for things like they said they would. Or Mr. Judson bringin us boxes of old clothes and raggedy magazines. Or Mrs. Cooper comin in our kitchen and touchin everything and sayin how clean it all was. Granny goin crazy, and Granddaddy Cain pullin her off the people, sayin, "Now, now, Cora." But next day loadin up the truck, with rocks all in his jaw, madder than Granny in the first place.

"I read a story once," said Cathy soundin like Granny teacher. "About this lady Goldilocks who barged into a house that wasn't even hers. And not invited, you understand. Messed over the people's groceries and broke up the people's furniture. Had the nerve to sleep in the folks' bed."

"Then what happened?" asked Tyrone. "What they do, the folks, when they come in to all this mess?"

"Did they make her pay for it?" asked Terry, makin a fist. "I'd've made her pay me."

I didn't even ask. I could see Cathy actress was very likely to just walk away and leave us in mystery about this story which I heard was about some bears.

"Did they throw her out?" asked Tyrone, like his father sounds when he's bein extra nasty-plus to the washin-machine man.

Literary Analysis

Read the first bracketed passage. Circle three words that show the **dialect** of the narrator.

Reading Skill

Read the second bracketed passage. Underline three things that **cause** Granny to want to move. What **effect** does moving have on Granddaddy?

_____

_____

_____

_____

_____

Reading Check

What fairy tale does Cathy tell the other children? Underline the sentence that gives you your answer.

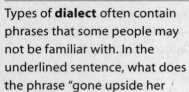

Literary Analysis

Types of **dialect** often contain phrases that some people may not be familiar with. In the underlined sentence, what does the phrase "gone upside her head" probably mean?

_____

_____

_____

_____

Reading Skill

The narrator says that "folks like to go for" Granddaddy Cain. What does Cathy think is the **cause** of this? Underline the sentences that tell you. Then, write the answer in your own words.

_____

_____

_____

_____

Reading Check

What does Granddaddy do with the hawk? Circle the sentence that tells you.

"Woulda," said Terry. "I woulda gone upside her head with my fist and—"

"You woulda done whatcha always do—go cry to Mama, you big baby," said Tyrone. So naturally Terry starts hittin on Tyrone, and next thing you know they tumblin out the tire and rollin on the ground. But Granny didn't say a thing or send the twins home or step out on the steps to tell us about how we can't afford to be fightin amongst ourselves. She didn't say nuthin. So I get into the tire to take my turn. And I could see her leanin up against the pantry table, staring at the cakes she was puttin up for the Christmas sale, mumblin real low and grumpy and holdin her forehead like it wanted to fall off and mess up the rum cakes.

Behind me I hear before I can see Granddaddy Cain comin through the woods in his field boots. Then I twist around to see the shiny black oilskin cuttin through what little left there was of yellows, reds, and oranges. His great white head not quite round cause of this bloody thing high on his shoulder, like he was wearin a cap on sideways. He takes the shortcut through the pecan grove, and the sound of twigs snapping overhead and underfoot travels clear and cold all the way up to us. And here comes Smilin and Camera up behind him like they was goin to do somethin. Folks like to go for him sometimes. Cathy say it's because he's so tall and quiet and like a king. And people just can't stand it. But Smilin and Camera don't hit him in the head or nuthin. They just buzz on him as he stalks by with the chicken hawk slung over his shoulder, squawkin, drippin red down the back of the oilskin.[2] He passes the porch and stops a second for Granny to see he's caught the hawk at last, but she's just starin and mumblin, and not at the hawk. So he nails the bird to the toolshed door, the hammerin crackin through the eardrums. And the bird flappin himself to death and droolin down the door to paint the gravel in the driveway red, then brown, then black. And the two men movin up on tiptoe like they was invisible or we were blind, one.

"Get them persons out of my flower bed, Mister Cain," say Granny moanin real low like at a funeral.

"How come your grandmother calls her husband 'Mister Cain' all the time?" Tyrone whispers all loud and noisy and from the city and don't know no better. Like his mama, Miss Myrtle, tell us never mind the formality as if

Vocabulary Development

formality (fawr MAL uh tee) *n.* attention to established rules or customs

2. **oilskin** (OYL skin) *n.* an oiled waterproof piece of cloth, often used as a raincoat.

we had no better breeding than to call her Myrtle, plain. And then this awful thing—a giant hawk—come wailin up over the meadow, flyin low and tilted and screamin, zigzaggin through the pecan grove, breakin branches and hollerin, snappin past the clothesline, flyin every which way, flyin into things <u>reckless</u> with crazy.

"He's come to claim his mate," say Cathy fast, and ducks down. We all fall quick and flat into the gravel driveway, stones scrapin my face. I squinch my eyes open again at the hawk on the door, tryin to fly up out of her death like it was just a sack flown into by mistake. Her body holdin her there on that nail, though. The mate beatin the air overhead and clutchin for hair, for heads, for landin space.

The camera man duckin and bendin and runnin and fallin, jigglin the camera and scared. And Smilin jumpin up and down swipin at the huge bird, tryin to bring the hawk down with just his raggedy ole cap. Granddaddy Cain straight up and silent, watchin the circles of the hawk, then aimin the hammer off his wrist. The giant bird fallin, silent and slow. Then here comes Camera and Smilin all big and bad now that the awful screechin thing is on its back and broken, here they come. And Granddaddy Cain looks up at them like it was the first time noticin, but not payin them too much mind cause he's listenin, we all listenin, to that low groanin music comin from the porch. And we figure any minute, somethin in my back tells me any minute now, Granny gonna bust through that screen with somethin in her hand and murder on her mind. So Granddaddy say above the buzzin, but quiet, "Good day, gentlemen." Just like that. Like he'd invited them in to play cards and they'd stayed too long and all the sandwiches were gone and Reverend Webb was droppin by and it was time to go.

They didn't know what to do. But like Cathy say, folks can't stand Granddaddy tall and silent and like a king. They can't neither. The smile the men smilin is pullin the mouth back and showin the teeth. Lookin like the wolf man, both of them. Then Granddaddy holds his hand out—this huge hand I used to sit in when I was a baby and he'd carry me through the house to my mother like I was a gift on a tray. Like he used to on the trains. They called the other men just waiters. But they spoke of Granddaddy separate and said, The Waiter. And said he had engines in his feet and motors in his hands and couldn't no train throw him off and couldn't nobody turn him round. They were big enough for motors, his hands were. He held that one hand out all still and it gettin to be not at all a hand but a person in itself.

Vocabulary Development

reckless (REK lis) *adj.* careless; rash

Reading Skill

What **causes** the film crew to duck and bend and become frightened?

_____

_____

What **effect** does the arrival of the screaming hawk have on Granddaddy Cain?

_____

_____

Stop to Reflect

Look at the words that Granddaddy uses to greet the two men. Then, circle the words that show what the narrator thinks Granddaddy means. Why do Granddaddy's words confuse the two men?

_____

_____

_____

Reading Check

What tool does Granddaddy use to kill the male hawk? Circle the sentence that tells the answer.

Literary Analysis

Which characters engage in **dialogue** in the first bracketed passage?

_____

_____

What does the dialogue show about how the characters feel?

_____

_____

_____

Stop to Reflect

Read the second bracketed passage. Do you agree with Granddaddy's action toward the film crew? Explain why or why not.

_____

_____

_____

_____

Reading Skill

In what way does **visualizing** the scene in the third bracketed passage help you understand the **effects** of Granddaddy's action?

_____

_____

_____

_____

Reading Check

What explanation does Smilin give for filming? Circle the text that tells you.

"He wants you to hand him the camera," Smilin whispers to Camera, tiltin his head to talk secret like they was in the jungle or somethin and come upon a native that don't speak the language. The men start untyin the straps, and they put the camera into that great hand speckled with the hawk's blood all black and crackly now. And the hand don't even drop with the weight, just the fingers move, curl up around the machine. But Granddaddy lookin straight at the men. They lookin at each other and everywhere but at Granddaddy's face.

"We filmin for the county, see," say Smilin. "We puttin together a movie for the food stamp program . . . filmin all around these parts. Uhh, filmin for the county."

"Can I have my camera back?" say the tall man with no machine on his shoulder, but still keepin it high like the camera was still there or needed to be. "Please, sir."

Then Granddaddy's other hand flies up like a sudden and gentle bird, slaps down fast on top of the camera and lifts off half like it was a calabash[3] cut for sharing.

"Hey," Camera jumps forward. He gathers up the parts into his chest and everything unrollin and fallin all over. "Whatcha tryin to do? You'll ruin the film." He looks down into his chest of metal reels and things like he's protectin a kitten from the cold.

"You standin in the misses' flower bed," say Granddaddy. "This is our own place."

The two men look at him, then at each other, then back at the mess in the camera man's chest, and they just back off. One sayin over and over all the way down to the meadow, "Watch it, Bruno. Keep ya fingers off the film." Then Granddaddy picks up the hammer and jams it into the oilskin pocket, scrapes his boots, and goes into the house. And you can hear the squish of his boots headin through the house. And you can see the funny shadow he throws from the parlor window onto the ground by the string-bean patch. The hammer draggin the pocket of the oilskin out so Granddaddy looked even wider. Granny was hummin now—high not low and grumbly. And she was doin the cakes again, you could smell the molasses from the rum.

Vocabulary Development

native (NAY tiv) *n.* an original inhabitant of a region
molasses (muh LAS iz) *n.* a thick, usually dark-brown syrup

3. **calabash** (KAL uh bash) *n.* large, gourdlike fruit.

"There's this story I'm goin to write one day," say Cathy dreamer. "About the proper use of the hammer."

"Can I be in it?" Tyrone say with his hand up like it was a matter of first come, first served.

"Perhaps," say Cathy, climbin onto the tire to pump us up. "If you there and ready."

Reader's Response: Do you sympathize with the family in this story? Do you have any sympathy for the two men? Explain your answers.

_____

_____

_____

_____

Reading Skill

What **causes** Tyrone to put up his hand?

_____

_____

_____

_____

Reading Check

What does Cathy plan to do one day? Underline the sentence that tells you.

Blues Ain't No Mockin Bird

1. **Respond:** Which character would you most like to meet? Why?

_____

_____

_____

2. **Compare:** Look at the chart below. In the first column, compare the ways that the Camera and Smilin are like the hawks. In the second column, compare the ways Granddaddy's actions are like the actions of the male hawk. In the third column, explain whether you think the hawks represent Granddaddy and Granny, Smilin and Camera, or both pairs.

Hawks and Cameramen	Hawks and Granddaddy	What the Hawks Represent

3. **Literary Analysis:** Explain how the spelling and grammar in the following passage show that it is an example of **dialect**. "Granny always got somethin to say. She teaches steady with no let-up."

_____

_____

_____

4. **Reading Skill:** What is the **cause** of Granddaddy's decision to disassemble the men's camera?

_____

_____

_____

Writing: Informal Letter

Write an **informal letter** from the point of view of one of the characters. Choose a character that is not the main character. Write all or part of the letter in his or her dialect. Use the following items to prepare you to write in the dialect.

- List three examples of the character's dialect in the story.

  _____

  _____

- Rewrite the following sentences in the character's dialect:

  1. We are filming the birds flying in the sky.

     _____

     _____

  2. He was trying to stand in my wife's garden.

     _____

     _____

It might be helpful first to write the letter without dialect. Then, go back and change the language. This will help you write your informal letter.

Listening and Speaking: Dialogue

With a partner, jot down notes for what each character in the dialogue says. Consider starting with the cameraman reporting what happened at Granny's house.

What the Cameraman Says	What the Boss Says in Reply
_____	_____
_____	_____
_____	_____
_____	_____
_____	_____

The Invalid's Story
Mark Twain

Summary The narrator must deliver the remains of a close friend. A mix-up on the train leads to a mistaken smell. The characters try many ways to get rid of the smell. This affects the narrator's health.

Writing About the Big Question

Is conflict necessary? In "The Invalid's Story," the two main characters try to resolve a problem but do not have all the facts. Complete this sentence:

Lack of information can lead to a humorous conflict because

_____.

Note-taking Guide

Use this chart to list the three most important events in the story.

1	2	3
The narrator gets on a train to transport his dead friend's remains to Wisconsin.		

The Invalid's Story

1. **Interpret:** Why does Thompson say the corpse "wants to travel alone"?

   _____

   _____

2. **Compare and Contrast:** The men believe that the strong smell is coming from the corpse. However, it is actually coming from the cheese. In what ways does this contrast add to the humor of the story?

   _____

   _____

3. **Evaluate:** Fill in this chart with sad and humorous details from the story. In the third column, explain whether you think the story is sad, funny, or both.

Sad Details	Humorous Details	Evaluation
_____	_____	_____
_____	_____	_____
_____	_____	_____
_____	_____	_____

4. **Literary Analysis:** Explain how the use of **dialect** makes the characters and setting more vivid. Vivid means "stronger" or "more true to life."

   _____

   _____

5. **Reading Skill:** What **effect** does the smell have on the men?

   _____

   _____

Writing: Informal Letter

Write an **informal letter** from Thompson's point of view. Write all or part of the letter in Thompson's dialect. Use the following items to prepare you to write in his dialect.

- List three examples of Thompson's dialect from the story.

_____

_____

_____

- Rewrite the following sentences in the character's dialect:

    1. It would have been better if we moved the bed to the other side of the room.

_____

_____

    2. I think it is a curious situation.

_____

   It might be helpful first to write the letter without dialect. Then, go back and change the language. This will help you write your informal letter.

Listening and Speaking: Dialogue

With a partner, jot down notes for what each character in the dialogue says. Consider starting with the narrator reporting on the reason for his train journey.

What the Narrator Says	What the Doctor Says
_____	_____
_____	_____
_____	_____
_____	_____
_____	_____

Student Guide

About Student Guides

A **guide** is an expository text that provides information to help readers understand a subject. Guides often include heads and subheads that identify topics and subtopics.

A **student guide** helps student students understand a subject or work of literature. Reading a student guide can be helpful as an aid or reference. However, it is not a replacement for reading a complete original text or work of literature.

Reading Skill

A student guide may include a summary or a critique of a literary work. A **summary** is a short description of a text. A **critique** gives an opinion about a text. Being able to tell the difference between a summary and a critique will help you understand an author's purpose for writing.

Use this checklist to analyze the student guide to Sandra Cisneros's novel, *The House on Mango Street*. Your answers will help you decide if it is a summary or a critique.

Question	Summary	Critique
Does the text give an opinion about Cisneros's book?	☐ No	☐ Yes
Does the text restate ideas from Cisneros's book?	☐ Yes	☐ No
Does the text present new ideas about Cisneros's book?	☐ No	☐ Yes
Does the text outline the events of Cisneros's book?	☐ Yes	☐ No

Features:

- information intended to help students
- organization that follows that of the original work
- heads and subheads that identify topics and subtopics

Student Guide to
THE HOUSE ON MANGO STREET
BY SANDRA CISNEROS

Mary Patterson Thornburg

PART ONE

The House on Mango Street; Hairs; Boys & Girls; My Name

In the first chapter, the speaker reveals a little about her family and her life. She talks about the house she lives in and about some of the other places she has lived. The family has moved numerous times and, at the same time, has been growing, until now there are four children: the speaker has two brothers (Carlos and Kiki) and one sister (Nenny), besides her two parents. The speaker was ashamed of the last place they lived. This new house is small, with crumbling bricks, small windows, a small backyard, and no front yard, but it has three bedrooms and the speaker's parents own it.

In "Hairs," the speaker describes how everyone in her family has different kinds of hair, and how her mother's hair smells comfortably like bread before it's baked.

Carlos and Kiki, the two boys, play together outside but can't be seen talking to girls, the speaker tells us in "Boys & Girls." She herself has to watch out that her sister doesn't get into trouble, but Nenny is not the "best friend" she wants or would choose. Someday, though, she will have a best friend.

Then, in "My Name," she tells us who she is: Esperanza, which in English translates to hope; it was also the name of her great-grandmother, a strong woman who suffered because her culture did not like strong women. Esperanza doesn't like her name, but at least it is better than her sister's—Magdalena—and sounds better in Spanish than in English. But her sister's name has a nickname—Nenny—whereas her own does not.

> The author gives information about the content of the first chapter of *The House on Mango Street.* **Does the author present an opinion or take a position in this paragraph?**

PART TWO

Cathy Queen of Cats; Our Good Day; Laughter; Gil's Furniture Bought & Sold; Meme Ortiz; Louie, His Cousin & His Other Cousin

A girl named Cathy, one of Esperanza's neighbors, tells Esperanza about the neighborhood. She says she'll be Esperanza's friend for a few days, but then her family is moving. Cathy says she's related to the Queen of France, and someday her family will inherit some property, but for now they have to move because the neighborhood is going downhill.

Cathy has warned Esperanza about the two girls across the street, but in "Our Good Day" Esperanza decides to be their friend anyway. She gives the two girls (Lucy and Rachel) some money because they are all going in together to buy a bicycle from a neighborhood boy. Cathy leaves, and Esperanza, Lucy, and Rachel take a ride on their new, wobbly bicycle.

> Here the author discusses a particular incident from the novel. **Does the author express new ideas or restate main ideas and events from the novel?**

In "Laughter," Esperanza says she and Nenny don't look alike, but that there are likenesses between them deeper than looks.

The girls visit a neighborhood second-hand store ("Gil's Furniture…"). Nenny asks the owner about a music box, and he opens the lid and lets them listen. Nenny asks how much it costs, but the storeowner says it's not for sale.

Cathy has moved, and a boy called Meme Ortiz moves into her house. There's a backyard with a large tree in it. The children hold the First Annual Tarzan Jumping Contest in this tree, and Meme wins, breaking both arms.

 Is conflict necessary?
How do the conflicts described in *The House on Mango Street* relate to the conflicts of real-life children and teens?

Thinking About the Student Guide

1. What is the first chapter of *The House on Mango Street* about?

_____

_____

2. What do the bold heads in the student guide indicate?

_____

_____

TALK ABOUT IT Reading Skill

3. What type of information does the author present in the student guide—facts or opinions?

_____

4. Is the author of the student guide trying to convince you, the reader, of anything? Explain.

_____

WRITE ABOUT IT   Timed Writing: Analysis (30 minutes)

Write a short essay in which you analyze the student guide. In your essay, tell whether the guide is a summary or a critique of *The House on Mango Street*. Give reasons for your response and include details from the student guide as support. Use the sentence starters below to help you begin writing.

The student guide is a [summary / critique] because _____

_____

The author's purpose in writing the student guide was to _____

_____

Before Hip-Hop Was Hip-Hop

Essays and articles are short works of nonfiction. The people and events that are discussed are real. Speeches are nonfiction works that are delivered by a speaker to an audience.

- An **essay** discusses a specific topic. It often includes the writer's personal opinions.

- An **article** provides factual information about a topic, a person, or an event.

- A **speech** is written to be read aloud. It presents a topic and may persuade, inform, explain, or entertain.

The writer contributes more than information to nonfiction.

- **Style** is the way the author uses language. The style may be formal or informal. Style includes word choice and figures of speech. Sentence structure and type of organization also determine the author's style. Style shows the author's personality.

- **Tone** is the author's attitude toward the subject and the audience. You can "hear" tone in an author's choice of words and details. The tone of nonfiction can often be described with a single word. *Playful, serious,* or *sarcastic* are just a few of the ways to describe tone.

- **Perspective** is the author's point of view about the subject. Authors may express their opinions directly or indirectly. **Bias** occurs when a writer gives a one-sided view. You can spot bias when the author ignores certain facts. You can also detect it in emotional language. Emotional language may unfairly sway the audience's feelings.

- **Purpose** is the author's reason for writing. Common purposes are to inform, to persuade, and to entertain.

Categories of Nonfiction

Nonfiction can be grouped by the author's purpose. This chart will help you identify different types of nonfiction.

Type of Nonfiction	Characteristics	Examples
Narrative Essay	• tells a story of actual events or of a person's life experiences	• autobiography • memoir
Reflective Essay	• expresses the writer's thoughts and feelings in response to a personal experience or to an idea	• personal essay • journal
Descriptive Essay	• creates an impression about a person, an object, or an experience • presents physical and sensory details	• character sketch • scientific observation
Expository Essay	• provides information, discusses ideas, or explains a process	• analytical essay • research report
Persuasive Essay	• attempts to convince readers that they should think or act a certain way	• editorial • political speech
Procedural Essay	• gives instructions for completing specific tasks	• consumer publication • software instructions

Before Hip-Hop Was Hip-Hop
Rebecca Walker

Summary Rebecca Walker talks about being a teenager during the 1980s. She traces the growth of hip-hop music. Walker shows how hip-hop became a revolution that affected language and dress as well as music. For the writer, hip-hop created a new sense of unity among young people.

Note-taking Guide

Use this chart to help you recall the author's ideas and feelings about hip-hop.

She thinks that hip-hop is now prepackaged.

Rebecca Walker's Ideas and Feelings About Hip-Hop

Before Hip-Hop Was Hip-Hop
Rebecca Walker

© Pearson Education

Activate Prior Knowledge

What do you know about the 1980s? Who was President of the United States? What were some of the popular bands? What clothes were in fashion? List facts you know about the time period.

_____

_____

_____

Nonfiction

Writers consider their audience, purpose, and subject when choosing their **style** of language. Rebecca Walker uses informal English that contains everyday speech and popular expressions. It uses contractions and may include sentence fragments. Underline examples of informal English in the bracketed paragraphs. Why do you suppose Walker chose informal English?

_____

_____

Reading Check

Why is the author amazed by the "vast empire of hip-hop"? Underline the text that tells you.

_____

_____

If you ask most kids today about hip-hop, they'll spit out the names of recording artists they see on TV: Eminem, P. Diddy, J. Lo, Beyonce. They'll tell you about the songs they like and the clothes they want to buy. They'll tell you about the <u>indisputable</u> zones of hip-hop like "EO" (East Orange, New Jersey), the "ATL" (Atlanta, Georgia), and the "West Side" (Los Angeles, California), neighborhoods they feel they know because they've seen them in all the glossiest, "flossiest" music videos. Hip-hop is natural to these kids, like air or water, just there, a part of the digital landscape that streams through their lives.

I watch this cultural sea change with fascination. It astounds me that hip-hop has grown into a global industry, a force that <u>dominates</u> youth culture from Paris to Prague, Tokyo to Timbuktu. I can't believe that in small, all-white towns like Lincoln, Nebraska, high school boys wear their clothes in the latest "steelo": pants sagging off their waists, sports jerseys hanging to their knees, baseball hats cocked to one side. Even in the pueblos of Mexico, where mariachi bands and old school crooners still rule, it is hip-hop that sells cars, sodas, and children's toys on TV. The vast empire of hip-hop amazes me because I knew hip-hop before it was hip-hop. I was there when it all began.

Way back then, in what today's ninth graders might call the ancient eighties, there was no MTV or VH-1. We found out about music by listening to the radio, flipping through the stacks at the record store, or buying "mix tapes" from local deejays at two dollars apiece. Back then, we carried combs in our back pockets and clipped long strands of feathers to the belt loops of our designer jeans. We wore our names in cursive gold letters around our necks or in big brass letters on our belt buckles. We picked up words and inverted them, calling something that we thought was really cool, "hot," and something that had a whole lot of life, "def."

We didn't know a whole new language was rolling off our tongues as we flipped English upside down and pulled some Spanish and even a few words from Africa into our <u>parlance</u>. We didn't know that young people for years to

Vocabulary Development

indisputable (in di SPYOO tuh buhl) *adj.* definitely true
dominates (DAHM uh nayts) *v.* has power and control over something
parlance (PAR luhns) *n.* manner of speaking

come would recycle our fashions and sample the bass lines from our favorite tracks. We thought we were just being kids and expressing ourselves, showing the grown-ups we were different from them in a way that was safe and fun. In fact we were at the epicenter[1] of one of America's most significant cultural revolutions, making it happen. Who knew?

Not me.

When I moved from Washington, D.C. to the Bronx the summer before seventh grade, I had one box of records, mostly albums I had ordered from the Columbia Record Club. In 1982, if you promised to buy a record a month for one whole year, the Club sent you eight records for a penny. I had Bruce Springsteen's "The River," REO Speedwagon's "The Letter," "Belladonna" by Stevie Nicks. I had "Stairway to Heaven," by Led Zeppelin and the soundtrack from the movie Saturday Night Fever, which I played so many times I thought my mother would go crazy from listening to me belt out the lyrics with those lanky, swanky Bee Gees.

Along with my albums I had loads of 45s, what today we would call singles, little records with just two songs on them, that I bought at the record store near my school for just a dollar a piece. I had Chaka Khan's "I'm Every Woman," and Luther Vandross' "Never Too Much," and Chuck Brown and Soul Searcher's big hit, "Bustin' Loose." I had Michael Jackson's "Rock with You" and even Aretha Franklin's cover of "You Make me Feel Like a Natural Woman" which I sang along to in the mornings as I styled my hair.

If you had asked me then about rap music I would have shrugged my shoulders and looked at you like you were crazy. Rap music? What's that?

But then I started seventh grade and my whole world turned upside down. At Public School 141, I went to classes with kids from all over the Bronx. There were kids whose families came from Puerto Rico and the Dominican Republic, and kids whose families came from Russia and China. There were kids who were African-American and kids who were Irish-American, kids who were Italian-American and kids who were Greek-American. There were kids whose families were poor, kids whose families were well off, and kids whose families were somewhere in between. Some were Jewish, and others devout Catholics.

1. **epicenter** (EP uh sent er) *n.* focal or central point.

Nonfiction

Perspective is the author's point of view about the subject. Read the underlined lists of bands, artists, and songs. What do these details show about Walker's perspective on music?

_____

_____

_____

Nonfiction

Tone is the author's attitude toward the subject or the audience. How does the bracketed paragraph contribute to the author's tone?

_____

_____

Stop to Reflect

How much influence do your friends have on the music and clothes you like? Explain.

_____

_____

_____

Nonfiction

In what way do the examples of the Asian American girl and the preppy boy illustrate the author's **purpose**?

_____

_____

_____

Nonfiction

Essays can be **narrative, descriptive, expository, persuasive, procedural,** or **reflective**. What types of nonfiction writing does Walker use in the bracketed passage?

_____

_____

What is her **purpose** in using these types of nonfiction?

_____

_____

Reading Check ✐

What did Walker find interesting about her Public School 141 schoolmates? Underline the text that tells you.

Some were Muslim. Some of the Asian kids were even Buddhist.

The charge created by so many different elements coming together was <u>palpable</u>. The school crackled with energy, and as you can imagine, things weren't always smooth. There were some pretty <u>entrenched</u> cliques, and a few vicious fights on the schoolyard. But there was also so much "flavor." You could hear Spanish spoken with a thick "Nuyorican" accent to a kid wearing a "yamulke." A seemingly reserved Asian-American girl would get out of her parents' car, wait for them to drive off, and then unzip her coat to reveal a fire engine red Adidas sweatsuit. A guy in a preppy, button down shirt would "sport" gold chains with pendants of every denomination: the Jewish Star of David, the Arabic lettering for Allah, and a shiny gold cross. He was everything, that was his "steelo," and everyone gave him "props" for it.

When I got to 141, I felt like a blank canvas. Nothing had prepared me for the dynamism, the screaming self-expression of the place and its students. For the first few weeks I secretly studied the habits of the seventh, eighth and ninth graders with whom I walked the halls and shared the cafeteria. I was transfixed by the way they infused their words with attitude and drama, moving their hands and heads as they spoke. I was captivated by the way many of them walked and ran and joked with each other with confidence and <u>bravado</u>. I noted what they wore and how they wore it: the razor sharp creases of their Jordache jeans, the spotless sneakers with the laces left loose and untied.

Slowly, I began to add some of what I saw into my "look." I convinced my grandmother to buy me a name chain to wear around my neck, and my stepmother to buy me dark dyed designer jeans. I bought my first pair of Nike sneakers, red, white and blue Air Cortez's, with money I saved from my allowance.

One by one, I started to make friends—Diane, Loida, James, Jesus, Maya. When James and Jesus[2] weren't making fun of me for being so "square," they took me to parties on the Grand Concourse, the big boulevard lined with old apartment buildings and department stores that

---

Vocabulary Development

palpable (PAL puh buhl) *adj.*   l n

entrenched (n TRENCHD) *adj.*   u l   bl h

bravado (b uh VAH   h) *n.* p   n   u g

---

2. **Jesus** (hay SOOS)

ran through the Bronx. The parties were incredible, filled with young people who didn't drink, smoke or fight, but who just wanted to dance and laugh and ooh and ahhh over the "scratching" sounds and funky beats the DJ's coaxed out of their turntables.

A lot of the kids at the parties were "breakers" or "poppers and lockers," which meant they could breakdance, a style of movement that blends the Brazilian martial art of Capoeira with a dance called the Robot, and incorporates classical dance moves as well. The "breakers" moved in "crews" that competed against each other. Standing in a circle we watched as members of the different groups "moonwalked" into the center, and then hurled themselves to the floor, spinning on their heads, kicking their legs into the air, and making elaborate hand gestures, each more intricate and acrobatic than the last. Everyone at the party who wasn't "breaking" was a judge by default, and we registered our scores by clapping and yelling.

When Loida and Diane weren't "capping on" or making fun of my clothes, they were "hipping" me to Kiss 98.7 and WBLS, the radio stations that had started to slip some of the songs we liked into their rotation. Songs like "Planet Rock" by Soul Sonic Force and "Take Me Home" by Lisa Lisa and the Cult Jam. After school and on the weekends, they took me to the street vendors that sold the accessories we all coveted: the big knockoff Porsche sunglasses everybody wanted but not everybody could afford, and the heavy gold chains people collected around their necks like so many pieces of string. Loida and Diane also took me around the city on the bus, familiarizing me with the routes of the M1 and M3 and M7, showing me all the different neighborhoods like Little Italy and Chinatown, Bed-Stuy and Harlem.

I remember looking out the big sliding glass windows of the bus at the lines drawn in concrete and glass and thinking that while the world outside seemed so divided, inside, in my circle, among my friends, those lines didn't seem to exist. Loida was Dominican and Diane was Puerto Rican. Our friend Mary was Irish-American, and Lisa was Italian-American. Maya's family was from Haiti. Julius was Russian-American. We were different ages, with different likes and dislikes, but we were united in our love of hip-hop. We loved the "dope"[3] beats, the ever changing and ever expanding <u>lexicon</u>, the outrageous dance moves, the cocky swagger, the feeling that we were part of something

Vocabulary Development

lexicon (LEK si kahn) *n.* the special vocabulary of a particular group

---

3. **dope** (dohp) *adj.* slang term meaning "great; irresistible."

Nonfiction

Slang is used in casual speech. It consists of made-up words and unusual comparisons. Underline examples of slang on this page. What effect does the use of slang have on the author's **tone?**

_____

_____

Nonfiction

Read the bracketed paragraph. What is the **author's purpose** in including these descriptions?

_____

_____

Stop to Reflect

In addition to music, what else do you think could bridge the gaps between different cultures?

_____

_____

© Pearson Education

Stop to Reflect

Do you agree with Walker's vision of hip-hop music today? How would you describe hip-hop music to someone who had never heard it?

_____

_____

_____

_____

Nonfiction

Bias occurs when a writer gives a one-sided view. Do you think Walker's opinions on hip-hop today are biased? Why or why not?

_____

_____

_____

_____

Reading Check

What did the author learn from hip-hop? Circle the text that tells you.

dynamic and "fresh"[4] that was bigger than any one of us. That world, that other realm that we created on the streets and in our minds, that streamed from the radio in the privacy of our bedrooms and coursed between us as we talked on the phone, that was where we lived.

That was where we felt free.

Looking back on it now, I can see that hip-hop was born of the diversity I found at 141. Unlike the hip-hop of today, it didn't come pre-packaged from a marketing department with millions of dollars to spend. Our hip-hop was the product of a bunch of kids from a bunch of different places trying to talk to each other, trying to create a common language that could cut through the many languages people spoke at home. Intuitively, kids were making a community where there was none; we were affirming our sameness in a world that seemed to only emphasize our difference. That desire to come together irrespective of superficial differences and sometimes in celebration of them, was what gave hip-hop authenticity, that was what kept it honest and as crucial to our well being as food. It's what kept it real.

I can't say much about hip-hop today, but I can say that old hip-hop, original hip-hop, changed my life forever. I only lived in the "Boogie Down Bronx" for a year, but those twelve months gave me so much. I learned that art could bring people together and make them forget their differences. I learned how good it could feel to move with a "posse," a group of friends who had my back no matter what. I learned that I could express myself and communicate with others through what I wore and how I walked and what music I liked. I learned that it doesn't take money or a special degree to transform the grit and drive and hardness of the city into something beautiful.

Loyalty. Community. Self-confidence. Creativity. Hip-hop taught me more about real life than anything I learned that year in class.

I hope when kids today look at shiny videos by their favorite hip-hop artists, they will see through the

Vocabulary Development

intuitively (in TOO i tiv lee) _adv._ instinctively; because of feelings instead of facts

irrespective (ir i SPEK tiv) _adv._ regardless

superficial (soo per FISH uhl) _adj._ visible or obvious; on the surface

4. **fresh** (fresh) _adj._ slang term meaning "new."

expensive cars and exotic locations, the women in skimpy outfits and the men trying to approximate a "gangsta" lean. I hope they will remember that hip-hop was born without a formula and without a lot of expensive props or violent undertones. I hope they will marvel at the fact that in the early days of hip-hop, young people were making it up as they went along, following their hearts, following what felt good. I hope they will think about what it takes to create culture that is unique and transcendent and honest, and I hope they begin to dream about creating a new world for themselves.

I hope hip-hop inspires them to make their own revolution.

Nonfiction

Reflective essays express the writer's thoughts and feelings. Underline three thoughts or feelings that Walker expresses on this page.

© Pearson Education

Before Hip-Hop Was Hip-Hop

1. **Analyze Cause and Effect:** How did hip-hop help Walker and her friends bridge their differences?

   _____

   _____

2. **Interpret:** Why was it so important for Walker and her friends to define themselves through dress, slang, dance, and music?

   _____

   _____

3. **Types of Nonfiction:** How would you describe the **tone** of the **essay**? Explain the reasons for your choice by giving examples from the essay.

   _____

   _____

4. **Types of Nonfiction:** Describe Walker's **style** in one sentence. Use the chart below to analyze Walker's style. In each column, write examples from the text that support your idea.

   _____

Level of Formality	Word Choice	Sentence Patterns

Timeline

Create a popular culture **timeline** of Rebecca Walker's life. Look at the tips below. Use your notes to create your timeline.

- Search the Internet for biographical information about Rebecca Walker. Also search for information about music, fashion, and dances during the 1980s.

  Major events from Walker's life:

  _____

  _____

  _____

  Major cultural events from the 1980s:

  _____

  _____

  _____

- Watch the video interview with Rebecca Walker, and review your source material. Use this information to answer the following questions.

  1. What biographical information did you learn about Walker?

     _____

     _____

     _____

  2. How did growing up in the 1980s affect Walker?

     _____

     _____

     _____

  3. What major events in Walker's life happened at the same time as some important events in the 1980s?

     _____

     _____

     _____

A Celebration of Grandfathers • On Summer

Literary Analysis

An author's **style** is his or her unique way of using language. Some elements that contribute to an author's style are these:

- **Diction:** the words the author uses
- **Syntax:** the arrangement of words in sentences
- **Tone:** the author's attitude toward the audience or subject

A writer's diction and syntax may be described as *formal* or *informal*, *technical* or *ordinary*, or *sophisticated* or *down-to-earth*. Tone may be described as *serious*, *playful*, *friendly*, or *harsh*.

Reading Skill

The **main idea** is the central message, insight, or opinion in a work of nonfiction. **Supporting details** are the pieces of evidence that a writer uses to prove the main idea. These details can include facts, statistics, quotations, or anecdotes. To **identify the main idea and supporting details** in a work, **generate questions prior to reading**. Before you read, ask yourself questions such as these:

- *Why did the author choose this title?*
- *How might events in the author's life influence his or her attitude?*

As you read, look for details that answer those questions and point to the main idea. Use the chart below to help you.

Question	Detail/Answer	Main Idea?

A Celebration of Grandfathers

Rudolfo A. Anaya

Summary In this essay, Anaya remembers the quiet ways of the "old ones." They understood the seasons and appreciated the land in which they lived. Anaya urges readers to understand and respect their grandparents.

Writing About the Big Question

Is knowledge the same as understanding? "A Celebration of Grandfathers" gives information to show what the author's grandfather and people of his generation were like and what they valued. Complete this sentence:

Knowing what people do and how they live can give **insight** into who

they are because _____.

Note-taking Guide

Use this chart to record what the author believes about older people.

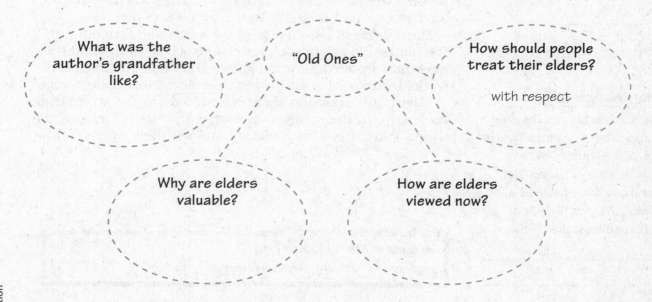

What was the author's grandfather like?

"Old Ones"

How should people treat their elders?

with respect

Why are elders valuable?

How are elders viewed now?

A Celebration of Grandfathers
Rudolfo A. Anaya

© Pearson Education

Activate Prior Knowledge

How has a grandparent or another older person affected your life?

_____

_____

_____

_____

Reading Skill

The **main idea** is the most important message in a work of nonfiction. **Supporting details** are the evidence that support the main idea. Read the first bracketed passage. Which details support the author's main idea about what the young learned from old people?

_____

_____

_____

_____

Literary Analysis

Style is the author's way of using language. One element of style is **tone,** or the author's attitude toward the subject. Read the second bracketed passage. Describe the tone the author creates to discuss the "ancianos."

_____

_____

_____

Underline two phrases or sentences to support your view.

Buenos días le de Dios, abuelo."[1] God give you a good day, grandfather. This is how I was taught as a child to greet my grandfather, or any grown person. It was a greeting of respect, a cultural value to be passed on from generation to generation, this respect for the old ones.

The old people I remember from my childhood were strong in their beliefs, and as we lived daily with them we learned a wise path of life to follow. They had something important to share with the young, and when they spoke the young listened. These old abuelos and abuelitas[2] had worked the earth all their lives, and so they knew the value of nurturing, they knew the sensitivity of the earth. The daily struggle called for cooperation, and so every person contributed to the social fabric, and each person was respected for his contribution.

The old ones had looked deep into the web that connects all animate and <u>inanimate</u> forms of life, and they recognized the great design of the creation.

These *ancianos*[3] from the cultures of the Rio Grande, living side by side, sharing, growing together, they knew the rhythms and cycles of time, from the preparation of the earth in the spring to the digging of the acequias[4] that brought the water to the dance of harvest in the fall. They shared good times and hard times. They helped each other through the epidemics and the personal tragedies, and they shared what little they had when the hot winds burned the land and no rain came. They learned that to survive one had to share in the process of life.

Hard workers all, they tilled the earth and farmed, ran the herds and spun wool, and carved their saints and their kachinas[5] from cottonwood late in the winter nights. All worked with a deep faith which <u>perplexes</u> the modern mind.

Their faith shone in their eyes; it was in the strength of their grip, in the creases time wove into their faces. When they spoke, they spoke plainly and with few words, and

Vocabulary Development
inanimate (in AN uh mit) *adj.* not living
perplexes (per PLEKS iz) *v.* confuses or puzzles

1. **Buenos días le de Dios, abuelo** (BWAY nohs DEE ahs lay day DEE ohs ah BWAY loh)
2. **abuelitas** (ah bway LEE tahs) grandmothers.
3. **ancianos** (ahn see AHN ohs) old people; ancestors.
4. **acequias** (ah say KEE ahs) irrigation ditches.
5. **kachinas** (kah CHEE nahs) small wooden dolls, representing the spirit of an ancestor or a god.

they meant what they said. When they prayed, they went straight to the source of life. When there were good times, they knew how to dance in celebration and how to prepare the foods of the fiestas.[6] All this they passed on to the young, so that a new generation would know what they had known, so the string of life would not be broken.

Today we would say that the old abuelitos lived authentic lives.

Newcomers to New Mexico often say that time seems to move slowly here. I think they mean they have come in contact with the inner strength of the people, a strength so solid it causes time itself to pause. Think of it. Think of the high, northern New Mexico villages, or the lonely ranches on the open llano.[7] Think of the Indian pueblo[8] which lies as solid as rock in the face of time. Remember the old people whose eyes seem like windows that peer into a distant past that makes absurdity of our contemporary world. That is what one feels when one encounters the old ones and their land, a pausing of time.

We have all felt time stand still. We have all been in the presence of power, the knowledge of the old ones, the majestic peace of a mountain stream or an aspen grove or red buttes rising into blue sky. We have all felt the light of dusk permeate the earth and cause time to pause in its flow.

I felt this when first touched by the spirit of Ultima, the old *curandera*[9] who appears in my first novel, *Bless Me, Ultima.* This is how the young Antonio describes what he feels:

> When she came the beauty of the llano unfolded before my eyes, and the gurgling waters of the river sang to the hum of the turning earth. The magical time of childhood stood still, and the pulse of the living earth pressed its mystery into my living blood. She took my hand, and the silent, magic powers she possessed made beauty from the raw, sun-baked llano, the green river valley, and the blue bowl which was the white sun's home. My bare feet felt the throbbing earth, and my body trembled with excitement. Time stood still . . .

Reading Skill

Which **details** on this page and on the previous page support the underlined sentence? Give three examples.

_____

_____

_____

Literary Analysis

Diction refers to the words an author uses. It is another element of **style.** The author uses Spanish words. Circle these words on this page. How does using Spanish show the way the author feels about his culture?

_____

_____

Stop to Reflect

Anaya portrays the slow movement of time as something positive. Do you agree or disagree with this point of view? Explain.

_____

_____

_____

Reading Check

How does Antonio feel when he meets Ultima? Underline two statements that tell you.

Vocabulary Development

absurdity (ab SER duh tee) *n.* something ridiculous or nonsensical
permeate (PER mee ayt) *v.* spread or flow throughout

6. **fiestas** (fee ES tahs) *n.* celebrations, feasts.
7. **llano** (YAH noh) plain.
8. **pueblo** (PWAY bloh) *n.* village or town.
9. **curandera** (koo rahn DAY rah) medicine woman.

© Pearson Education

Reading Skill

In the bracketed passage, Anaya includes an anecdote, or a short personal account about a hunting trip on the Taos mountain. What **main idea** about the grandfather does this anecdote support?

_____

_____

Literary Analysis 🔍

Syntax, or the arrangement of words in sentences, is an element of an author's **style.** Read the underlined sentence. How does the syntax of this sentence emphasize the physical characteristics of Anaya's grandfather?

_____

_____

_____

Reading Check

Why did Anaya's parents send him to stay with his grandfather during summers? Underline the text that tells you.

At other times, in other places, when I have been privileged to be with the old ones, to learn, I have felt this inner reserve of strength upon which they draw. I have been held motionless and speechless by the power of curanderas. I have felt the same power when I hunted with Cruz, high on the Taos mountain, where it was more than the incredible beauty of the mountain bathed in morning light, more than the shining of the quivering aspen, but a connection with life, as if a shining strand of light connected the particular and the cosmic. That feeling is an epiphany of time, a standing still of time.

But not all of our old ones are curanderos or hunters on the mountain. My grandfather was a plain man, a farmer from Puerto de Luna[10] on the Pecos River. He was probably a descendent of those people who spilled over the mountain from Taos, following the Pecos River in search of farmland. There in that river valley he settled and raised a large family.

Bearded and walrus-mustached, he stood five feet tall, but to me as a child he was a giant. I remember him most for his silence. In the summers my parents sent me to live with him on his farm, for I was to learn the ways of a farmer. My uncles also lived in that valley, the valley called Puerto de Luna, there where only the flow of the river and the whispering of the wind marked time. For me it was a magical place.

I remember once, while out hoeing the fields, I came upon an anthill, and before I knew it I was badly bitten. After he had covered my welts with the cool mud from the irrigation ditch, my grandfather calmly said: "Know where you stand." That is the way he spoke, in short phrases, to the point.

One very dry summer, the river dried to a trickle, there was no water for the fields. The young plants withered and died. In my sadness and with the impulses of youth I said, "I wish it would rain!" My grandfather touched me, looked up into the sky and whispered, "Pray for rain." In his language there was a difference. He felt connected to the cycles that brought the rain or kept it from us. His prayer was a meaningful action, because he was a participant with the forces that filled our world, he was not a bystander.

A young man died at the village one summer. A very tragic death. He was dragged by his horse. When he was found I cried, for the boy was my friend. I did not understand why death had come to one so young. My

Vocabulary Development

epiphany (ee PIF uh nee) *n.* a revealing moment

10. **Puerto de Luna** (PWEHR toh day LOO nah) Port of the Moon, the name of a town.

grandfather took me aside and said: "Think of the death of the trees and the fields in the fall. The leaves fall, and everything rests, as if dead. But they bloom again in the spring. Death is only this small transformation in life."

These are the things I remember, these fleeting images, few words.

I remember him driving his horse-drawn wagon into Santa Rosa in the fall when he brought his harvest produce to sell in the town. What a tower of strength seemed to come in that small man huddled on the seat of the giant wagon. One click of his tongue and the horses obeyed, stopped or turned as he wished. He never raised his whip. How unlike today when so much teaching is done with loud words and threatening hands.

I would run to greet the wagon, and the wagon would stop. "Buenos días le de Dios, abuelo," I would say. This was the prescribed greeting of esteem and respect. Only after the greeting was given could we approach these venerable old people. "Buenos días te de Dios, mi hijo,"[11] he would answer and smile, and then I could jump up on the wagon and sit at his side. Then I, too, became a king as I rode next to the old man who smelled of earth and sweat and the other deep <u>aromas</u> from the orchards and fields of Puerto de Luna.

We were all sons and daughters to him. But today the sons and daughters are breaking with the past, putting aside los abuelitos. The old values are threatened, and threatened most where it comes to these relationships with the old people. If we don't take the time to watch and feel the years of their final transformation, a part of our humanity will be lessened.

I grew up speaking Spanish, and oh! how difficult it was to learn English. Sometimes I would give up and cry out that I couldn't learn. Then he would say, "Ten paciencia."[12] Have patience. *Paciencia,* a word with the strength of centuries, a word that said that someday we would overcome. *Paciencia,* how soothing a word coming from this old man who could still sling hundred-pound bags over his shoulder, chop wood for hours on end, and hitch up his own horses and ride to town and back in one day.

"You have to learn the language of the Americanos,"[13] he said. "Me, I will live my last days in my valley. You will live in a new time, the time of the gringos."[14]

Vocabulary Development

aromas (uh ROH muhz) *n.* strong, pleasant smells

11. **mi hijo** (mee EE hoh) my son.
12. **Ten paciencia** (tayn pah see EN see ah)
13. **Americanos** (ah may ree KAH nohs) Americans.
14. **gringos** (GREENG ohs) *n.* foreigners; North Americans.

© Pearson Education

Literary Analysis

In the first bracketed passage, Anaya's **tone** is one of admiration and respect as he describes his grandfather Anaya's **diction** sets this tone. Circle three words in this passage that set the tone.

Reading Skill

What **main idea** about the loss of values does Anaya state in the second bracketed passage?

_____

_____

Reading Check

Why does Anaya's grandfather tell him that he must learn English? Underline the text that tells you.

Literary Analysis 🔍

In the first bracketed passage, Anaya begins two sentences with the word "gone." What point does this **syntax** emphasize?

_____

_____

_____

_____

Stop to Reflect 📖

How have the roles of grandfather and grandson been reversed?

_____

_____

_____

_____

_____

Reading Skill 📖

Read the second bracketed passage. What **details** support the **main idea** that Anaya's grandfather was both an ordinary and an extraordinary man?

_____

_____

_____

_____

_____

Reading Check ✏️

Why must Anaya tell his grandfather to "Have patience"? Underline the text that tells you.

A new time did come, a new time is here. How will we form it so it is fruitful? We need to know where we stand. We need to speak softly and respect others, and to share what we have. We need to pray not for material gain, but for rain for the fields, for the sun to nurture growth, for nights in which we can sleep in peace, and for a harvest in which everyone can share. Simple lessons from a simple man. These lessons he learned from his past which was as deep and strong as the currents of the river of life, a life which could be stronger than death.

He was a man; he died. Not in his valley, but nevertheless cared for by his sons and daughters and flocks of grandchildren. At the end, I would enter his room which carried the smell of medications and Vicks, the faint <u>pungent</u> odor of urine, and cigarette smoke. Gone were the aroma of the fields, the strength of his young manhood. Gone also was his patience in the face of crippling old age. Small things bothered him; he shouted or turned sour when his expectations were not met. It was because he could not care for himself, because he was returning to that state of childhood, and all those wishes and desires were now wrapped in a crumbling old body.

"Ten paciencia," I once said to him, and he smiled. "I didn't know I would grow this old," he said. "Now, I can't even roll my own cigarettes." I rolled a cigarette for him, placed it in his mouth and lit it. I asked him why he smoked, the doctor had said it was bad for him. "I like to see the smoke rise," he said. He would smoke and doze, and his quilt was spotted with little burns where the cigarettes dropped. One of us had to sit and watch to make sure a fire didn't start.

I would sit and look at him and remember what was said of him when he was a young man. He could mount a wild horse and break it, and he could ride as far as any man. He could dance all night at a dance, then work the acequia the following day. He helped neighbors, they helped him. He married, raised children. Small legends, the kind that make up everyman's life.

He was 94 when he died. Family, neighbors, and friends gathered; they all agreed he had led a rich life. I remembered the last years, the years he spent in bed. And as I remember now, I am reminded that it is too easy to romanticize old age. Sometimes we forget the pain of the transformation into old age, we forget the natural breaking down of the body. Not all go gentle into the last years, some go crying and cursing, forgetting the names

---

Vocabulary Development

pungent (PUN juhnt) *adj.* strong-smelling

of those they loved the most, withdrawing into an internal anguish few of us can know. May we be granted the patience and care to deal with our ancianos.

For some time we haven't looked at these changes and needs of the old ones. The American image created by the mass media is an image of youth, not of old age. It is the beautiful and the young who are praised in this society. If analyzed carefully, we see that same damaging thought has crept into the way society views the old. In response to the old, the mass media have just created old people who act like the young. It is only the healthy, pink-cheeked, outgoing, older persons we are shown in the media. And they are always selling something, as if an entire generation of old people were salesmen in their lives. Commercials show very lively old men, who must always be in excellent health according to the new myth, selling insurance policies or real estate as they are out golfing; older women selling coffee or toilet paper to those just married. That image does not illustrate the real life of the old ones.

Real life takes into account the natural cycle of growth and change. My grandfather pointed to the leaves falling from the tree. So time brings with its transformation the often painful, wearing-down process. Vision blurs, health wanes; even the act of walking carries with it the painful reminder of the autumn of life. But this process is something to be faced, not something to be hidden away by false images. Yes, the old can be young at heart, but in their own way, with their own dignity. They do not have to copy the always-young image of the Hollywood star.

My grandfather wanted to return to his valley to die. But by then the families of the valley had left in search of a better future. It is only now that there seems to be a return to the valley, a revival. The new generation seeks its roots, that value of love for the land moves us to return to the place where our ancianos formed the culture.

I returned to Puerto de Luna last summer, to join the community in a celebration of the founding of the church. I drove by my grandfather's home, my uncles' ranches, the neglected adobe[15] washing down into the earth from whence it came. And I wondered, how might the values of my grandfather's generation live in our own? What can we retain to see us through these hard times? I was to become a farmer, and I became a writer. As I plow and plant my words, do I nurture as my grandfather did in his fields and orchards? The answers are not simple.

TAKE NOTES

Stop to Reflect

Do you agree or disagree with Anaya's belief about media representations of old people? Explain your answer.

_____

_____

_____

Literary Analysis

What **diction** in the bracketed paragraph does Anaya use to connect the idea of life with nature? Underline examples in the paragraph.

Reading Skill

What **main idea** is supported by the **detail** of the neglected adobe homes?

_____

_____

_____

Vocabulary Development

anguish (ANG gwish) *n.* great pain or suffering

15. **adobe** (uh DOH bee) *n.* sun-dried clay brick.

Stop to Reflect

Anaya talks about how certain sounds and smells make him remember his grandfather. What are some smells and sounds that you connect with an important person in your life? Why do you connect these sounds and smells with that person?

_____

_____

_____

_____

_____

"They don't make men like that anymore," is a phrase we hear when one does honor to a man. I am glad I knew my grandfather. I am glad there are still times when I can see him in my dreams, hear him in my <u>reverie</u>. Sometimes I think I catch a whiff of that earthy aroma that was his smell, just as in lonely times sometimes I catch the fragrance of Ultima's herbs. Then I smile. How strong these people were to leave such a lasting impression.

So, as I would greet my abuelo long ago, it would help us all to greet the old ones we know with this kind and respectful greeting: "Buenos días le de Dios."

Reader's Response: How do the "old ones" in Anaya's compare with the "old ones" in your own life?

_____

_____

_____

_____

_____

_____

_____

_____

Vocabulary Development
reverie (REV uh ree) *n.* daydream

A Celebration of Grandfathers

1. **Distinguish:** How are the qualities of old people that Anaya remembers different from the images that Anaya says have been created by American mass media?

   _____

   _____

   _____

2. **Draw Conclusions:** What opinion does Anaya offer on the way people should be treated as they grow old?

   _____

   _____

   _____

3. **Literary Analysis:** Use this chart to record examples of the **diction** and **tone** Anaya uses. Then, on the basis of his diction and tone, write three adjectives in the center of the chart that describe Anaya's **style**.

Diction	Style	Tone

4. **Reading Skill:** State the **main idea** of Anaya's essay in your own words.

   _____

   _____

   _____

   _____

   _____

Writing: Book Jacket Copy

Write a few paragraphs of **book jacket copy** for the biography of an older person whom you admire. Be sure to include the most important events of that person's life. Use the items below to determine what information to include in your book jacket copy.

- List at least five words that describe the person's character.

_____

_____

_____

- What makes this person stand out from others?

_____

_____

_____

Listening and Speaking: Panel Discussion

With a partner, jot down notes for use in a panel discussion on the American image as it is created by the mass media.

Images of People in Media	Images of Old Age	Messages about Old Age
_____	_____	_____
_____	_____	_____
_____	_____	_____

My Position: _____

_____

_____

On Summer
Lorraine Hansberry

Summary Lorraine Hansberry explains that when she was young, summer was not her favorite season. She thought that summer was too bright and too noisy. She did not like summer's heat. Over time, her opinion of summer changed. She came to connect summer with strong-willed people.

 Writing About the Big Question

Is knowledge the same as understanding? In "On Summer," Lorraine Hansberry's growing understanding of life has changed her feelings about summer. Complete this sentence:

Learning the facts of peoples' lives may change how we comprehend them

because _____.

Note-taking Guide
Use this chart to record the writer's changing feelings about summer.

How does Hansberry feel about summer?	
As a Child	As an Adult
It is uncomfortable.	

On Summer

1. **Infer:** Why do you think Hansberry includes the section about her grandmother in her essay?

_____

_____

_____

2. **Interpret:** At the end of the essay, Hansberry calls summer "the noblest of seasons." What do you think she means by this phrase?

_____

_____

_____

3. **Literary Analysis:** Review the last two paragraphs of "On Summer." Use the chart below to record examples of the **diction** and **tone** Hansberry uses in describing summer. Then, on the basis of her diction and tone in these paragraphs, write three adjectives in the center of the chart to describe Hansberry's **style**.

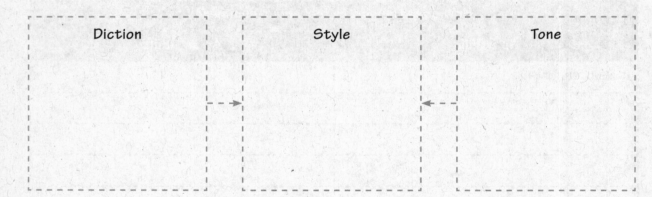

Diction	Style	Tone

4. **Reading Skill:** State the main idea of "On Summer" in your own words.

_____

_____

_____

Writing: Book Jacket Copy

Write a few paragraphs of **book jacket copy** for the biography of an older person whom you admire. Be sure to include the most important events of that person's life. Use the list below to determine what information to include in your book jacket copy.

- List at least five words that describe the person's character.

  _____

- What makes this person stand out from others?

  _____

Listening and Speaking: Panel Discussion

With a partner, jot down notes for taking part in a panel discussion on the seasons.

My Favorite Season:

_____

Reasons to Like This Season:

_____

_____

Reasons to Dislike This Season:

_____

_____

Single Room, Earth View • The News

Literary Analysis

Expository text is nonfiction that presents information or discusses ideas. This type of text can also explain a process. The writer may use many different techniques to provide support, depth, and context:

- **Description:** including **imagery**—language that appeals to the senses and **figurative language**—a comparison of two things
- **Comparison and contrast:** showing similarities and differences between two or more items
- **Cause and effect:** explaining the relationship between events, actions, or situations by showing how one can result in another

Reading Skill

The **main idea** is the central message or opinion in a work of nonfiction. The **supporting details** are the pieces of evidence that a writer uses to prove his or her point. **Reread** passages that do not seem to support the work's main idea. This action will help you **identify the main or controlling idea and supporting details** in a work.

- As you read, note key details to decide what the main idea might be.
- You may find details that do not seem to support the main idea. Reread passages to make sure that you have read them correctly.
- Revise your guesses about the main idea if you need to.

   Use the chart shown to record the details of a work. Write the main idea they might support.

```
┌────────────────┐         ┌────────────────┐
│    Details     │         │    Details     │
│                │         │                │
│                │         │                │
└────────────────┘         └────────────────┘
          ╲                   ╱
           ╲                 ╱
          ┌──────────────────┐
          │    Main Idea     │
          │                  │
          │                  │
          └──────────────────┘
```

Single Room, Earth View
Sally Ride

Summary Sally Ride tells about her space shuttle voyage. Ride is amazed at the way Earth looks from space. She recounts the many details she can see. Ride's time in space changes her feelings about Earth.

 Writing About the Big Question

Is knowledge the same as understanding? In "Single Room, Earth View," astronaut Sally Ride explains what it is like to see Earth from the space shuttle. Complete this sentence:

Looking at Earth from space may change how we comprehend the world

because _____.

Note-taking Guide
Use this chart to identify what Sally Ride sees from space.

What Sally Ride Sees from Space	
Oceans	the different colors of the oceans
Geographical Sites	
Human-Made Structures	
Natural Occurrences	
Environmental Problems	

Single Room, Earth View
Sally Ride

Everyone I've met has a glittering, if vague, mental image of space travel. And naturally enough, people want to hear about it from an astronaut: "How did it feel . . . ?" "What did it look like . . . ?" "Were you scared?" Sometimes, the questions come from reporters, their pens poised and their tape recorders silently reeling in the words; sometimes, it's wide-eyed, ten-year-old girls who want answers. I find a way to answer all of them, but it's not easy.

Imagine trying to describe an airplane ride to someone who has never flown. An <u>articulate</u> traveler could describe the sights but would find it much harder to explain the difference in perspective provided by the new view from a greater distance, along with the feelings, impressions, and insights that go with that new perspective. And the difference is enormous: Spaceflight moves the traveler another giant step farther away. Eight and one-half thunderous minutes after launch, an astronaut is orbiting high above the Earth, suddenly able to watch typhoons form, volcanoes smolder, and meteors streak through the atmosphere below.

While flying over the Hawaiian Islands, several astronauts have marveled that the islands look just like they do on a map. When people first hear that, they wonder what should be so surprising about Hawaii looking the way it does in the atlas. Yet, to the astronauts it is an absolutely startling sensation: The islands really *do* look as if that part of the world has been carpeted with a big page torn out of Rand-McNally, and all we can do is try to convey the surreal quality of that scene.

In orbit, racing along at five miles per second, the space shuttle circles the Earth once every 90 minutes. I found that at this speed, unless I kept my nose pressed to the window, it was almost impossible to keep track of where we were at any given moment—the world below simply changes too fast. If I turned my concentration away for too long, even just to change film in a camera, I could miss an entire land mass. It's embarrassing to float up to a window, glance outside, and then have to ask a crewmate, "What continent is this?"

We could see smoke rising from fires that dotted the entire east coast of Africa, and in the same orbit only moments later, ice floes jostling for position in the Antarctic. We could see the Ganges River dumping its

© Pearson Education

Activate Prior Knowledge

Think of a photograph you have seen of Earth. Make sure that it was one that was taken from space. On the lines below, list three details that you remember about the photograph.

_____

_____

_____

_____

_____

Reading Skill

The **main idea** is the main message in a nonfiction story. **Supporting details** are the evidence an author uses to support the main idea. Read the bracketed passage. Which details support the author's idea that Earth looks different from space?

_____

_____

_____

Reading Check

How fast do the astronauts travel in orbit? Underline the text that tells you.

Vocabulary Development

articulate (ahr TIK yuh lit) *adj.* expressing oneself clearly and easily

murky, sediment-laden water into the Indian Ocean and watch ominous hurricane clouds expanding and rising like biscuits in the oven of the Caribbean.

Mountain ranges, volcanoes, and river deltas appeared in salt-and-flour relief, all leading me to assume the role of a novice geologist. In such moments, it was easy to imagine the dynamic upheavals that created jutting mountain ranges and the internal wrenchings that created rifts and seas. I also became an instant believer in plate tectonics; India really is crashing into Asia, and Saudi Arabia and Egypt really *are* pulling apart, making the Red Sea wider. Even though their respective motion is really no more than mere inches a year, the view from overhead makes theory come alive.

Spectacular as the view is from 200 miles up, the Earth is not the awe-inspiring "blue marble" made famous by the photos from the moon. From space shuttle height, we can't see the entire globe at a glance, but we can look down the entire boot of Italy, or up the East Coast of the United States from Cape Hatteras to Cape Cod. The panoramic view inspires an appreciation for the scale of some of nature's phenomena. One day, as I scanned the sandy expanse of Northern Africa, I couldn't find any of the familiar landmarks—colorful outcroppings of rock in Chad, irrigated patches of the Sahara. Then I realized they were obscured by a huge dust storm, a cloud of sand that enveloped the continent from Morocco to the Sudan.

Since the space shuttle flies fairly low (at least by orbital standards; it's more than 22,000 miles lower than a typical TV satellite), we can make out both natural and manmade features in surprising detail. Familiar geographical features like San Francisco Bay, Long Island, and Lake Michigan are easy to recognize, as are many cities, bridges, and airports. The Great Wall of China is not the only man-made object visible from space.

The signatures of civilization are usually seen in straight lines (bridges or runways) or sharp delineations (abrupt transitions from desert to irrigated land, as in California's Imperial Valley). A modern city like New York doesn't leap from the canvas of its surroundings, but its straight piers and concrete runways catch the eye—and around them, the city materializes. I found Salina, Kansas

Vocabulary Development

sediment (SED uh muhnt) *n.* solid material, such as sand, that sinks to the bottom of a body of water

novice (NAH vis) *adj.* new to an activity; inexperienced

delineations (di lin ee AY shuhns) *n.* divisions that are easy to see

---

Literary Analysis

An **expository essay** is a short piece of nonfiction that presents information or discusses ideas. These essays often contain vivid **descriptive language** that appeals to the senses. Read the bracketed passage. What senses does the descriptive language have you use?

_____

_____

Stop to Reflect

Which places that Ride describes do you think would be most interesting to see? Explain.

_____

_____

_____

_____

_____

Reading Check 🖊

Volcanoes, mountains, and lakes are examples of geological features. What are three geographical features Ride sees from space? Underline the text that tells you.

Literary Analysis

What is Ride **describing** in the first bracketed paragraph?

_____

_____

What point is she making about the environment in her description?

_____

_____

_____

_____

_____

Reading Skill

Reread the second bracketed paragraph. What **supporting details** does Ride use for her claim that Earth looks different from space? Underline the text that tells you.

Literary Analysis

Comparison and contrast is another technique that writers use in an **expository essay**. This technique shows the similarities and differences between items. What is the difference between looking at the ocean from space and looking at it from a boat?

_____

_____

_____

(and pleased my in-laws, who live there) by spotting its long runway amid the wheat fields near the city. Over Florida, I could see the launch pad where we had begun our trip, and the landing strip, where we would eventually land.

Some of civilization's more unfortunate effects on the environment are also evident from orbit. Oil slicks glisten on the surface of the Persian Gulf, patches of pollution-damaged trees dot the forests of central Europe. Some cities look out of focus, and their colors muted, when viewed through a pollutant haze. Not surprisingly, the effects are more noticeable now than they were a decade ago. An astronaut who has flown in both Skylab and the space shuttle reported that the horizon didn't seem quite as sharp, or the colors quite as bright, in 1983 as they had in 1973.

Of course, informal observations by individual astronauts are one thing, but more precise measurements are continually being made from space: The space shuttle has carried infrared film to document damage to citrus trees in Florida and in rain forests along the Amazon. It has carried even more sophisticated sensors in the payload bay. Here is one example: sensors used to measure atmospheric carbon monoxide levels, allowing scientists to study the environmental effects of city emissions and land-clearing fires.

Most of the Earth's surface is covered with water, and at first glance it all looks the same: blue. But with the right lighting conditions and a couple of orbits of practice, it's possible to make out the intricate patterns in the oceans—eddies and spirals become visible because of the subtle differences in water color or reflectivity.

Observations and photographs by astronauts have contributed significantly to the understanding of ocean dynamics, and some of the more intriguing discoveries prompted the National Aeronautics and Space Administration to fly an oceanographic observer for the express purpose of studying the ocean from orbit. Scientists' understanding of the energy balance in the oceans has increased significantly as a result of the discoveries of circular and spiral eddies tens of kilometers in diameter, of standing waves hundreds of kilometers long, and of spiral eddies that sometimes trail into one another for thousands of kilometers. If a scientist wants to study features on this scale, it's much easier from an orbiting vehicle than from the vantage point of a boat.

Vocabulary Development

eddies (ED eez) *n.* round water movements

Believe it or not, an astronaut can also see the wakes of large ships and the <u>contrails</u> of airplanes. The sun angle has to be just right, but when the lighting conditions are perfect, you can follow otherwise invisible oil tankers on the Persian Gulf and trace major shipping lanes through the Mediterranean Sea. Similarly, when atmospheric conditions allow contrail formation, the thousand-mile-long condensation trails let astronauts trace the major air routes across the northern Pacific Ocean.

Part of every orbit takes us to the dark side of the planet. In space, night is very, very black—but that doesn't mean there's nothing to look at. The lights of cities sparkle; on nights when there was no moon, it was difficult for me to tell the Earth from the sky—the twinkling lights could be stars or they could be small cities. On one nighttime pass from Cuba to Nova Scotia, the entire East Coast of the United States appeared in twinkling outline.

When the moon is full, it casts an eerie light on the Earth. In its light, we see ghostly clouds and bright reflections on the water. One night, the Mississippi River flashed into view, and because of our viewing angle and orbital path, the reflected moonlight seemed to flow downstream—as if Huck Finn had tied a candle to his raft.

Of all the sights from orbit, the most spectacular may be the magnificent displays of lightning that ignite the clouds at night. On Earth, we see lightning from below the clouds; in orbit, we see it from above. Bolts of lightning are <u>diffused</u> by the clouds into bursting balls of light. Sometimes, when a storm extends hundreds of miles, it looks like a transcontinental brigade is tossing fireworks from cloud to cloud.

As the shuttle races the sun around the Earth, we pass from day to night and back again during a single orbit—hurtling into darkness, then bursting into daylight. The sun's appearance unleashes spectacular blue and orange bands along the horizon, a clockwork miracle that astronauts witness every 90 minutes. But I really can't describe a sunrise in orbit. The drama set against the black backdrop of space and the magic of the materializing colors can't be captured in an astronomer's equations or an astronaut's photographs.

Vocabulary Development

contrails (KAHN trayls) *n.* white trails of condensed water vapor that form behind aircraft in flight

diffused (di FYOOZD) *v.* spread out

Literary Analysis

To what does Ride **compare** the lights on Earth at night?

_____

_____

Reading Skill

What **details** in the first bracketed passage support the **main idea** that the moon casts an eerie light on Earth?

_____

_____

_____

_____

_____

Stop to Reflect

Read the second bracketed passage. How might the quick switch back and forth between darkness and daylight affect you? Do you think this switch would be hard or easy to get used to? Explain your answer.

_____

_____

_____

_____

Reading Check

What does Ride say may be the most spectacular sight from orbit? Circle the text that tells you.

© Pearson Education

Stop to Reflect

What do you think is different about the environment and perspective in space flight?

_____

_____

_____

I once heard someone (not an astronaut) suggest that it's possible to imagine what spaceflight is like by simply extrapolating from the sensations you experience on an airplane. All you have to do, he said, is mentally raise the airplane 200 miles, mentally eliminate the air noise and the turbulence, and you get an accurate mental picture of a trip in the space shuttle.

Not true. And while it's natural to try to liken spaceflight to familiar experiences, it can't be brought "down to Earth"—not in the final sense. The environment is different, the perspective is different. Part of the fascination with space travel is the element of the unknown—the conviction that it's different from earthbound experiences. And it is.

Reader's Response: Did any of Ride's observations about Earth surprise you? Why?

_____

_____

_____

_____

_____

Vocabulary Development

extrapolating (ek STRAP uh layt ing) *v.* arriving at a conclusion by using what you already know

Single Room, Earth View

1. **Interpret:** Why do you think Ride found it easier to imagine the workings of geological forces when she saw Earth from space?

_____

_____

2. **Assess:** Have Ride's descriptions of Earth changed the way you think about the planet? Explain your answer.

_____

_____

_____

3. **Literary Analysis:** Use this chart to give examples of Ride's use of **description**, **comparison and contrast**, and **cause and effect**. In the first box, write the example. In the second box, explain how the example adds depth and context to the information Ride presents.

	Example	Effect
Description		
Comparison/ Contrast		
Cause and Effect		

4. **Reading Skill:** State the **main idea** of "Single Room, Earth View" in your own words.

_____

_____

Writing: Script

Write a **script** for a public service announcement that persuades people to become candidates for astronaut training. Answer the following questions before you begin.

- How can I appeal to my audience's emotions?

_____

_____

_____

_____

- What persuasive words or phrases might attract people to astronaut training?

_____

_____

_____

_____

Research and Technology: Journal Entries

Make notes below for your two journal entries on the training of astronauts. Be sure to keep track of your information sources.

Physical Training: _____

_____

_____

Scientific Training: _____

_____

_____

Sources I used: _____

_____

The News
Neil Postman

Summary Neil Postman writes about the different features of television news programs. He explains the limitations of television. The essay shows how these weaknesses affect the audience.

 Writing About the Big Question

Is knowledge the same as understanding?
In "The News," the author describes the pros and cons of television news. Complete this sentence:

We react in different ways to the presentation of news information on

television and to the presentation in other media because _____

_____.

Note-taking Guide

Use this chart to record how television news programs and newspapers are different. Then, write how they are alike.

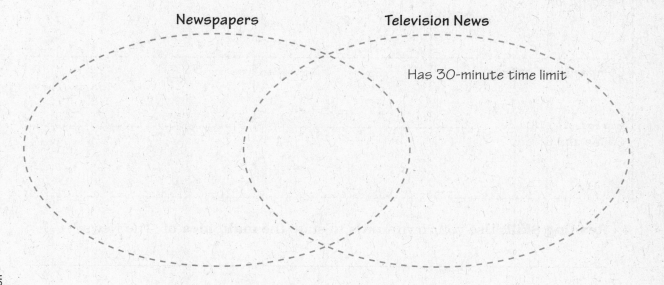

Newspapers   Television News

Has 30-minute time limit

The News

1. **Interpret:** Postman sees a similarity between television news and theater. What problem does he see in this similarity?

   _____

   _____

   _____

2. **Cause and Effect:** What effects do time limits have on television news?

   _____

   _____

   _____

3. **Literary Analysis:** Fill in the chart shown. Find passages in which Postman uses **description, comparison and contrast**, or **cause and effect**. Find one example of each technique. Then, explain the effect of each example.

	Example	Effect
Description		
Comparison/Contrast		
Cause and Effect		

4. **Reading Skill:** Use your own words to state the **main idea** of "The News."

   _____

   _____

   _____

Writing: Script

Write a public service announcement **script** that encourages people to use different news sources. Answer the following questions before you begin your script.

- What action do I want my audience to take?

  _____

  _____

  _____

  _____

- What persuasive words or phrases will help persuade people to use different types of news sources?

  _____

  _____

  _____

  _____

Make sure that you have used a clear organization to present a logical argument.

Research and Technology: Journal Entries

Make notes below for your two journal entries on how journalists prepare to write a news story. Be sure to keep track of your information sources.

Researching Information (Who? What? When? Where? Why? How?):

_____

_____

_____

Interviewing People Involved in the Story: _____

_____

_____

Planning the Visuals: _____

_____

Sources I Used: _____

_____

Technical Documents

About Technical Documents

Technical documents explain how things work. They show how things are made. Some common parts of a technical document include:

- technical language and data
- specifications and other facts
- graphical sources such as diagrams and charts

Reading Skill

Connecting ideas and details across and within texts helps to build your understanding of what you are reading. To connect details within a text, look for pieces of information that logically relate to each other—for instance, all the details on a particular aspect of a topic. Consider all of these details together, even if they are scattered throughout the text. As you analyze, remember to consider details and data presented in **graphical sources,** such as pictures, graphs, and charts.

As you read the technical document, use a graphic organizer to connect ideas and details within the text.

Subtopic	Idea or Detail	Location in Text
space shuttle fuel tank	located under spacecraft, between solid rocket boosters	Space Shuttle illustration

Build Understanding

Knowing these words will help you read this technical document.

components (kuhm POH nuhnts) *n.* parts
modifications (mahd uh fuh KAY shuhnz) *n.* changes
orbiter (AWR bi ter) *n.* spacecraft that goes around a planet or moon

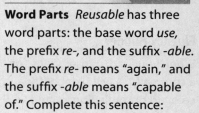

Shuttle Statistics

Length
Space Shuttle:
56.14 meters (184.2 feet)
Orbiter:
37.23 meters (122.17 feet)

Height
Orbiter on runway:
17.27 meters (56.67 feet)

Wingspan
23.79 meters (78.06 feet)

Weight*
At liftoff: 2,041,166 kilograms
(4.5 million pounds)

End of mission: 104,326 kilograms (230,000 pounds)

Maximum cargo to orbit
28,803 kilograms (63,500 pounds)

SRB Separation
Two minutes after launch

External Tank Separation
8.5 minutes after launch

Altitude: 109.26 kilometers
(59 nautical miles)

Velocity: 28,067 kph
(17,440 mph)

Orbit
185 to 643 kilometers
(115 to 400 statute miles)

Velocity: 27,875 kph
(17,321 mph)

*weight will vary depending on payloads and on board consumables.

Space Shuttle Basics

The space shuttle is the world's first reusable spacecraft, and the first spacecraft in history that can carry large satellites both to and from orbit. The shuttle launches like a rocket, maneuvers in Earth orbit like a spacecraft and lands like an airplane. Each of the three space shuttle orbiters now in operation—Discovery, Atlantis and Endeavour—is designed to fly at least 100 missions. So far, altogether they have flown a combined total of less than one-fourth of that.

Text Structure
Headings help readers quickly find a fact. Scan the list headings to find how much the space shuttle weighs at the end of a mission. Write your answer.

_____

Vocabulary Builder
Word Parts *Reusable* has three word parts: the base word *use*, the prefix *re-*, and the suffix *-able*. The prefix *re-* means "again," and the suffix *-able* means "capable of." Complete this sentence:

A reusable spacecraft is a

spacecraft that is _____

_____

_____.

Comprehension Builder
Why is the space shuttle important? On the lines below, write two reasons that are mentioned in the first paragraph.

1. _____

_____

2. _____

_____

Columbia was the first space shuttle orbiter to be delivered to NASA's Kennedy Space Center, Fla., in March 1979. Columbia and the STS-107 crew were lost Feb. 1, 2003, during re-entry. The orbiter Challenger was delivered to KSC in July 1982 and was destroyed in an explosion during ascent in January 1986. Discovery was delivered in November 1983. Atlantis was delivered in April 1985. Endeavour was built as a replacement following the Challenger accident and was delivered to Florida in May 1991. An early space shuttle orbiter, the Enterprise, never flew in space but was used for approach and landing tests at the Dryden Flight Research Center and several launch pad studies in the late 1970s.

The space shuttle consists of three major components: the orbiter which houses the crew; a large external fuel tank that holds fuel for the main engines; and two solid rocket boosters which provide most of the shuttle's lift during the first two minutes of flight. All of the components are reused except for the external fuel tank, which burns up in the atmosphere after each launch.

The longest the shuttle has stayed in orbit on any single mission is 17.5 days on mission STS-80 in November 1996. Normally, missions may be planned for anywhere from five to 16 days in duration. The smallest crew ever to fly on the shuttle numbered two people on the first few missions. The largest crew numbered eight people. Normally, crews may range in size from five to seven people. The shuttle is designed to reach orbits ranging from about 185 kilometers to 643 kilometers (115 statute miles to 400 statute miles) high.

The shuttle has the most reliable launch record of any rocket now in operation. Since 1981, it has boosted more than 1.36 million kilograms (3 million pounds) of cargo into orbit. More than 600 crew members have flown on its missions. Although it has been in operation for almost

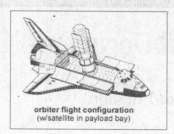

orbiter flight configuration
(w/satellite in payload bay)

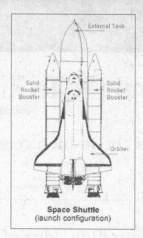

External Tank

Solid Rocket Booster

Solid Rocket Booster

Orbiter

Space Shuttle
(launch configuration)

20 years, the shuttle has continually evolved and is significantly different today than when it first was launched. NASA has made literally thousands of major and minor modifications to the original design that have made it safer, more reliable and more capable today than ever before.

Since 1992 alone, NASA has made engine and system improvements that are estimated to have tripled the safety of flying the space shuttle, and the number of problems experienced while a space shuttle is in flight has decreased by 70 percent. During the same period, the cost of operating the shuttle has decreased by one and a quarter billion dollars annually—a reduction of more than 40 percent. At the same time, because of weight reductions and other improvements, the cargo the shuttle can carry has increased by 7.3 metric tons (8 tons).

NASA is prepared to continue flying the shuttle for at least the next decade and plans to continue to improve the shuttle during the next five years, with goals of increasing its safety by improving the highest-risk components. NASA will also be working with the Columbia Accident Investigation Board to correct any problems the board may find as it works to determine the cause of the Columbia accident.

In managing and operating the space shuttle, NASA holds the safety of the crew as its highest priority.

© Pearson Education

Text Structure

Looking at diagrams will give you some quick background knowledge. This knowledge will help you understand the text. What is one thing you can learn by looking at the diagrams on this page?

_____

_____

_____

_____

Comprehension Builder

Reread the first bracketed passage. Summarize the improvements that have been made to the space shuttle.

_____

_____

_____

Vocabulary Builder

Proper Nouns Proper nouns name particular persons, places, things, or ideas. They begin with capital letters. Underline the proper nouns in the second bracketed paragraph.

Thinking About the Technical Document

1. The document discusses the launch record and design improvements. Why?

   _____

2. What is the main, or controlling, idea of the technical document?

   _____

TALK ABOUT IT Reading Skill

3. The writer describes some of the shuttle parts. The diagram also shows the parts. Why do you think the subtopic of shuttle parts appears in both places in the text?

   _____

4. Which parts of the document discuss the space shuttle *Columbia*?

   _____

WRITE ABOUT IT Timed Writing: Essay (35 minutes)

Write an essay about the importance of safety in the space shuttle program. In your essay, connect details from within the technical document to support your ideas. Answer these questions to help get you started:

- What is the space shuttle *Enterprise* used for?

   _____

- Why has NASA made so many modifications to the original design of the shuttle?

   _____

- Why is NASA working with the Columbia Accident Investigation Board?

   _____

Carry Your Own Skis • Libraries Face Sad Chapter

Literary Analysis

A **persuasive essay** is a short nonfiction work that tries to convince a reader that he or she should think or act in a particular way. Persuasive essays usually include one or both of the following:

- **Appeals to reason:** logical arguments based on verifiable evidence, such as facts, statistics, or expert testimony
- **Appeals to emotion:** statements intended to affect listeners' feelings about a subject. These statements often include charged language—words with strong positive or negative associations.

An **author's motive** in a persuasive essay is his or her reason for, or interest in, persuading readers to accept his or her position.

Reading Skill

Persuasive appeals are the arguments the author makes. To **analyze and evaluate persuasive appeals**, identify passages in which the author makes an argument in support of his or her position. Then, **reread** those passages to test the author's logic and reasoning. Ask yourself the following questions;

- Is the author's argument supported by evidence, or is it based on faulty assumptions?
- Does the author link ideas clearly, or make leaps in logic?
- Is the argument consistent, or is it contradictory?

Use this chart to record your analysis of the author's arguments. Then, decide whether the author has made a convincing persuasive appeal.

Claim	Logical?

Evaluation

© Pearson Education

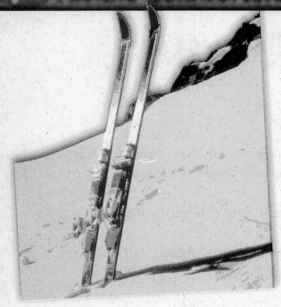

Carry Your Own Skis
Lian Dolan

Summary Lian Dolan recalls how her mother and her aunt taught their children to ski. Everyone was expected to take charge of his or her own gear. The rule was "carry your own skis." As an adult, Dolan learned how the "carry your own skis" rule meant being responsible.

 Writing About the Big Question

Is knowledge the same as understanding? In "Carry Your Own Skis," the author draws an analogy between carrying your own skis and taking responsibility for yourself. Complete this sentence:

Personal responsibility is a **concept** that many people do not truly

understand because _____

_____.

Note-taking Guide
Use this chart to compare those who carry their own skis with those who do not carry their own skis.

Those Who Carry Their Own Skis	Those Who Do Not Carry Their Own Skis
Have fun	Miss all of the fun

Carry Your Own Skis

Lian Dolan

When my mother was forty, she took up skiing. Or, more correctly, she and her twin sister took up skiing. They got on a bus, went to ski camp for a week, and learned to ski. After that, they'd get in the car and head up to Ladies Day at Powder Hill as often as they could to practice their stem christies.[1] Don't let the name fool you, Powder Hill (which later became the more Everest-like "Powder Ridge") was no pushover bunny slope.[2]

This was in the mid-sixties, when skiing was work—decades before valet parking, fondue lunches, and gear that actually keeps you dry, warm, and safe. My mother and my aunt took up the kind of skiing that entailed wooden skis, tie boots, and rope tows[3] that could jerk your arm out of its socket. This was the kind of skiing where skiers, not the Sno-Cats, groomed the hill[4] in the morning. Ticket buyers were expected to sidestep up and down slopes and herringbone the lift lines.[5] The typical A-frame lodge had a big fireplace, a couple of bathrooms, rows of picnic tables, and maybe some hot chocolate for sale. At the end of the day, there were no hot toddies by a roaring fire in furry boots or drinks in the hot tub of a slopeside condo. Instead, my mother and her sister faced the <u>inevitability</u> of a station wagon with a dead battery and the long, dark drive back home in wet clothes.

Why did they learn to ski? It wasn't to spend some quality time outdoors together away from their responsibilities at home. They learned to ski so that they could take their collective children skiing, all seventeen of us. My mother's eight children and my aunt's nine. And learn to ski we did, eagerly. There was, however, one rule my mother had about skiing: Carry your own skis.

My mother didn't teach us to ski until we could carry our own skis from the car to the lodge in the morning and—this is key—from the lodge back to the car at the end of the day. Even cold, wet, and tired, we had to get

Vocabulary Development

inevitability (in ev i tuh BIL i tee) *n.* quality of being certain to happen

---

1. **stem christies** turns made by angling one ski and then bringing the other into alignment.
2. **bunny slope** gently sloping hill used for practice by beginning skiers.
3. **rope tows** moving ropes that skiers hold to be pulled to the top of the hill.
4. **groomed the hill** packed and smoothed the snow.
5. **herringbone the lift lines** walk uphill to chair lift by stepping with skis pointed outward to avoid sliding back down the hill. The skis leave a "herringbone" pattern—a line of connected v-shapes—on the snow.

Activate Prior Knowledge

Think about something difficult that you learned to do as a child. Are you glad you learned the activity? Explain.

_____

_____

_____

_____

Reading Skill

Persuasive appeals are arguments the author makes to convince readers that they should think or act a certain way. How do the details about ski lodges of the 1960s support the author's position that skiing used to be a less-luxurious sport?

_____

_____

_____

Literary Analysis

A **persuasive essay** tries to talk the reader into thinking or acting a certain way by making **appeals to emotions**. Explain how the details "cold, wet, and tired" appeal to your emotions.

_____

_____

_____

Reading Check

What is Dolan's mother's one rule about skiing? Underline the text that tells you.

TAKE NOTES

Literary Analysis ✏️

Appeals to emotions are statements that affect a reader's feelings about the subject of the essay. Underline details in the first bracketed passage that appeal to the emotions. Explain your answers.

_____

_____

_____

_____

_____

Stop to Reflect 📖

Do you think it was reasonable of Dolan's mother to expect all of her children to carry their own skis? Why or why not?

_____

_____

_____

_____

Reading Skill 📖

Reread the second bracketed passage. How does the author support her claim that some kids operate by different rules?

_____

_____

_____

_____

_____

our skis, poles, and boots back to that station wagon on our own. No falling behind. No dragging. And no whining. My mother had the responsibility for her gear, the giant lunch, the car, and the occasional trip to the ER for broken legs. We were in charge of our own gear and meeting at the end of the day. These were the conditions to be allowed to accompany siblings and cousins to the slopes. Carry your own skis or sit in the lodge all day.

No one wanted to get left in the lodge. A cold, wet day on the ice-blue slopes of New England, freezing in leather boots and the generation of ski clothes before microfibers was far preferable to being left out of all that fun. Miss the lunches of soggy tuna fish sandwiches and mini chocolate bars? No way! Sit in the lodge instead of side-slipping your way down a sheet of ice disguised as a trail or tramping through three feet of snow to get the pole you dropped under the chair lift? Not me! Forgo that last run of the day in near darkness, cold and alone and crying because your siblings have skied on ahead without you? Who'd want to miss all that fun? Sitting in the lodge all day just wasn't an option once we reached ski age. We were expected to participate. We learned to carry our own skis.

The lesson was simple, really. Be responsible for yourself and your stuff or you miss out. No one wanted to miss out. Getting across the icy parking lot and back seemed a small price to pay for the <u>potential</u> of great fun. And even if you dropped your poles or the bindings cut into your hands or you fell on your rear end, that was part of the experience. The "carry your own skis" mentality filtered into almost every area of our life as we were growing up. Doing homework, getting to practice, applying to college—be responsible for yourself and your stuff or you miss out.

I began to notice the people who hadn't learned to carry their own skis when I was as young as eleven. I didn't have a name for this concept yet, but I had the notion that maybe other kids operated by a different set of rules. They thought that somewhere, somebody was going to take care of things for them. I remember the girls at summer camp who never signed up to pack out or pack in for a camping trip, expecting that someone else would provide food or do all the cleanup for them. But me? I would sign up to make the PB&Js and to clean up the mess. I'd load the canoes onto the truck and take 'em off again. And the tent? I'd put it up and I'd take it down. I didn't know any different. As a result, I was invited to go

Vocabulary Development

potential (puh TEN shuhl) _n._ possibility

on a lot of camping trips. The lodge and back, baby—that was my attitude.

In high school, the kids who didn't carry their own skis called their parents to bring in assignments they'd forgotten or to ask for a ride home instead of walking or taking the late bus. In college, the no-ski carriers all had pink T-shirts—a sure sign that they had never done laundry before—and they complained about how much work they had. Isn't that what college was about—doing your own laundry and finishing your work? Then you could get to the fun stuff.

The real world is <u>riddled</u> with people who have never learned to carry their own skis—the blame-shifters, the no-RSVPers, the coworkers who never participate in those painful group birthdays except if it's their own. I admit it: I don't really get these people.

I like the folks who clear the dishes, even when they're the guests. Or the committee members who show up on time, assignment completed and ready to pitch in on the next event. Or the neighbor who drives the carpool even though her kids are sick. I get these people. These people have learned to carry their own skis.

In early adulthood, carrying my own skis meant getting a job, paying off my student loans, and working hard for the company that was providing my paycheck. If I did those things, then I could enjoy the other areas of my life. Dull, yes, but freeing, too. When I wasn't responsible for myself or my stuff, I felt lousy. Sometimes I could get to the lodge, but I just couldn't get back to the station wagon at the end of the day. It was an unfamiliar feeling to let someone down by missing a deadline at work or not showing up for an early-morning run . . . On days like that, the parking lot seemed bigger and icier than I had anticipated.

Now I have a life that includes a husband, two children, a dog, a house, friends, schools, and a radio show that involves lots of other people, including four sisters. The "stuff" of my life may seem much heavier than two skis, two boots, and two poles, but it isn't really—just a little bit trickier to carry. I have to do more balancing and let go of the commitments that I'd probably drop anyway. If I commit to more than I can handle, I miss out. That's when I think of Powder Hill.

The funny thing is, some of the worst moments of my childhood were spent on skis or in pursuit of skiing. The truth is, I didn't really like skiing as a kid. And I wasn't

Vocabulary Development

riddled (RID ld) *v.* affected in every part

 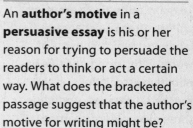

Literary Analysis

An **author's motive** in a **persuasive essay** is his or her reason for trying to persuade the readers to think or act a certain way. What does the bracketed passage suggest that the author's motive for writing might be?

_____

_____

_____

_____

Stop to Reflect

How do you feel about people who do not take responsibility for themselves?

_____

_____

_____

_____

_____

Reading Skill

In her **persuasive appeal,** how does Dolan connect her life today with her experiences skiing?

_____

_____

Reading Check

How did Dolan feel when she was not responsible for herself? Underline the answers in the text.

Literary Analysis

To make **appeals to emotions,** writers often use charged language, which consists of words with strong positive or negative associations. In the bracketed passage, underline three examples of charged language.

Reading Skill

Analyze and evaluate persuasive appeals in Dolan's essay. Does the author clearly connect lessons learned from skiing with ideas about life? Explain.

_____

_____

_____

_____

a very good skier. Most days, skiing for me was about freezing rain and constantly trying to catch up to my older, faster, more talented siblings. The hard falls on the hard ice. I can still feel the damp long underwear and the wet wool during the endless ride home. But whether I liked to ski or not didn't really matter. I was expected to learn to ski, and I did. And I also learned that in life you need to be responsible for yourself and your stuff or you miss out. The lodge and back, baby.

Reader's Response: What emotions did Dolan make you feel? Explain.

_____

_____

_____

_____

_____

_____

Carry Your Own Skis

1. **Connect:** In what aspects of life does the author say the "carry your own skis" lesson has guided her behavior?

_____

_____

_____

2. **Take a Position:** Do you agree or disagree with Dolan's claim that people who do not take responsibility miss out on things? Explain.

_____

_____

_____

3. **Literary Analysis:** Use this chart to identify three passages where Dolan argues for "the 'carry your own skis' mentality." In the left column, write the passage. In the right column, indicate whether each passage is an **appeal to reason** or to **emotion**. Explain.

Passage	Reason or Emotion

4. **Reading Skill:** Did the author **persuade** you to accept her position? Explain.

_____

_____

_____

Writing: Abstract

Write an **abstract** of "Carry Your Own Skis." Answer this list of questions a reader might have about a work before deciding whether to read it. Your notes will help you write your abstract.

• What is the author's purpose?

_____

_____

_____

• What would a reader learn from reading this work?

_____

_____

_____

Research and Technology: Persuasive Presentation

Practice your presentation before delivering it to your class. Use this checklist to be sure you are meeting the needs of your audience, purpose, and occasion:

Am I...	Yes or No
using informal, or "everyday," language during most of my presentation?	
explaining technical language—words specific to my topic—when I use it?	
making eye contact with my audience?	
using appropriate gestures?	
speaking slowly enough to be understood?	
speaking loudly enough for everyone to hear?	
enunciating, or clearly pronouncing my words?	
using proper grammar?	

Libraries Face Sad Chapter
Pete Hamill

Summary Pete Hamill liked to read when he was a child. He saw the library as a treasure house. Today, libraries in New York City have problems. Hamill says they do not have enough money. He suggests a "voluntary tax" to support library services.

 ## Writing About the Big Question

Is knowledge the same as understanding? In "Libraries Face Sad Chapter," the author urges readers to contribute to a fund to support public libraries. Complete this sentence:

Libraries, as a source of information and a place for research, are still

important because _____.

Note-taking Guide
Use this web to write the reasons that Hamill gives for visiting a library.

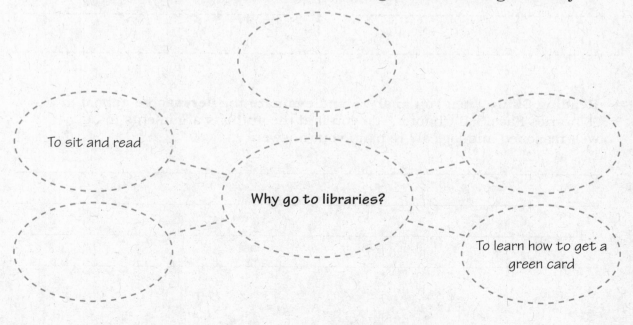

To sit and read

Why *go to* libraries?

To learn how to get a green card

Libraries Face Sad Chapter

1. **Respond:** Do you share Hamill's feelings about public libraries? Why or why not?

_____

_____

_____

2. **Interpret:** What does Hamill mean by calling books "another kind of food"?

_____

_____

3. **Literary Analysis:** In the left column of this chart, identify three passages in which Hamill asserts his position on public libraries. In the right column, indicate whether each passage is an **appeal to reason** or to **emotion**. Explain.

Passage	Reason or Emotion

4. **Reading Skill:** When you **analyze and evaluate** the **persuasive appeal** in "Libraries Face Sad Chapter," do you find the author's arguments to be well-reasoned and logical? Explain your answer.

_____

_____

_____

_____

Writing: Abstract

Write an **abstract** of "Libraries Face Sad Chapter." Answer this list of questions
that a reader might have about a piece of writing before deciding whether to read it.
Your notes will help you write your abstract.

- What is the author's purpose?

  _____

  _____

  _____

- What would a reader learn from reading this work?

  _____

  _____

  _____

Research and Technology: Persuasive Presentation

Practice your presentation before delivering it to your class. Use this checklist to
be sure you are meeting the needs of your audience, purpose, and occasion:

Am I . . .	Yes or No
using informal, or "everyday," language during most of my presentation?	
explaining technical language—words specific to my topic—when I use it?	
making eye contact with my audience?	
using appropriate gestures?	
speaking slowly enough to be understood?	
speaking loudly enough for everyone to hear?	
enunciating, or clearly pronouncing my words?	
using proper grammar?	

I Have a Dream • First Inaugural Address

Literary Analysis

A **persuasive speech** is one meant to convince listeners to think or act in a certain way. Persuasive speeches may appeal to reason or emotion or both. Speakers often use **rhetorical structures and devices** to engage the audience. Rhetorical structures and devices are patterns of words and ideas that create emphasis and stir emotion in the audience.

- **Parallelism:** repeating a grammatical structure or an arrangement of words to create a sense of rhythm and energy
- **Restatement:** expressing the same idea in different words to clarify and stress important points
- **Repetition:** using the same words or images to strengthen and connect ideas
- **Analogy:** making a comparison that shows a similarity between unlike things

Reading Skill

Persuasive techniques are devices intended to make people agree with the speaker. Persuasive speeches present evidence or facts that support the speaker's argument. A speaker may also use language that appeals to people's emotions. He or she may also use rhetorical devices such as those listed above.

Read aloud to hear the effect of persuasive techniques. Doing so will help you analyze and evaluate the techniques. Notice the emotional effect of certain words and the rhythm and energy created by specific word patterns. Think about the purpose and the effect of these persuasive techniques. Use the chart to organize your analysis.

Technique:	
Purpose	Effect

I Have a Dream
Martin Luther King, Jr.

Summary In this famous speech, Dr. Martin Luther King, Jr. gives a speech about what America would be like without racism and inequality. He hopes that all people will one day be free.

 Writing About the Big Question

Is knowledge the same as understanding? In "I Have a Dream," Dr. Martin Luther King, Jr. makes a logical and emotional speech to help listeners understand his dream of freedom and equality. Complete these sentences:

The concept of equality is ambiguous to some people because

_____.

Note-taking Guide
Use this chart to recall the details of Dr. King's dream.

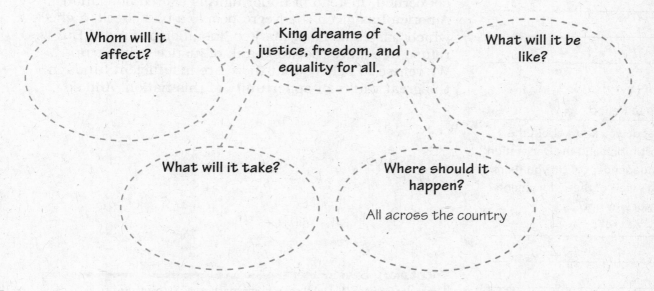

I Have a Dream
Martin Luther King, Jr.

Activate Prior Knowledge

Think of what you already know about Martin Luther King, Jr. Why does the United States honor him with a national holiday every year?

_____

_____

_____

Reading Skill

One **persuasive technique** is using language that appeals to people's emotions. When you **read aloud**, you can recognize words and phrases that appeal to emotions. Read the bracketed passage. Underline words or phrases that affect the reader's emotions. What emotions do these words make you feel?

_____

_____

_____

Stop to Reflect

What do you know about the Constitution and the Declaration of Independence? Do you share King's view of these documents? Why or why not?

_____

_____

_____

_____

Five score years ago, a great American, in whose symbolic shadow we stand today, signed the Emancipation Proclamation. This <u>momentous</u> decree came as a great beacon light of hope to millions of Negro slaves who had been seared in the flames of withering injustice. It came as a joyous daybreak to end the long night of captivity.

But one hundred years later, the Negro is still not free. One hundred years later, the life of the Negro is still sadly crippled by the manacles of segregation and the chains of discrimination. One hundred years later, the Negro lives on a lonely island of poverty in the midst of a vast ocean of material prosperity. One hundred years later, the Negro is still <u>languished</u> in the corners of American society and finds himself an exile in his own land. So we have come here today to dramatize a shameful condition.

In a sense we have come to our nation's Capital to cash a check. When the architects of our republic wrote the magnificent words of the Constitution and the Declaration of Independence, they were signing a promissory note[1] to which every American was to fall heir. This note was a promise that all men, yes, black men as well as white men, would be guaranteed the <u>unalienable</u> rights of life, liberty, and the pursuit of happiness.

It is obvious today that America has defaulted on this promissory note insofar as her citizens of color are concerned. Instead of honoring this sacred obligation, America has given the Negro people a bad check; a check which has come back marked 'insufficient funds.' But we refuse to believe that the bank of justice is bankrupt. We refuse to believe that there are insufficient funds in the great vaults of opportunity of this nation. And so

Vocabulary Development

momentous (moh MEN tuhs) *adj.* very important, especially because of its effect on the future

languished (LANG wishd) *v.* prevented from developing or improving

unalienable (un AY lee uhn uh buhl) *adj.* cannot be taken away

1. **promissory** (PRAHM i sawr ee) **note** written promise to pay a specific amount.

we've come to cash this check—a check that will give us upon demand the riches of freedom and the security of justice. We have also come to this <u>hallowed</u> spot to remind America of the fierce urgency of *now*. This is no time to engage in the luxury of cooling off or to take the tranquilizing drug of gradualism.

Now is the time to make real the promises of Democracy.

Now is the time to rise from the dark and desolate valley of segregation to the sunlit path of racial justice.

Now is the time to lift our nation from the quicksands of racial injustice to the solid rock of brotherhood.

Now is the time to make justice a reality for all of God's children.

It would be fatal for the nation to overlook the urgency of the moment. This sweltering summer of the Negro's legitimate discontent will not pass until there is an <u>invigorating</u> autumn of freedom and equality. Nineteen sixty-three is not an end, but a beginning. Those who hope that the Negro needed to blow off steam and will now be content will have a rude awakening if the nation returns to business as usual. There will be neither rest nor tranquillity in America until the Negro is granted his citizenship rights. The whirlwinds of revolt will continue to shake the foundations of our nation until the bright day of justice emerges.

But there is something that I must say to my people who stand on the warm threshold which leads into the palace of justice. In the process of gaining our rightful place we must not be guilty of wrongful deeds. Let us not seek to satisfy our thirst for freedom by drinking from the cup of bitterness and hatred. We must forever conduct our struggle on the high plane of dignity and discipline. We must not allow our creative protest to <u>degenerate</u> into physical violence. Again and again we must rise to the majestic heights of meeting physical force with soul force. The marvelous new militancy which has engulfed the Negro community must not lead us to a distrust of all white people, for many of our white brothers, as evidenced by their presence here today, have come to realize that their destiny is tied up with our destiny. And they have come to realize that their

Literary Analysis

Parallelism occurs when you repeat words or a structure of words to create a sense of rhythm. What set of words is repeated on the page? Underline an example.

How does this parallel structure help emphasize King's ideas?

_____

_____

_____

Reading Skill ✎

Read aloud the bracketed passage. Underline words or phrases that affect the reader's emotions. Pay attention to the effect of the references to nature. What emotions does this passage make you feel?

_____

_____

_____

Reading Check

How should people react to violence, or physical force? Circle the text that tells you.

© Pearson Education

Vocabulary Development

hallowed (HAL ohd) *adj.* sacred

invigorating (in VIG uhr ayt ing) *adj.* energizing; life-giving

degenerate (de JEN uhr ayt) *v.* grow worse

Literary Analysis

Restatement is another **persuasive technique**. Restatement means saying the same thing more than once in different ways. It is used to make an important point. Read the underlined sentence. What important idea about white people and African Americans does King restate in this sentence?

_____

_____

_____

Stop to Reflect

Dr. King made this speech in 1963. Do you think his dreams have come true? Explain.

_____

_____

_____

_____

Reading Skill

Read aloud the bracketed passage. What feelings do you get from the dream that King expresses in this passage?

_____

_____

_____

Reading Check

What does King dream will happen in Georgia? Circle the text that tells you.

---

freedom is <u>inextricably</u> bound to our freedom. <u>We cannot walk alone.</u>

And as we walk, we must make the pledge that we shall always march ahead. We cannot turn back. There are those who are asking the devotees of civil rights, 'When will you be satisfied?' We can never be satisfied as long as the Negro is the victim of the unspeakable horrors of police brutality. We can never be satisfied as long as our bodies, heavy with the fatigue of travel, cannot gain lodging in the motels of the highways and the hotels of the cities. We cannot be satisfied as long as the Negro's basic mobility is from a smaller ghetto to a larger one. We can never be satisfied as long as a Negro in Mississippi cannot vote and a Negro in New York believes he has nothing for which to vote. No, no, we are not satisfied, and we will not be satisfied until justice rolls down like waters and righteousness like a mighty stream.

I am not unmindful that some of you have come here out of great trials and tribulations. Some of you have come fresh from narrow jail cells. Some of you have come from areas where your quest for freedom left you battered by the storms of persecution and staggered by the winds of police brutality. You have been the veterans of creative suffering. Continue to work with the faith that unearned suffering is <u>redemptive</u>.

Go back to Mississippi, go back to Alabama, go back to South Carolina, go back to Georgia, go back to Louisiana, go back to the slums and ghettos of our northern cities, knowing that somehow this situation can and will be changed. Let us not wallow in the valley of despair.

I say to you today, my friends, so even though we face the difficulties and frustrations of the moment I still have a dream. It is a dream deeply rooted in the American dream.

I have a dream that one day this nation will rise up and live out the true meaning of its <u>creed</u>: 'We hold these truths to be self-evident; that all men are created equal.'

I have a dream that one day on the red hills of Georgia the sons of former slaves and the sons of former slaveowners will be able to sit down together at the table of brotherhood.

I have a dream that one day even the state of Mississippi, a state sweltering with the heat of injustice,

---

Vocabulary Development

inextricably (in iks TRI kuh blee) *adv.* connected in a way that cannot be broken

redemptive (ri DEMP tiv) *adj.* saving; freeing

creed (kreed) *n.* statement of belief

sweltering with the heat of oppression, will be transformed into an oasis of freedom and justice.

I have a dream that my four little children will one day live in a nation where they will not be judged by the color of their skin but by the content of their character.

I have a dream today.

I have a dream that one day down in Alabama, with its vicious racists, with its governor still having his lips dripping with the words of interposition and nullification,[2] one day right down in Alabama little black boys and black girls will be able to join hands with little white boys and white girls as sisters and brothers.

I have a dream today.

I have a dream that one day every valley shall be exalted, every hill and mountain shall be made low, the rough places will be made plains, and the crooked places will be made straight, and the glory of the Lord shall be revealed, and all flesh shall see it together.[3]

This is our hope. This is the faith that I go back to the South with. With this faith we will be able to hew out of the mountain of despair a stone of hope. With this faith we will be able to transform the jangling discords of our nation into a beautiful symphony of brotherhood. With this faith we will be able to work together, to pray together, to struggle together, to go to jail together, to stand up for freedom together, knowing that we will be free one day.

This will be the day when all of God's children will be able to sing with new meaning

My country, 'tis of thee,
Sweet land of liberty,
Of thee I sing:
Land where my fathers died,
Land of the pilgrims' pride,
From every mountainside
Let freedom ring.

And if America is to be a great nation this must become true. So let freedom ring from the prodigious hilltops of New Hampshire. Let freedom ring from the mighty

Literary Analysis

Repetition is using the same words or images to strengthen important points in a speech. Read the first bracketed passage. Underline the phrase that King repeats. What idea does this repetition emphasize? Think about what King hopes will happen one day.

_____

_____

_____

Reading Skill

Read aloud the second bracketed passage. What emotional impact does King's appeal to patriotism and America's ideals have on the listener?

_____

_____

_____

Stop to Reflect

Imagine that Dr. King is alive today. What problems in the world do you think he would talk about? What injustices would he fight against?

_____

_____

_____

_____

Vocabulary Development

hew (hyoo) *v.* carve with a cutting tool

prodigious (pruh DIJ uhs) *adj.* wonderful; of great size

2. **interposition** (in ter puh ZI shuhn) **and nullification** (nul uh fi KAY shuhn) disputed doctrine that a state can reject federal laws considered to be violations of its rights. Governor George C. Wallace used this doctrine to reject federal civil rights legislation.

3. **every valley...all flesh shall see it together** reference to a biblical passage (Isaiah 40:4–5). King likens the struggle of African Americans to the struggle of the Israelites.

Literary Analysis

What **rhetorical structure** is King using in the bracketed passage?

_____

_____

Underline the text that supports your answer.

Reading Skill

Read the last paragraph of this **persuasive speech**. Do you think this last paragraph is an appeal to emotion or to reason? Explain your answer.

_____

_____

_____

_____

mountains of New York. Let freedom ring from the heightening Alleghenies of Pennsylvania!

Let freedom ring from the snowcapped Rockies of Colorado!

Let freedom ring from the <u>curvacious</u> peaks of California!

But not only that; let freedom ring from Stone Mountain of Georgia!

Let freedom ring from Lookout Mountain of Tennessee!

Let freedom ring from every hill and molehill of Mississippi. From every mountainside, let freedom ring.

And when this happens, when we let freedom ring, when we let it ring from every village and every hamlet, from every state and every city, we will be able to speed up that day when all of God's children, black men and white men, Jews and Gentiles, Protestants and Catholics, will be able to join hands and sing in the words of the old Negro spiritual, 'Free at last! free at last! thank God almighty, we are free at last!'

Reader's Response: What do you imagine it would have been like to have been in King's audience in 1963?

_____

_____

_____

_____

_____

Vocabulary Development

curvacious (ker VAY shuhs) _adj._ gracefully curving

© Pearson Education

I Have a Dream

1. **Interpret:** King quotes lines from "My Country 'Tis of Thee." What message does he send to his audience by quoting these lines?

   _____

   _____

2. **Connect:** King mentions different parts of the United States. How does his mention of these places relate to the overall message of his speech?

   _____

   _____

3. **Literary Analysis:** Fill in the chart with examples of King's use of **rhetorical structures and devices**. Then, write what effect each device causes.

	Example	Effect
Restatement		
Repetition		
Parallelism		

4. **Reading Skill:** King uses the **persuasive technique** of language that appeals to emotions. He also uses **rhetorical structures and devices**. Do you think he used both of these techniques effectively in his speech? Explain.

   _____

   _____

Writing: Expository Essay

Find and read the Bill of Rights of the U.S. Constitution. Then, write a brief **expository essay** in which you analyze how the Bill of Rights is related to King's "I Have a Dream" speech. Use a chart to organize information and ideas for your essay.

Ideas in "I Have a Dream"	Ideas in the Bill of Rights	How the ideas are related

Listening and Speaking: Television News Report

Make prewriting notes and gather possible sources for your news report and commentary on Dr. King's "I Have A Dream" speech.

Background Information About the Civil Rights Movement:

_____

_____

_____

Notable Excerpts from the Speech: _____

_____

_____

_____

Effect of Dr. King's Speech on the Crowd: _____

_____

Possible Sources: _____

_____

First Inaugural Address
Franklin D. Roosevelt

Summary This is the speech President Franklin Delano Roosevelt gave on his first day as president. He talks about the problems of the Great Depression and how he plans to fix them. President Roosevelt speaks of hope. He says that people need to rely on one another.

 Writing About the Big Question

Is knowledge the same as understanding? In "First Inaugural Address," President Roosevelt acknowledges the realities of the Great Depression and promises to do whatever is necessary to help the nation recover. Complete this sentence:

For leaders to inspire confidence, they must comprehend

_____

because _____.

Note-taking Guide

Use this chart to record details about Roosevelt's speech.

Who is giving this speech?	
Why is he giving this speech?	
In what year is he giving this speech?	
What is the greatest problem for the country at this time?	
What is the main promise that is made in the speech?	

First Inaugural Address

1. **Interpret:** Roosevelt describes financial leaders as "unscrupulous money changers," "false leaders," and "self-seekers." What message does he send to the American people by describing financial leaders in this way?

_____

_____

2. **Speculate:** How do you think Roosevelt's listeners felt on hearing about earlier Americans?

_____

3. **Literary Analysis:** Use the chart below to list examples of **rhetorical structures and devices** in Roosevelt's speech. Then, describe the effect that each example has on his audience.

	Example	Effect
Restatement		
Repetition		
Parallelism		
Analogy		

4. **Reading Skill:** Identify a passage in which Roosevelt uses language that appeals to emotions as a **persuasive technique**.

_____

_____

_____

Writing: Expository Essay

Find and read the portion of the Emergency Relief Appropriation Act of 1935 that established the Works Progress Administration. Then, write a brief **expository essay** in which you analyze how the text is related to Roosevelt's first inaugural address. Use a chart to organize information and ideas for your essay.

Ideas in inaugural address	Ideas in Emergency Relief Appropriation Act of 1935	How the ideas are related

Listening and Speaking: Television News Report

Make prewriting notes and gather possible sources for your news report and commentary on President Roosevelt's first inaugural address.

Notable Excerpts from the Address: _____

_____

_____

Effect of President Roosevelt's Speech on the Crowd:

_____

_____

Possible Sources: _____

_____

Historical Research Study

About Historical Research Studies

A writer judges and interprets a speech, a document, or an event in history in a **historical research study**. The writer looks at what the words meant when they were written and what they mean now. The writer also shows how the ideas connect to other ideas and events. A historical study usually has these parts:

- an introduction with a main idea
- a summary of the historical work
- facts and opinions that are in the work
- quotations, examples, and statistics
- explanations
- connections to other ideas
- a conclusion that restates the main idea

Reading Skill

Before you accept the opinion of an author, evaluate his or her credibility. When you **evaluate credibility,** you decide whether the author is knowledgeable and fair. Some authors may express bias, or an opinion that something is either good or bad. Credible authors avoid bias and present a variety of information, including opposing viewpoints. Use the chart below to evaluate the credibility of the author of "Nothing to Fear: Lessons in Leadership from FDR."

Checklist for Evaluating an Author's Argument

- Does the author present a clear argument?
- Is the argument supported by evidence?
- How comprehensive is the evidence?
- Is the argument structured in a logical way?
- Does the author use sound reasoning, or only emotional appeals?

---

from Nothing to Fear: Lessons in Leadership from FDR

Alan Axelrod

"This great nation will endure as it has endured, will revive and will prosper. So, first of all, let me assert my firm belief that the only thing we have to fear is fear itself—nameless, unreasoning, unjustified terror which paralyzes needed efforts to convert retreat into advance."

—First inaugural address, March 4, 1933

In *Defending Your Life*, a charmingly provocative 1991 movie written and directed by its star, Albert Brooks, we discover that the only truly unforgivable sin in life is fear. Killed in a head-on crash with a bus, yuppie Brooks finds himself transported to Judgment City, where he must "defend his life" before a pair of judges who will decide whether he is to be returned to Earth for another crack at life or be permitted to progress to the next plane of existence. His attorney (for the benevolent managers of the universe provide defense assistance) explains to him the nature of fear, which is, he says, a "fog" that obscures everything and that makes intelligent, productive action impossible.

It is a stimulating thought—that fear is not so much the sensation accompanying the realization of danger, but a fog, an obscurer of truth, an interference with how we may productively engage reality. Certainly this is the way FDR saw it. In 1921 polio threatened first to kill him and then paralyzed him, subjected him to a life of relentless pain, and nearly ended his career in public service. He could then and there have given in

Text Structure

Quotations sometimes appear in italics at the beginning of an article. This type of text structure makes the words stand out from the article. What effect does this have on the reader?

_____

_____

Comprehension Builder

Summarize the main idea in the quotation.

_____

_____

_____

Vocabulary Builder

Idioms *Another crack at life* means "another chance at life." Complete this sentence to practice using the idiom.

By surviving polio, FDR was

given _____

_____.

Text Structure

Readers can gather information from pictures. Look at the picture on this page. What can you learn about President Roosevelt?

_____

_____

_____

Cultural Understanding

Polio is a serious illness. Many people died or became crippled because of polio in the first part of the twentieth century. In 1955, a vaccine developed by Jonas Salk began to be given to children. The vaccine nearly ended polio in the United States.

Vocabulary Builder

Compound Words The word *sugarcoating* combines the words *sugar,* which means "a sweet substance," and *coating,* which means "a thin covering." In the line "There is no sugarcoating of reality here!", *sugarcoating* means "making something look better than it is." Complete this sentence with the word *sugarcoating:*

FDR avoids _____ by telling people the truth about the economy.

Franklin D. Roosevelt with a local child, 1941.

to the fog of fear, but he chose not to. He chose instead to understand polio, to see clearly the extent of his disability, and then to assess—also clearly—his options for overcoming that disability. He did not blink at the odds. He looked at them, contemplated them, assessed them, and then acted on them.

Now, more than a decade later, assuming the office of president of the United States, he began by asking the American people to sweep aside the fog of fear, "nameless, unreasoning, unjustified terror which paralyzes needed efforts to convert retreat into advance." He didn't ask them to stop being afraid, but to stop letting fear obscure their vision of reality. He asked the people to confront what they feared, so that they could see clearly what needed to be done and thereby overcome (and the word is significant) the terror that *paralyzes*.

In the second paragraph of his inaugural speech, FDR lifted the fog of fear. What did he reveal to his audience, the American people?

Values have shrunken to fantastic levels; taxes have risen; our ability to pay has fallen; government of all kinds is faced by serious curtailment of income; the means of exchange are frozen in the currents of trade; the withered leaves of industrial enterprise lie on every side; farmers find no markets for their produce; the savings of many years in thousands of families are gone.

There is no sugarcoating of reality here! The fog has lifted, the scene is sharply etched and downright frightening: "a host of unemployed citizens face the grim problem of existence, and an equally great number toil with little return. Only a foolish optimist can deny the dark realities of the moment."

Franklin D. Roosevelt addressing Congress, 1941.

FDR did not blink at reality and he did not allow his audience to do so either. He embarked on this catalog of economic disasters by defining them as "our common difficulties," which "concern, thank God, only material things."

The fog was lifted and the president's listeners could see the reality they already knew, a reality of poverty and despair, to be sure; yet with the fog of fear lifted, they could see it in a new light: Our common difficulties "concern, thank God, only material things."

Not one to blink at disaster, FDR also saw a way out of it:

> Yet our distress comes from no failure of substance. We are stricken by no plague of locusts. Compared with the perils which our forefathers conquered because they believed and were not afraid, we have still much to be thankful for. Nature still offers her bounty and human efforts have multiplied it. Plenty is at our doorstep. . .

Lift the fog of fear and you could see that the Great Depression was not of natural, supernatural, or inevitable origin. It was not a plague of biblical proportion. Our kind has conquered worse in the past. Nature has not failed us.

What, then, was the problem?

Text Structure

Look at the picture. What can you learn about President Roosevelt from this picture?

_____

_____

_____

Vocabulary Builder

Possessive Nouns Possessive nouns show ownership. Most possessive nouns are formed by adding 's to the end of the noun. Find the possessive noun in the bracketed paragraph. Use that possessive noun to complete the following sentence:

Members of Congress listened

to the _____
inaugural speech.

Fluency Builder

Read the quotation that begins "Yet our distress" silently. With a partner, take turns reading the quotation aloud with expression.

Plenty is at our doorstep, but a generous use of it languishes in the very sight of the supply. Primarily this is because rulers of the exchange of mankind's good have failed through their own stubbornness and their own incompetence, have admitted their failure, and have abdicated. Practices of unscrupulous money changers stand indicted in the court of public opinion, rejected by the hearts and minds of men.

The failure was a failure of particular human beings and the particular policies they pursued. "True," Roosevelt continued, these particular people "have tried, but their efforts have been cast in the pattern of an outworn tradition."

Faced by failure of credit they have proposed only the lending of more money. Stripped of the lure of profit by which to induce our people to follow their false leadership, they have resorted to exhortation, pleading tearfully for restored confidence. They know only the rules of a generation of self-seekers. They have no vision, and when there is no vision the people perish.

As a leader FDR always navigated between the radically new and unprecedented, on the one hand, and the age-old and unchanging, on the other. Early in the speech he evoked the Old Testament image of a plague of locusts. He used another biblical image, this one from the New Testament, in referring to the "unscrupulous money changers." Then he went on to speak of the Depression as a problem created by old ways of thinking. It was, he said, a problem that could not be solved by "efforts . . . cast in the pattern of outworn tradition," the pattern of a "generation of self-seekers."

The implication was unmistakable: Conquering the Depression would require new thinking. And yet FDR once again linked this need for fresh imagination and bold, new action with the timeless wisdom of Judeo-Christian tradition. In Proverbs 29:18 we are told, "Where there is no vision, the people perish," and FDR tells us that the Depression was created and is perpetuated by leaders who "have no vision, and when there is no vision the people perish." He continued with his echo of the Gospels:

> The money changers have fled from their high seats in the temple of our civilization. We may now restore that temple to the ancient truths. The measure of the restoration lies in the extent to which we apply social values more noble than mere monetary profit.

An inauguration is a beginning, as Roosevelt was well aware, and in his acceptance speech to the Democratic National Convention, he had already pledged to the American people a "New Deal." Americans would soon discover, during the dazzling first hundred days of the Roosevelt presidency, just how new a deal it would be, as program after innovative program was ushered into being. Yet all of this innovation was aimed at restoring the "temple of our civilization . . . to the ancient truths," the age-old redemption of the temple of the spirit from the grasp of the materialistic money changers.

> Happiness lies not in the mere possession of money; it lies in the joy of achievement, in the thrill of creative effort. The joy and moral stimulation of work no longer must be forgotten in the mad chase of evanescent profits. These dark days will be worth all they cost us if they teach us that our true

Vocabulary Builder

Suffixes Find and underline the word *timeless* in the first bracketed paragraph. *Timeless* is an adjective with two word parts: the base word *time* and the suffix *-less,* which means "without." Something that is timeless does not become old-fashioned. Circle the word that *timeless* describes.

Vocabulary Builder

Word Families The word *innovative* in the second bracketed paragraph belongs to the word family *innovate. Innovate* means "to start to use new ideas, methods, or inventions." In the same paragraph, circle another word that belongs to the word family *innovate.*

Fluency Builder

With a partner, practice reading aloud the quotation that begins "Happiness lies not" with expression.

destiny is not to be ministered unto but to minister to ourselves and our fellow men.

Here then, in the space of the first few minutes of his first speech as leader of the American people, is what Franklin Roosevelt made visible in the absence of the fog of fear: that the economic disaster is serious, urgent, even life-threatening, yet it is an economic disaster, one concerning "thank God, only material things." Roosevelt's speech does not allow his listeners to turn away from the disaster. His words invite them to see beyond it, both to its cause in human errors, in the short-sighted pursuit of immediate material profit, and in the absence of greater vision, to its eventual resolution.

That resolution is the subject of the rest of the speech, which broadly out-lines innovative goals, policies, and programs aimed at ending the Great Depression. Yet the proposed means of resolution, radical as

Franklin D. Roosevelt delivering a radio address, 1938.

they may be, rest on restoring the "temple of our civilization . . . to the ancient truths." Paramount among these truths is a realization that "happiness lies not in the mere possession of money," that morals and ethics must not be sacrificed in "the mad chase of evanescent profits," and that our "true destiny is not to be ministered unto but to minister to ourselves and our fellow men."

Thinking About the Historical Research Study

1. Axelrod says that fear is a fog. What does this mean?

   _____

2. Axelrod says that Roosevelt "navigated between the radically new . . . and the age-old and unchanging." How does Axelrod support this belief?

   _____

   _____

TALK ABOUT IT **Reading Skill**

3. How does the article demonstrate Axelrod's knowledge about President Roosevelt?

   _____

4. Axelrod may be biased in favor of President Roosevelt because the article presents FDR positively. What is missing from the article that would give it more balance?

   _____

WRITE ABOUT IT ➤ **Timed Writing: Persuasive Essay (35 minutes)**

Write a persuasive essay in which you offer a solution to a problem in your school or community. In your essay, clearly explain the problem and describe your solution. Offer examples and evidence to support your ideas. Use the following graphic organizer to choose your topic:

Problem	Solution	Do I have strong feelings about this problem?

Elements of Poetry

Poetry is a form of writing that combines the exact meanings of words with the emotional connections of words. Poets experiment with the sounds and rhythms of language. Poems are written in **stanzas**, or groups of lines. Stanza types include the following:

- **Couplets:** have two lines
- **Quatrains:** have four lines

Poets use **figurative language** to express ideas or feelings in fresh ways. The chart contains the most common types of figurative language.

Figurative Language	Definition	Example
Metaphors	- comparison of two unlike things without using the words *like, as, than,* or *resembles*	The sky is a patchwork quilt.
Similes	- comparison of two unlike things using the connecting words *like, as, than,* or *resembles*	The sky is like a patchwork quilt.
Personification	- giving human feelings, thoughts, actions, or attitudes to an object or animal	The snowflakes played a game of hide and seek.
Onomatopoeia	- the use of a word whose sound imitates its meaning	*buzz, hiss, thud, sizzle*
Imagery	- descriptive language used to create word pictures, or **images** - **sensory language** uses details related to the five senses to enhance images	The icy water froze my fingers until they were numb.

Poets use **sound devices** to give a musical quality to their writing. The chart contains the most common sound devices.

Sound Device	Definition	Example
Rhythm	• stressed and unstressed syllables • **meter:** a controlled pattern of rhythm	"I like hot days, hot days/ Sweat is what you got days" (Myers)
Rhyme	• repetition of identical or similar sounds in stressed syllables • **rhyme scheme:** a pattern of end rhymes • **free verse:** no set meter or rhyme scheme	"From what I've tasted of desire/ I hold with those who favor fire" (Frost)
Alliteration	• repetition of beginning consonant sounds • **assonance:** repetition of vowel sounds in nearby words • **consonance:** repetition of consonants within nearby words in which the vowel sounds differ	"maggie and milly and molly and may" (Cummings) "Ball hates to take bat's bait" (Swenson) "He clasps the crag with crooked hands" (Tennyson)
Repetition	• use of any language element more than once	"From the bells, bells, bells, bells," (Poe)

There are three main types of poetry.
- In a **narrative** poem, the poet tells a story in verse. An **epic** is a long, narrative poem about gods or heroes. A **ballad** is a narrative that is like a song. It can be about an adventure or a romance.
- In a **dramatic** poem, the poet tells a story through a character's thoughts or statements.
- In a **lyric** poem, the poet expresses the feelings of a single speaker.

Some poems are characterized by their form. Their structures have certain patterns of rhyme, rhythm, line structure, and stanza format.
- A **haiku** has three unrhymed lines of five, seven, and five syllables.
- A **sonnet** is a fourteen-line lyric poem with formal patterns of rhyme, rhythm, and line structure.

Uncoiling • A Voice
Pat Mora

Summaries "Uncoiling" shows the power of nature. Pat Mora recreates the chaos of a desert storm and shows its effects. "A Voice" tells the story of the poet's mother. Mora's mother is a Mexican American. She had to adjust to life in the United States. She teaches her children to use their voices well and proudly.

Note-taking Guide
Use this chart to identify the main image of each poem.

	What is the main image of the poem?	What details support this image?
Uncoiling	a storm	
A Voice		

Uncoiling
Pat Mora

With thorns, she scratches
    on my window, tosses her hair dark with rain,
    <u>snares</u> lightning, cholla,[1] hawks, butterfly
       swarms in the tangles.

5 She sighs clouds,
    head thrown back, eyes closed, roars
           and rivers leap,
boulders retreat like crabs
into themselves.

10 She <u>spews</u> gusts and thunder,
    spooks pale women who scurry to
      lock doors, windows
        when her tumbleweed skirt starts its spin.

    They sing lace lullabies
15   so their children won't hear
      her uncoiling
        through her lips, howling
         leaves off trees, flesh
          off bones, until she becomes

20 sound, spins herself
    to sleep, sand stinging her ankles,
      whirring into her raw skin like stars.

© Pearson Education

Vocabulary Development

snares (snayrz) *v.* catches in a trap
spews (spyooz) *v.* sprays

1. **cholla** (CHOH yah) *n.* spiny cactus found in the southwestern United States and Mexico.

Activate Prior Knowledge

If you had to compare a storm to something else, what would it be? Think of at least two different comparisons you could make. How would the impression of the storm change with the different comparisons?

_____

_____

_____

Poetry

Personification is when a writer gives human actions or attitudes to objects. Underline the human actions that the storm performs.

_____

_____

Poetry

Sound devices like **alliteration** and **rhyme** give a musical quality to writing. What sound device is Mora using in the last **stanza,** or group of lines?

_____

What is the **image,** or word picture, created by the sound device?

_____

_____

Reading Check

What things get caught in the storm's "hair"? Circle the text that tells you.

Poetry

Figurative language expresses ideas and feelings in fresh ways. Read the first bracketed passage. What impressions do you get about the father from the comparisons Mora makes?

_____

_____

_____

Poetry

Repetition is the use of any language element more than once. Underline the repetition you find in the second bracketed passage. What point is Mora trying to make?

_____

_____

_____

Poetry

What type of **figurative language** is the author using in lines 22–23?

_____

What information does she convey with her comparison?

_____

Stop to Reflect

What do you think Mora means by the underlined statement?

_____

_____

_____

A Voice
Pat Mora

Even the lights on the stage unrelenting
as the desert sun couldn't hide the other
students, their eyes also unrelenting,
students who spoke English every night

5 as they ate their meat, potatoes, gravy.
Not you. In your house that smelled like
rose powder, you spoke Spanish formal
as your father, the judge without a courtroom

in the country he floated to in the dark
10 on a flatbed truck. He walked slow
as a hot river down the narrow hall
of your house. You never dared to race past him

to say, "Please move," in the language
you learned effortlessly, as you learned to run,
15 the language forbidden at home, though your mother
said you learned it to fight with the neighbors.

You like winning with words. You liked
writing speeches about patriotism and democracy.
You liked all the faces looking at you, all those eyes.
20 "How did I do it?" you ask me now. "How did I do it

when my parents didn't understand?"
The family story says your voice is the voice
of an aunt in Mexico, spunky as a peacock.
Family stories sing of what lives in the blood.

25 You told me only once about the time you went
to the state capitol, your family proud as if
you'd been named governor. But when you looked
around, the only Mexican in the auditorium,

Vocabulary Development

spunky (SPUNG kee) *adj.* courageous; spirited

you wanted to hide from those strange faces.
30 Their eyes were pinpricks, and you faked
hoarseness. You, who are never at a loss
for words, felt your breath stick in your throat

like an ice cube. "I can't," you whispered.
"I can't." Yet you did. Not that day but years later.
35 You taught the four of us to speak up.
This is America, Mom. The undoable is done

in the next generation. Your breath moves
through the family like the wind
moves through the trees.

Poetry

What type of **figurative language** does the author use in the bracketed **stanza**?

_____

What point is she trying to make?

_____

_____

Reading Check

Does Mora's mother speak in front of the large audience? Underline the text that tells you.

Uncoiling • A Voice

1. **Infer:** In "Uncoiling," what type of storm does the poet describe?

   _____

   _____

2. **Analyze:** In "A Voice," Pat Mora shows what happened when her mother had to deliver a speech. How does that day change the subject's life and that of her family?

   _____

   _____

   _____

3. **Poetry:** In "Uncoiling," Mora uses **personification** to make the storm seem human. How does the storm's behavior compare with the actions of the women in the poem?

   _____

   _____

4. **Poetry:** Both "Uncoiling" and "A Voice" have **images** of breathing, speaking, or making sounds. Use the first column of the chart to record these images. In the second column, write what they mean. In the third column, write their effects.

What It Says	What It Means	Effect

Report

Describe Pat Mora's views about her dual heritage and literary career in a **report**. Use the following tips to write notes for your report.

- Search the Internet for biographical information about Mora.

    What I learned about Mora:

    _____

    _____

- Search through the author's collected poems. Find at least five poems that deal with her dual-language heritage. *Confetti: Poems for Children* and *Agua Santa: Holy Water* are two of Mora's poetry collections.

    What I learned from Mora's poems:

    _____

    _____

- Watch the video interview with Pat Mora. Use it and your source material to answer these questions.

    1. What did you learn about Mora's feelings about her Mexican roots and the Spanish language?

        _____

        _____

    2. How has her heritage affected her career?

        _____

        _____

        _____

Poetry Collection 1 • Poetry Collection 2

Literary Analysis

Figurative language is language that is used imaginatively rather than literally. Figurative language includes one or more **figures of speech**, literary devices that make unexpected comparisons or change the usual meaning of words. The following are specific types of figures of speech:

- **Simile:** a comparison of two apparently unlike things using *like, as, than,* or *resembles*: "The sky is <u>like</u> a patchwork quilt."

- **Metaphor:** a comparison of one thing as if it were another: "The sky <u>is</u> a patchwork quilt."

- **Personification:** giving human characteristics to a nonhuman subject: "The <u>sea</u> was <u>angry</u> that day, my friends."

- **Paradox:** a statement, an idea, or a situation that seems contradictory but actually expresses a truth: "The more things change, the more they stay the same."

As you read, use the chart below to record examples of each type of figurative language you find.

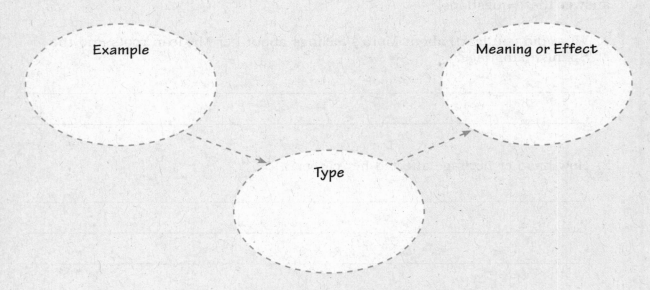

Reading Skill

Reading fluently is reading smoothly and continuously while also comprehending the text and appreciating the writer's artistry. To improve your fluency when reading poetry, **read in sentences**. Use punctuation rather than the ends of lines to determine where to pause or stop reading.

Poetry Collection 1

Summaries In "Dream Deferred," the speaker asks what happens to a dream that is ignored. "Dreams" describes the importance of dreams. In "I Wandered Lonely as a Cloud," the speaker recalls a time when daffodils made him feel less lonely. In "Meciendo," the speaker rocks her son to sleep. In "Sonnets on Love XIII," the speaker compares an ancient remark to his love for his beloved.

Writing About the Big Question

How does communication change us? The poets in this collection communicate ideas that help us think about the world in new ways. Use this sentence starter to develop your ideas about the Big Question:

When the speaker of a poem asks the audience to **respond** to a question,

the reader is pushed to _____ and _____.

Note-taking Guide

Use this chart to write the purpose of each poem.

Dream Deferred	Dreams	I Wandered Lonely as a Cloud	Meciendo	Sonnets on Love XIII
to imagine what happens if dreams are ignored				

Why do you think many poets refer to nature in their work?

_____

_____

_____

Reading Check

How many questions are in "Dream Deferred"? Circle each question the speaker asks.

Reading Skill

Reading fluently is reading smoothly and continuously while also understanding the text and appreciating the writer's artistry. **Read in sentences** to improve your fluency when reading poetry. Read the bracketed section. How many sentences are in this stanza?

_____

Literary Analysis 🔍

A **metaphor** is a description of one thing as if it were another. Identify one metaphor in "Dreams."

_____

_____

_____

Dream Deferred
Langston Hughes

Harlem

What happens to a dream <u>deferred</u>?

    Does it dry up
    like a raisin in the sun?
5 Or <u>fester</u> like a sore—
    And then run?
    Does it stink like rotten meat?
    Or crust and sugar over—
    like a syrupy sweet?

10 Maybe it just sags

    like a heavy load.
    Or does it explode?

Vocabulary Development

deferred (di FERD) *adj.* put off until a future time
fester (FES ter) *v.* to get worse or infected as a result of having been left untreated too long

Dreams
Langston Hughes

Hold fast to dreams
For if dreams die
Life is a broken-winged bird
That cannot fly.

5 Hold fast to dreams
For when dreams go
Life is a barren field
Frozen with snow.

I Wandered Lonely as a Cloud
William Wordsworth

I wandered lonely as a cloud
That floats on high o'er vales[1] and hills,
When all at once I saw a crowd,
A host, of golden daffodils;
5   Beside the lake, beneath the trees,
Fluttering and dancing in the breeze.

Continuous as the stars that shine
And twinkle on the milky way,
They stretched in never-ending line
10 Along the margin of a bay:
Ten thousand saw I at a glance,
Tossing their heads in sprightly dance.

The waves beside them danced; but they
Outdid the sparkling waves in glee;
15 A poet could not but be gay,
In such a jocund[2] company;
I gazed—and gazed—but little thought
What wealth the show to me had brought:

For oft, when on my couch I lie
20 In vacant or in pensive mood,
They flash upon that inward eye
Which is the bliss of solitude;
And then my heart with pleasure fills,
And dances with the daffodils.

Literary Analysis

A **simile** is a comparison of two unlike things. To what does the speaker compare the daffodils in the simile in lines 7–8?

_____

_____

Reading Skill

When you **read in sentences,** use punctuation rather than the ends of lines to determine where to pause or stop reading. After which words should you stop reading in this poem?

_____

Stop to Reflect

Figurative language is language that is used imaginatively rather than literally. How does the use of figurative language contribute to the overall effect of this poem?

_____

_____

_____

Reading Check

What dances beside the daffodils? Circle the lines that tell you.

Vocabulary Development

sprightly (SPRYT lee) *adj.* light and elflike

oft (awft) *adv.* often

pensive (PEN siv) *adj.* thinking deeply or seriously

---

1. **o'er vales** over valleys.
2. **jocund** (JAHK uhnd) *adj.* cheerful.

© Pearson Education

Reading Skill

Read in sentences to help you read this poem. How many sentences are in this translation?

_____

Literary Analysis

This poem uses **personification**. It gives human characteristics to nonhuman subjects. Read the second stanza. How does the wind act like a person?

_____

_____

Reading Check

What action is the speaker doing throughout the poem? Underline the text that tells you.

Meciendo
Gabriela Mistral

El mar sus millares de olas
mece, divino.
Oyendo a los mares amantes,
mezo a mi niño.

5 El viento errabundo en la noche
mece a los trigos.
Oyendo a los vientos amantes,
mezo a mi niño.

Dios Padre sus miles de mundos
10 mece sin ruido.
Sintiendo su mano en la sombra,
mezo a mi niño.

Rocking (Meciendo)
Gabriela Mistral translated by Doris Dana

The sea rocks her thousands of waves.
The sea is divine.
Hearing the loving sea,
I rock my son.

5 The wind wandering by night
rocks the wheat.
Hearing the loving wind,
I rock my son.

God, the Father, soundlessly rocks
10 His thousands of worlds.
Feeling His hand in the shadow,
I rock my son.

Sonnets on Love XIII

Jean de Sponde translated by David R. Slavitt

Background

Archimedes (ahr kuh MEE deez) (287?–212 B.C.) has been called the founder of theoretical mechanics. He was a brilliant Greek mathematician and inventor who once boasted that, given a place to stand in space and a long enough lever, he could move the Earth itself. Legend has it that when he made a great discovery, he jumped up and shouted "Eureka!" ("I have found it!").

> "Give me a place to stand," Archimedes said,
> "and I can move the world." Paradoxical, clever,
> his remark which first explained the use of the
>   lever
> was an academic joke. But if that dead
>
> 5 sage could return to life, he would find a clear
> demonstration of his idea, which is not
> pure theory after all. That putative[1]
>   spot
> exists in the love I feel for you, my dear.
>
> What could be more immovable or stronger?
> 10 What becomes more and more secure, the longer
> it is battered by inconstancy and the stress
>
> we find in our lives? Here is that fine fixed point
> from which to move a world that is out of joint,
> as he could have done, had he known a love
>   like this.

Literary Analysis

Identify which of the following **figures of speech** appears in the first stanza of this poem: **simile, metaphor, personification,** or **paradox.**

_____

Reading Skill

You should **read in sentences** to help you understand this poem. In what line does the sentence that starts in line 4 end?

_____

Reading Check

Lines 4–5 refer to a "dead sage." Underline the sentence that tells you who this "dead sage" is.

Reader's Response: Which of these poems affected you the most? Explain.

_____

_____

Vocabulary Development

paradoxical (par uh DAHK si kuhl) *adj.* strange and impossible because it does not make sense

sage (sayj) *n.* wise person

---

1. **putative** (PYOOT uh tiv) *adj.* supposed; known by reputation.

Poetry Collection 1

1. **Interpret:** Restate in your own words the advice that "Dreams" offers.

   _____

   _____

2. **Compare and Contrast:** Explain how the natural sights and sounds of "I Wandered Lonely as a Cloud" and "Meciendo" affect each speaker.

   _____

   _____

   _____

3. **Literary Analysis:** Think of one example of **personification** from Poetry Collection 1.

   _____

   _____

4. **Reading Skill:** Using the graphic organizer below, rewrite one stanza in Poetry Collection 1 as a prose paragraph.

Stanza	Paragraph

Writing: Choose a Genre

Using one of the descriptions in the Poetry Collection as a model, write about nature. Choose the genre in which you will write—poem or descriptive essay. Use this graphic organizer to choose a topic:

My Experiences in Nature	Photographs I Have Seen of Nature

Listening and Speaking: Informal Presentation

Use the lines to make prewriting notes for your informal presentation about dreams, nature, or love.

My Speech Topic: _____

My Central Idea: _____

_____

Ideas for Body Language and Eye Contact: _____

_____

_____

My Conclusion: _____

_____

Poetry Collection 2

Summaries The speaker in "All Watched Over by Machines of Loving Grace" imagines a world in which technology and nature exist in harmony. " 'Hope' is the thing with feathers—" compares hope to a bird that never stops singing. The speaker of "Much Madness is divinest Sense—" says that, sometimes, madness shows the best sense. In "The War Against the Trees," the speaker compares the bulldozing of trees to a war against nature.

? Writing About the Big Question

How does communication change us? The poets in this collection share thoughts of how technology, war, and even ideas can change us and how we regard the world. Use this sentence starter to develop your ideas about the Big Question:

As a result of advances in computer technology, relationships between

people have become _____ because _____.

Note-taking Guide

Use this chart to write the topic of each poem.

All Watched Over by Machines of Loving Grace	"Hope" is the thing with feathers—	Much Madness is divinest Sense—	The War Against the Trees
a world run by computers			

Poetry Collection 2

1. **Interpret:** In "All Watched Over by Machines of Loving Grace," the speaker compares computers to flowers. What does this comparison suggest about the speaker's feelings about computers in the real world?

   _____

2. **Draw Conclusions:** Reread "The War Against the Trees." What does the image of war suggest about the speaker's feelings toward the trees and what is happening to them? Explain.

   _____

3. **Literary Analysis:** Identify one example of **personification** in Poetry Collection 2.

   _____

4. **Reading Skill:** Rewrite one stanza in Poetry Collection 2 as a prose paragraph. Use the chart below. Look at the example in the chart for help.

Stanza	Paragraph
I've heard it in the chillest land— And on the strangest Sea— Yet, never, in Extremity, It asked a crumb—of Me.	I've heard it in the chillest land and on the strangest Sea, yet, never, in Extremity, it asked a crumb of me.

Writing: Choose a Genre

Using one of the descriptions in the Poetry Collection as a model, write about nature. Choose the genre in which you will write—poem or descriptive essay. Use this graphic organizer to choose a topic:

My Experiences in Nature	Photographs I Have Seen of Nature

Listening and Speaking: Informal Presentation

Use the lines to make prewriting notes for your informal presentation about a topic covered in one of the poems.

My Speech Topic: _____

My Central Idea: _____

_____

Ideas for Body Language and Eye Contact: _____

_____

_____

My Conclusion: _____

_____

Poetry Collection 3 • Poetry Collection 4

Literary Analysis

Poets use **sound devices** to emphasize the sound relationships among words. These devices include the following:

- **Alliteration:** the repetition of initial consonant sounds in stressed syllables: *"The fair breeze blew, the white foam flew . . ."*
- **Consonance:** the repetition of final consonant sounds in stressed syllables with different vowel sounds, as in *sit* and *cat*
- **Assonance:** the repetition of similar vowel sounds in stressed syllables that end with different consonants, as in *seal* and *meet*
- **Onomatopoeia:** the use of a word whose sound imitates its meaning, such as *pop* or *hiss*

All of these sound devices engage the reader's senses and create musical and emotional effects.

Reading Skill

Reading fluently is reading smoothly and continuously while also comprehending the text and appreciating the writer's artistry. To avoid being tripped up by the meaning as you read, **use your senses**. To do so, notice language that appeals to the five senses. Record examples of sensory language in the chart below.

Senses	Words That Appeal to Senses
Sight	
Hearing	
Smell	
Taste	
Touch	

Poetry Collection 3

Summaries In "Summer," the speaker describes a hot day in the summer. In "The Eagle," the poet imagines an eagle perched on a cliff high in the sky. In "Analysis of Baseball," the poet describes the action in a game of baseball.

 Writing About the Big Question

How does communication change us? In "Analysis of Baseball," the speaker shares personal impressions of "America's pastime." Use this sentence starter to develop your ideas about the Big Question:

Reading someone else's **interpretation** of a common experience can

illuminate one's understanding of that experience because _____

_____.

Note-taking Guide

Use this chart to record the topic and events of each poem.

	The topic of the poem	Two events that take place in the poem
Summer	joys of summer	
The Eagle		an eagle falls
Analysis of Baseball		

Summer
Walter Dean Myers

I like hot days, hot days
Sweat is what you got days
Bugs buzzin from cousin to cousin
Juices dripping
5　Running and ripping
Catch the one you love days

Birds peeping
Old men sleeping
Lazy days, daisies lay
10　Beaming and dreaming
Of hot days, hot days,
Sweat is what you got days

The Eagle
Alfred, Lord Tennyson

He clasps the crag[1] with crooked hands;
Close to the sun in lonely lands,
Ring'd with the azure world, he stands.

The wrinkled sea beneath him crawls;
5　He watches from his mountain walls,
And like a thunderbolt he falls.

© Pearson Education

Vocabulary Development

beaming (BEE ming) *v.* smiling
clasps (klasps) *v.* grips
azure (AZH uhr) *adj.* sky blue

1. **crag** (krag) *n.* steep, rugged rock that rises above others or projects from a rock mass.

Activate Prior Knowledge

Think about your favorite season. What do you like about this time of year? Explain.

_____

_____

_____

_____

Reading Skill

Use your senses to avoid being confused by the meaning of what you read. To which of the five senses does the poem "Summer" appeal? Explain.

_____

_____

_____

_____

Literary Analysis

Alliteration is the repetition of initial consonant sounds in stressed syllables. Read the bracketed stanza. Circle examples of alliteration.

Reading Check

What is the eagle doing on the mountain? Underline the answer.

Reading Skill

Reading fluently is reading smoothly and continuously while also understanding the text and appreciating the writer's artistry. Reading in sentences can help you read fluently. Read the bracketed stanza. How many sentences are in this section?

_____

To which **senses** does this section appeal? Explain.

_____

_____

_____

Literary Analysis

Onomatopoeia is the use of a word whose sound imitates its meaning, such as *pop* or *hiss*. Circle the onomatopoeia in lines 26–30.

Stop to Reflect

The speaker tells what baseball is about in this poem. Do you think this poem can be appreciated by someone who is unfamiliar with the rules of baseball? Why or why not?

_____

_____

_____

Analysis of Baseball
May Swenson

It's about
the ball,
the bat,
and the mitt.
5   Ball hits
bat, or it
hits mitt.
Bat doesn't
hit ball, bat
10   meets it.
Ball bounces
off bat, flies
air, or thuds
ground (dud)
15   or it
fits mitt.

Bat waits
for ball
to mate.
20   Ball hates
to take bat's
bait. Ball
flirts, bat's
late, don't
25   keep the date.
Ball goes in
(thwack) to mitt,
and goes out
(thwack) back
30   to mitt.

Ball fits
mitt, but
not all
the time.
35 Sometimes
ball gets hit
(pow) when bat
meets it,
and sails
40 to a place
where mitt
has to quit
in disgrace.
That's about
45 the bases
loaded,
about 40,000
fans exploded.

It's about
50 the ball,
the bat,
the mitt,
the bases
and the fans.
55 It's done
on a diamond,
and for fun.
It's about
home, and it's
60 about run.

Reading Skill

Use your senses as you read lines 44–48. To what senses do the words "40,000 fans exploded" appeal? Explain.

_____

_____

_____

Literary Analysis 🔍

Consonance occurs when the final consonant sounds of words repeat. They appear in stressed syllables with different vowel sounds. What consonance is repeated frequently in lines 49–54?

_____

_____

What effect does this consonance create?

_____

_____

Reading Check

According to the speaker, what is baseball "about"? Underline the lines that tell you.

Reader's Response: How does each poem make you feel about its subject? Explain.

_____

_____

_____

_____

Analysis of Baseball **265**

Poetry Collection 3

1. **Interpret:** What kind of juices might be dripping in line 4 of "Summer"?

_____

_____

_____

2. **Infer:** What is the eagle watching for in line 5 of "The Eagle"?

_____

3. **Literary Analysis:** For each poem in Poetry Collection 1, use this chart to identify one example of each **sound device** listed. Then, explain the way each example adds to the musical feeling of each poem.

	Example	Effect
Alliteration		
Consonance		
Assonance		

4. **Reading Skill:** In what way does **reading fluently** help you appreciate a poem's sound devices?

_____

_____

_____

Writing: Editorial

Write an **editorial** related to one of the poems. An editorial is a short piece of writing that presents one side of an issue. Ask several people to respond to your editorial. Use this chart to address responses from readers.

Argument	Reader's Responses	How I Can Fix the Problem

These notes will help you revise any weaknesses in your editorial.

Listening and Speaking: Formal Presentation

Give a formal presentation about one of the poems you read. Make a poster or other graphic about the poem to display to your audience while you give your speech. Use this checklist to be sure you are meeting the needs of your audience, purpose, and occasion:

Am I…	Yes or No
using formal language?	
making eye contact with my audience?	
using appropriate gestures?	
speaking slowly enough to be understood?	
speaking loudly enough for everyone to hear?	
enunciating, or clearly pronouncing, my words?	
using proper grammar?	

Poetry Collection 4

Summaries In "The Bells," the poet uses words and repetition to imitate the sounds of bells. In "Slam, Dunk, & Hook," the speaker describes the action and excitement of the basketball games he played in his youth. In "Jabberwocky," the poet uses made-up words to tell of a forest monster called the Jabberwock.

Writing About the Big Question

How does communication change us? The speaker in "The Bells" describes a range of ideas associated with the sounds of different bells. Use this sentence starter to develop your ideas about the Big Question:

By reading about the **meaning** that someone finds in certain sounds, a

reader can learn to _____.

Note-taking Guide

Use this chart to write the main image of each poem.

What is the main image in each poem?		
The Bells	Slam, Dunk, & Hook	Jabberwocky
	basketball games	

Poetry Collection 4

1. **Infer:** Read line 5 of "Slam, Dunk, & Hook." What action causes the sound described by the speaker?

   _____

   _____

2. **Evaluate:** Do you think "Jabberwocky" pokes fun at heroism? Explain.

   _____

   _____

3. **Literary Analysis:** Use this chart to identify one example of each **sound device** listed. Find the examples in the poems in Poetry Collection 2. Then, tell how each example adds to the musical feeling of the poem.

	Example	Effect
Alliteration		
Consonance		
Assonance		

4. **Reading Skill:** In what way does **reading fluently** help you appreciate a poem's sound devices?

   _____

   _____

Writing: Editorial

Write an **editorial** related to one of the poems. Ask several people to respond to your editorial. Use this chart to address responses from readers.

Argument	Reader's Responses	How I Can Fix the Problem

These notes will help you revise any weaknesses in your editorial.

Listening and Speaking: Formal Presentation

Give a formal presentation about one of the poems you read. Make a poster or other graphic about the poem to display to your audience while you give your speech. Use this checklist to be sure you are meeting the needs of your audience, purpose, and occasion:

Am I...	Yes or No
using formal language?	
making eye contact with my audience?	
using appropriate gestures?	
speaking slowly enough to be understood?	
speaking loudly enough for everyone to hear?	
enunciating, or clearly pronouncing, my words?	
using proper grammar?	

Procedural Texts

About Procedural Texts

A **procedural text** explains how something works or tells how to complete a task. A procedural text should clearly state its objective, or goal. If the text describes steps in a process, the steps should be clear and easily understandable.

A **consumer publication** is a type of procedural text that provides general information explaining a topic. It may also include steps to complete a task.

Instructions are also procedural texts. These texts explain key features of a product or explain how to complete a specific task correctly.

Reading Skill

When you **analyze the clarity of the objectives** of a procedural text, you decide if the text achieves its goal in a clear and understandable way. In other words, you decide if a reader could easily use the text to complete a task or understand how something works.

Use this graphic organizer to analyze the clarity of the objectives of the consumer publication.

Objective or Goal: To introduce podcasting and explain how it is done	
Are all necessary steps included in the text?	
Are the steps clear?	
Are the steps presented in the proper order?	
Are common questions answered?	

Consumer Publication

Features:

- background about a topic
- some technical language
- step-by-step instructions

How Podcasting Works

by Stephanie Watson

This heading clearly states that this section will provide an introduction to the subject of podcasting.

Introduction to How Podcasting Works

Have you ever dreamed of having your own radio show? Are you a recording artist hoping to have your songs heard by the masses? Decades ago, you would have had to have a lot of connections—or a fortune—to get heard.

The text includes background information about podcasting and its purposes.

But now, thanks to the Internet and its instantaneous connection to millions of people, your dreams can become reality. Just as blogging has enabled almost anyone with a computer to become a bona fide reporter, a new technology called podcasting is allowing virtually anyone with a computer to become a radio disc jockey, talk show host or recording artist.

If you post it, they will come. Although podcasting is still primarily used by the techie set, it's beginning to catch on with the general public. Log onto one of several podcast sites on the Web, and you can download content ranging from music to philosophy. . . . Podcasting combines the freedom of blogging with the technology of MP3 to create an almost endless supply of content. Some say this new technology is democratizing the once corporate-run world of radio.

In this article, you'll learn how podcasting works, find out what tools you need to record and receive podcasts and hear what industry analysts have to say about the future of this burgeoning technology.

Podcasting is a free service that allows Internet users to pull audio files (typically MP3s) from a podcasting Web site to listen to on their computer or personal digital audio player. The name comes from a combination of the words **iPod** and **broadcasting.** Even though the name is derived from the iPod, you don't need an iPod to listen to a podcast. You can use virtually any MP3 player or your computer.

Boldface text highlights key technical words.

Unlike with Internet radio, users don't have to "tune in" to a particular broadcast; instead, they **subscribe** to a podcast, and the audio files are automatically downloaded to their computer via **RSS feed** as often as they request. The technology is similar to that used by TiVo, a personal video recorder that lets users set which programs they'd like to record and then automatically records those programs for later viewing.

Podcasting History

Podcasting was developed in 2004 by former MTV video jockey Adam Curry and software developer Dave Winer. Curry wrote a program, called iPodder, that enabled him to automatically download Internet radio broadcasts to his iPod. Several developers improved upon his idea, and podcasting was officially born. . . .

Right now, podcasting is free from government regulation. Podcasters don't need to buy a license to broadcast their programming, as radio stations do, and they don't need to conform to the the Federal Communication Commission's (FCC) broadcast decency regulations. . . .

Although several corporations and big broadcast companies have ventured into the medium, many podcasters are amateurs broadcasting from home studios. Because podcasters don't rely on ratings as radio broadcasters do, the subject matter of podcasts can range from the refined to the silly to the excruciatingly mundane. . . .

Several companies are trying to turn podcasting into a profitable business. Podcasting aggregators. . . are including advertising on their sites. The Podcast Network, based in Australia, runs commercials and sponsorships during its audio broadcasts. Television networks have gotten into the action. National Public Radio, the Canadian Broadcasting Corporation and the BBC have begun podcasting some of their shows. Corporations. . . have created their own podcasts to attract consumers.

Some experts say podcasting still has a long way to go before it catches on with the masses. But others believe it will eventually become as popular as text blogging, which grew from a few thousand blogs in the late '90s to more than 7 million today. Some podcasts are already providing thousands of downloads a day.

Creating and Listening to Podcasts

Virtually anyone with a computer and recording capabilities can create his or her own podcast. Podcasts may include music, comedy, sports, philosophy—even people's rants and raves. Here's how the process works.

To record a podcast:

1. Plug a USB headset with a microphone into your computer.

2. Install an MP3 recorder for Windows, Mac or Linux.

3. Create an audio file by making a recording (you can talk, sing or record music) and saving it as an MP3 file.

4. Finally, upload the MP3 audio file to one of the podcasting sites.

To listen to a podcast:

1. Go to a podcasting site and download the free software.

2. Click on the hyperlink for each podcast you want. You can listen right away on your computer (both Windows and Mac support podcasting) or download the podcast to your MP3 player.

3. You can also subscribe to one or more RSS feeds. Your podcasting software will check the RSS feeds regularly and automatically pull content that matches your playlist. When you dock your MP3 player to your computer, it automatically updates with the latest content.

The subheads in this section help readers to find information. **Analyze the clarity of the objectives in this section of the procedural text.**

Numbered lists provide step-by-step instructions.

 THE BIG ?

How does communication change us?

How has podcasting changed the exchange of information?

Thinking About the Consumer Publication

1. Why might someone be interested in recording a podcast?

   _____

2. How is a podcast different from Internet radio?

   _____

TALK ABOUT IT **Reading Skill**

3. The author's objective, or goal, is to introduce podcasting and explain how it is done. How does the author achieve this goal?

   _____

   _____

4. Is the author successful in achieving her objective? Explain.

   _____

   _____

WRITE ABOUT IT **Timed Writing: Podcast Script (30 minutes)**

Write a script for a podcast. In the script, discuss how technology affects the way students learn and communicate in the classroom. Also, include directions that other students can follow when posting a podcast. Use information from "How Podcasting Works" to help you write your script. In the space below, list five details that you will include in your podcast.

1. _____

2. _____

3. _____

4. _____

5. _____

Poetry Collection 5 • Poetry Collection 6

Literary Analysis

Narrative poetry is verse that tells a story and includes the same literary elements as narrative prose: a plot, or sequence of events; specific settings; and characters who participate in the action.

Like the narrative prose of a short story, a narrative poem conveys a **mood**, or **atmosphere**—an overall feeling created by the setting, plot, words, and images. For example, a narrative poem's mood can be gloomy, joyous, or mysterious. Poetry's emphasis on precise words and images makes mood a powerful element in a narrative poem.

Reading Skill

Paraphrasing is restating in your own words what someone else has written or said. A paraphrase retains the meaning but is simpler. Paraphrasing helps you read poetry because poems often contain **figurative language,** words that are used imaginatively rather than literally. To paraphrase a narrative poem, **picture the action**.

- Based on details in the poem, form a mental image of the setting, the characters, and the characters' actions.

- To be sure that your mental picture is accurate, pay attention to the way that the poet describes the scene.

- Then, use your own words to describe your mental image of the scene and the action taking place in it.

As you read, use this chart to record your paraphrases.

Lines of Poetry	Details in Lines of Poetry	Paraphrase

Poetry Collection 5

Summaries "Casey at the Bat" is about a Mudville baseball game. The fans count on their star player, Casey, to win the game. In "Fifteen," the speaker remembers when he found a motorcycle in the grass. He dreams about driving away on the bike. In "Twister Hits Houston," the speaker recalls when a tornado hit the family's house.

Writing About the Big Question

How does communication change us? In "Casey at the Bat," the fans of a baseball team voice their enthusiastic support for their star player. Use this sentence starter to develop your ideas about the Big Question:

When a crowd communicates its support or disapproval, an athlete might

react by _____.

Note-taking Guide

Use this chart to record the most important events in each poem.

Poem	Beginning Event	What Happens Next	What Happens Next	Final Event
Casey at the Bat	two players get on base	Casey comes up to bat		
Fifteen	teenage boy finds a wrecked motorcycle			
Twister Hits Houston				

Casey at the Bat
Ernest Lawrence Thayer

It looked extremely rocky for the Mudville nine
    that day;
The score stood two to four, with but an inning
    left to play.
So, when Cooney died at second, and Burrows
    did the same,
A pallor wreathed the features of the patrons of
    the game.

5 A straggling few got up to go, leaving there
    the rest,
With that hope which springs eternal within the
    human breast.
For they thought: "If only Casey would get a
    whack at that,"
They'd put even money now, with Casey at the bat.

But Flynn preceded Casey, and likewise so did
    Blake,
10 And the former was a pudd'n, and the latter was
    a fake.
So on that stricken multitude a deathlike silence
    sat;
For there seemed but little chance of Casey's
    getting to the bat.

But Flynn let drive a "single," to the wonderment
    of all.
And the much-despised Blakey "tore the cover off
    the ball."
15 And when the dust had lifted, and they saw what
    had occurred,
There was Blakey safe at second, and Flynn a-
    huggin' third.

Then from the gladdened multitude went up a
    joyous yell—
It rumbled in the mountaintops, it rattled in the
    dell;
It struck upon the hillside and rebounded on the
    flat;
20 For Casey, mighty Casey, was advancing to the
    bat.

Activate Prior Knowledge

Think of a high-pressure situation in which you were expected to perform well. How do you think the added pressure affected your ability to perform?

_____

_____

_____

Literary Analysis

Narrative poetry is verse that tells a story and includes a plot, specific settings, and characters. Read lines 1–4. What is the setting in this narrative poem?

_____

_____

Circle the details that hint at this.

Reading Skill

Paraphrasing is using your own words to restate what someone else has written or said. A paraphrase should keep the meaning but be simpler to read. Examine the important details of the scene and the action that takes place in the bracketed stanzas. Use your own words to retell what is said.

_____

_____

_____

_____

Literary Analysis

The **mood** or **atmosphere** of a literary work is an overall feeling created by the setting, plot, words, and images. In lines 23–28, what is the poem's mood as Casey steps up to bat?

_____

_____

_____

Reading Skill

Poems often contain **figurative language,** or words that are used imaginatively rather than literally. Underline the figurative language used in the bracketed stanza.

Reading Check

How many people were watching Casey during the game? Circle the text that tells you.

There was ease in Casey's manner as he stepped
    into his place,
There was pride in Casey's bearing and a smile
    on Casey's face;
And when responding to the cheers he lightly
    doffed his hat,
No stranger in the crowd could doubt 'twas Casey
    at the bat.

25 Ten thousand eyes were on him as he rubbed his
    hands with dirt,
Five thousand tongues applauded when he wiped
    them on his shirt;
Then when the <u>writhing</u> pitcher ground the ball
    into his hip,
Defiance glanced in Casey's eye, a sneer curled
    Casey's lip.

And now the leather-covered sphere came hurtling
    through the air,
30 And Casey stood a-watching it in haughty
    grandeur there.
Close by the sturdy batsman the ball unheeded
    sped;
"That ain't my style," said Casey. "Strike one,"
    the umpire said.

From the benches, black with people, there went
    up a muffled roar,
Like the beating of the storm waves on the stern
    and distant shore.
35 "Kill him! kill the umpire!" shouted someone on
    the stand;
And it's likely they'd have killed him had not
    Casey raised his hand.

With a smile of Christian charity great Casey's
    visage shone;
He stilled the rising tumult, he made the game
    go on;
He signaled to the pitcher, and once more the
    spheroid flew;
40 But Casey still ignored it, and the umpire
said,   "Strike two."

Vocabulary Development
writhing (RY<u>TH</u> ing) *adj.* twisting; turning

"Fraud!" cried the maddened thousands, and
   the echo answered "Fraud!"
But one scornful look from Casey and the
   audience was awed;
They saw his face grow stern and cold, they saw
   his muscles strain,
And they knew that Casey wouldn't let the ball
   go by again.

45 The sneer is gone from Casey's lips, his teeth are
   clenched in hate.
He pounds with cruel vengeance his bat upon
   the plate:
And now the pitcher holds the ball, and now he
   lets it go,
And now the air is shattered by the force of
   Casey's blow.

Oh, somewhere in this favored land the sun is
   shining bright,
50 The band is playing somewhere, and somewhere
   hearts are light:
And somewhere men are laughing, and somewhere
   children shout,
But there is no joy in Mudville: Mighty Casey has
   struck out.

Reading Skill

To **paraphrase** what happens in a poem, **picture the action.** Read the bracketed stanzas. Use your own words to describe what is happening.

_____

_____

_____

_____

Literary Analysis

In what way does the poem's **mood** change in the last stanza?

_____

_____

_____

What has caused the mood to change?

_____

_____

Reading Check

What does the crowd yell after the second strike? Underline the text that tells you.

Fifteen
William Stafford

Stop to Reflect

Do you think a poem is an effective way in which to tell a story? Why or why not?

_____

_____

_____

Reading Skill

Picture the action in lines 11 and 12, and then restate the phrase "meet the sky" in your own words.

_____

_____

_____

Literary Analysis

The characters in a **narrative poem** take part in the action. Who are the characters in this poem?

_____

_____

_____

Reading Check

Where did the speaker find the motorcycle? Underline the text that tells you.

_____

_____

_____

South of the bridge on Seventeenth
I found back of the willows one summer
day a motorcycle with engine running
as it lay on its side, ticking over
5 slowly in the high grass. I was fifteen.

I admired all that pulsing gleam, the
shiny flanks, the demure headlights
fringed where it lay; I led it gently
to the road and stood with that
10 companion, ready and friendly. I was fifteen.

We could find the end of a road, meet
the sky on out Seventeenth. I thought about
hills, and patting the handle got back a
confident opinion. On the bridge we indulged
15 a forward feeling, a tremble. I was fifteen.

Thinking, back farther in the grass I found
the owner, just coming to, where he had flipped
over the rail. He had blood on his hand, was pale—
I helped him walk to his machine. He ran his hand
20 over it, called me a good man, roared away.

I stood there, fifteen.

Vocabulary Development

demure (di MYUR) *adj.* modest
indulged (in DULGD) *v.* enjoyed something considered bad

Twister Hits Houston
Sandra Cisneros

Papa was on the front porch.
Mama was in the kitchen.
Mama was trying
to screw a lightbulb into a fixture.
5   Papa was watching the rain.
Mama, it's a cyclone for sure,
he shouted to his wife in the kitchen.
Papa who was sitting on his front porch
when the storm hit
10 said the twister ripped
the big black oak to splinter,
tossed a green sedan into his garden,
and banged the back door
like a mad cat wanting in.
15 Mama who was in the kitchen
said Papa saw everything,
the big oak ripped to kindling,
the green sedan land out back,
the back door slam and slam.
20 I missed it.
Mama was in the kitchen Papa explained.
Papa was sitting on the front porch.
The light bulb is still sitting
where I left it. Don't matter now.
25 Got no electricity anyway.

Reader's Response: Which of the poems in this collection do you think has the most exciting or interesting plot? Explain your answer.

_____

_____

_____

_____

TAKE NOTES

Reading Skill 📖

Paraphrase the description of the twister banging the back door in lines 13–14.

_____

_____

Literary Analysis 🔍

What is the plot, or sequence of events, in this **narrative poem?**

_____

_____

_____

_____

Stop to Reflect 📕

Remember a time when you saw a large storm. What was the storm like? What did you do during the storm?

_____

_____

_____

Reading Check ✏️

Where were Mama and Papa when the twister hit? Underline the text that tells you.

Poetry Collection 5

1. **Draw Conclusions:** How might Casey's personality have affected the game's outcome?

   _____

   _____

2. **Make a Judgment:** In "Twister Hits Houston," is the father's behavior appropriate for the situation? Explain your answer.

   _____

   _____

3. **Literary Analysis:** Using the chart below, identify and briefly describe the story elements in each **narrative poem** in Poetry Collection 1.

	Setting	Characters	Plot
Casey at the Bat			
Fifteen			
Twister Hits Houston			

4. **Reading Skill: Paraphrase** lines 29 through 32 of "Casey at the Bat."

   _____

   _____

Writing: Poem

Write a **poem**. In your poem, be sure your diction, or word choice, conveys a specific mood. Consult a thesaurus if necessary. Use this graphic organizer to help choose the words you will use:

Mood of Poem: _____	
Word	Definition

Listening and Speaking: Report

Prepare a **report** with a partner in which you analyze a motorcycle or an automobile commercial. In your report, discuss the visual and sound techniques that are used to make the audience want to purchase the item being advertised. Use this chart to organize your analysis:

Technique	Definition	Notes
editing	Cutting and rearranging of visual and audio elements	
reaction shots	Audio or visual portrayals of a person's reactions to something	
sequencing	Order of visual or sound messages	
background music	Music added to a scene	

Poetry Collection 6

Summaries In "The Raven," the speaker is sad because of the death of a woman. A raven appears. The speaker asks it questions but always receives the same response. In "The Horses," a war in the future has destroyed much of the planet. Horses appear and give the speaker hope. In "The Writer," the speaker reflects on his daughter who is writing a story. He does not want her to struggle in life.

Writing About the Big Question

How does communication change us? In "The Writer," a father is moved by the sound of his daughter typing a story. Use this sentence starter to develop your ideas about the Big Question:

Having **empathy** for someone who is in a difficult situation might make a

person realize that _____.

Note-taking Guide

Use this chart to record an event that happens in each poem. Then, note one effect of each event.

	Event	Effect
The Raven	The speaker hears a tapping at the door.	The speaker opens the door.
The Horses		
The Writer		

Poetry Collection 6

1. **Draw Conclusions:** In "The Raven," what words would you use to describe the speaker's state of mind at the end of the poem?

   _____

   _____

2. **Analyze:** Why does the speaker of "The Writer" remember the incident of the trapped starling? Explain your answer.

   _____

   _____

3. **Literary Analysis:** Use the chart below to describe details from each **narrative poem** that show the setting, characters, and plot.

	Setting	Characters	Plot
The Raven			
The Horses			
The Writer			

4. **Reading Skill: Picture the action** described in lines 1 and 2 of "The Raven." Then, **paraphrase** these lines.

   _____

   _____

Writing: Poem

Write a **poem**. In your poem, be sure your diction, or word choice, conveys a specific mood. Consult a thesaurus if necessary. Use this graphic organizer to help choose the words you will use:

Mood of Poem: _____	
Word	Definition

Listening and Speaking: Report

Prepare a **report** with a partner in which you analyze a commercial for a computer or other contemporary electronic device. In your report, discuss the visual and sound techniques that are used to make the audience want to purchase the item being advertised. Use this chart to organize your analysis:

Technique	Definition	Notes
editing	Cutting and rearranging of visual and audio elements	
reaction shots	Audio or visual portrayals of a person's reactions to something	
sequencing	Order of visual or sound messages	
background music	Music added to a scene	

Poetry Collection 7 • Poetry Collection 8

Literary Analysis

Rhyme is the repetition of sounds at the ends of words. There are several types of rhyme. **Exact rhyme** is the repetition of words that end with the same vowel and consonant sounds, as in *love* and *dove*. **Slant rhyme** is the repetition of words that end with similar sounds but do not rhyme perfectly, as in *prove* and *glove*. **End rhyme** is the rhyming of words at the ends of lines. **Internal rhyme** is the rhyming of words within a line.

A **rhyme scheme** is a regular pattern of end rhymes in a poem or stanza. A rhyme scheme is described by assigning one letter of the alphabet to each rhyming sound.

Meter is the rhythmical pattern in a line of poetry. It results from the arrangement of stressed (´) and unstressed (˘) syllables. When you read aloud a line with a regular meter, you can hear the steady rhythmic pulse of the stressed syllables.

As you read the poetry in this collection, notice rhyme and meter.

- Look for examples of different types of rhyme.
- Determine whether the lines follow a rhyme scheme.
- Notice whether the lines follow a regular meter.

Reading Skill

Paraphrasing is restating in your own words what someone else has written or said. A paraphrase should retain the essential meaning and ideas of the original but should be simpler to read. One way to simplify the text that you are paraphrasing is to **break down long sentences**. Divide long sentences into parts and paraphrase those parts.

As you read poetry and break down long sentences to paraphrase lines, use this chart to record your work.

Original Lines	Lines in Smaller Sentences	Paraphrase

Poetry Collection 7

Summaries In "The Road Not Taken," the speaker thinks of a time in the past. He had to choose which path to take. In "We never know how high we are," the speaker reflects on how people have the ability to do great things. She suggests that fear holds them back. "Macavity: The Mystery Cat" is about a cat who steals things. The police cannot catch the cat.

 ## Writing About the Big Question

How does communication change us? In the first poem in Collection 7, the speaker claims that "We never know how high we are / Till we are asked to rise." Use this sentence starter to develop your ideas about the Big Question:

A person can make someone **aware** of his or her potential by

_____.

Note-taking Guide

Use this chart to write the topic of each poem.

What is the topic of each poem?		
The Road Not Taken	We never know how high we are	Macavity: The Mystery Cat
taking a less-traveled path through life		

We never know how high we are

Emily Dickinson

We never know how high we are
Till we are asked to rise
And then if we are true to plan
Our statures touch the skies—
The Heroism we recite
Would be a normal thing
Did not ourselves the Cubits[1] <u>warp</u>
For fear to be a King—

Vocabulary Development

warp (wawrp) *v.* twist; distort

The Road Not Taken

Robert Frost

Two roads <u>diverged</u> in a yellow wood,
And sorry I could not travel both
And be one traveler, long I stood
And looked down one as far as I could
5   To where it bent in the undergrowth;

Then took the other, as just as fair,
And having perhaps the better claim,
Because it was grassy and wanted wear;
Though as for that, the passing there
10   Had worn them really about the same,

And both that morning equally lay
In leaves no step had trodden black.
Oh, I kept the first for another day!
Yet knowing how way leads on to way,
15   I doubted if I should ever come back.

I shall be telling this with a sigh
Somewhere ages and ages hence:
Two roads diverged in a wood, and I—
I took the one less traveled by,
20   And that has made all the difference.

Vocabulary Development

diverged (di VERJD) *v.* branched out in different directions

1. **Cubits** (KYOO bitz) *n.* ancient measure using the length of the arm from the end of the middle finger to the elbow (about 18–22 inches).

Activate Prior Knowledge

Think about your favorite poems. What do you like about these works—the images, or the subject matter? Explain.

_____

_____

_____

Literary Analysis

Exact rhyme is the repetition of words that end with the same vowel and consonant sounds, as in *love* and *dove*. Underline the words in "We never know how high we are" that show exact rhyme.

Reading Skill

Paraphrasing is using your own words to restate what someone else has written or said. A paraphrase should keep the meaning and ideas of the original but should be simpler to read. In your own words, restate the decision the speaker makes in lines 6–8 of "The Road Not Taken."

_____

_____

_____

Literary Analysis

A **rhyme scheme** is a regular pattern of end rhymes. What is the rhyme scheme of the bracketed stanza?

_____

© Pearson Education

Macavity: The Mystery Cat
T. S. Eliot

Literary Analysis

End rhyme is the rhyming of words at the ends of lines of poetry. **Internal rhyme** is the rhyming of words within a line of poetry. Read the bracketed stanza. Does this stanza use end rhyme or internal rhyme?

_____

_____

Underline the words that helped you answer this question.

Reading Skill

You can **break down long sentences** by treating colons, semicolons, and dashes like periods. Break lines 11–12 into a few sentences and write them below.

_____

_____

_____

Reading Check

How does Macavity confuse the London police? Underline the text that tells you.

Macavity's a Mystery Cat: he's called the Hidden
    Paw—
For he's the master criminal who can defy the Law.
He's the bafflement of Scotland Yard,[1] the Flying
    Squad's[2] despair:
5   For when they reach the scene of crime—
    Macavity's not there!

Macavity, Macavity, there's no one like Macavity,
He's broken every human law, he breaks the law
    of gravity.
His powers of levitation would make a fakir[3] stare,
10 And when you reach the scene of crime—
    Macavity's not there!
You may seek him in the basement, you may look
    up in the air—
But I tell you once and once again, *Macavity's
    not there!*

Macavity's a ginger cat, he's very tall and thin;
15 You would know him if you saw him, for his eyes
    are sunken in.
His brow is deeply lined with thought, his head
    is highly domed;
His coat is dusty from neglect, his whiskers are
    uncombed.
He sways his head from side to side, with
    movements like a snake;
20 And when you think he's half asleep, he's always
    wide awake.

Vocabulary Development

bafflement (BAF uhl muhnt) *n.* puzzlement; bewilderment

---

1. **Scotland Yard** London police.
2. **Flying Squad** criminal-investigation department.
3. **fakir** (fuh KIR) *n.* Muslim or Hindu beggar who claims to perform miracles.

Macavity, Macavity, there's no one like Macavity,
For he's a fiend in feline shape, a monster of
  depravity.
You may meet him in a by-street, you may see
  him in the square—
25 But when a crime's discovered, then *Macavity's not
  there!*

He's outwardly respectable. (They say he cheats
  at cards.)
And his footprints are not found in any file of
  Scotland Yard's.
And when the larder's looted, or the jewel-case
  is rifled,
30 Or when the milk is missing, or another Peke's[4]
  been stifled,
Or the greenhouse glass is broken, and the trellis
  past repair—
Ay, there's the wonder of the thing! *Macavity's
  not there!*

And when the Foreign Office find a Treaty's gone
  astray,
Or the Admiralty lose some plans and drawings
  by the way,
35 There may be a scrap of paper in the hall or on
  the stair—
But it's useless to investigate—*Macavity's not there!*
And when the loss has been disclosed, the Secret
  Service say:
'It *must* have been Macavity!'—but he's a mile
  away.
You'll be sure to find him resting, or a-licking of
  his thumbs,
40 Or engaged in doing complicated long division
  sums.

© Pearson Education

Vocabulary Development

depravity (dee PRAV uh tee) *n.* crookedness; corruption

4. **Peke** short for Pekingese, a small dog with long, silky hair and a pug nose.

Literary Analysis

Slant rhyme is the repetition of words that end with similar sounds but do not rhyme perfectly, as in *prove* or *glove*.
Internal rhyme is the rhyming of words within a line. Which two words in line 31 show both slant rhyme and internal rhyme? Explain.

_____

_____

_____

Stop to Reflect

What do you think is funny about the character of Macavity? Explain your answer.

_____

_____

_____

Reading Check

What crimes is Macavity connected with? Circle the text that tells you.

© Pearson Education

Reading Skill

To simplify the text you are **paraphrasing, break down long sentences** into shorter sentences. Read lines 43–44. Break down the sentences in these lines into three smaller sentences. Then, restate each sentence in your own words.

_____

_____

_____

_____

_____

Reading Check

What makes Macavity different from other cats? Circle the text that tells you.

Literary Analysis 🔍

A **rhyme scheme** is a regular pattern of end rhymes in a poem or stanza. Describe the rhyme scheme of the last stanza using letters of the alphabet.

_____

Macavity, Macavity, there's no one like Macavity,
There never was a Cat of such deceitfulness and
　suavity.
He always has an alibi, and one or two to spare:
At whatever time the deed took place—MACAVITY
　WASN'T THERE!
45　And they say that all the Cats whose wicked
　deeds are widely known
(I might mention Mungojerrie, I might mention
　Griddlebone)
Are nothing more than agents for the Cat who all
　the time
50　Just controls their operations: the Napoleon of
　Crime![5]

> **Reader's Response:** Which poem do you think sounds best when it is read aloud? Why?
>
> _____
>
> _____
>
> _____

_____

5. **the Napoleon of Crime** criminal mastermind; emperor of crime—just as Napoleon Bonaparte (1769–1821) was a masterful military strategist who had himself crowned emperor.

Poetry Collection 7

1. **Interpret:** Fill out this chart about "The Road Not Taken." The first column identifies the decision faced by the speaker. In the second column, tell what other kinds of decisions this choice might represent.

What Does It Say?	What Does It Mean?
The speaker must decide which road to take.	

2. **Speculate:** Which qualities of cats might have caused T. S. Eliot to associate them with criminal activities in "Macavity: The Mystery Cat"? Explain.

_____

_____

_____

3. **Literary Analysis:** Which poem has lines with a more regular **meter**, "The Road Not Taken" or "We never know how high we are"? Explain.

_____

_____

_____

4. **Reading Skill: Paraphrase** the first stanza of "The Road Not Taken" by rewriting it as a series of sentences.

_____

_____

_____

Writing: Poem

Write a **poem** using the same rhyme scheme as a poem in Poetry Collection 7. Select a topic for your poem. Then, ask yourself the following questions. Use these notes to help draft your poem.

- What feelings about this topic do I want to express?

  _____

  _____

  _____

- What images, details, phrases, or words do I want to use to describe this topic?

  _____

  _____

  _____

Listening and Speaking: Panel Discussion

Create a chart like the following to prepare for your panel discussion on Frost's "The Road Not Taken".

Personal Interpretation of Poem's Theme or Main Idea: _____
_____
Support in Text: _____
_____
Panel's Position Statement: _____

Book by Frost	Biographies of Frost	Critical Analyses of Frost's Poetry
_____	_____	_____
_____	_____	_____

Poetry Collection 8

Summaries In "Fire and Ice," the speaker considers two ways in which the world could end: by fire or by ice. In "maggie and milly and molly and may," the speaker describes how four young girls go to the beach one day. Each girl finds an ordinary object and learns something about herself. In "The Seven Ages of Man," the speaker describes seven stages of a person's life.

 Writing About the Big Question

How does communication change us? The speaker of "The Seven Ages of Man" compares the people of the world with actors in a play. Use this sentence starter to develop your ideas about the Big Question:

Communication between two people can seem like action in a play when

_____.

Note-taking Guide

Use this chart to record the purpose of each poem.

What is the purpose of each poem?		
Fire and Ice	maggie and milly and molly and may	The Seven Ages of Man
to consider how the world will end		

Poetry Collection 8

1. **Interpret:** Fill out this chart about "Fire and Ice." The first column tells the emotions that fire and ice represent. In the second column, explain why fire and ice are good metaphors for these emotions.

What Does It Say?	What Does It Mean?
Fire represents desire. Ice represents hate.	

2. **Connect:** At the end of "maggie and milly and molly and may," the speaker says that people can find themselves through nature. How does each character's experience support this statement?

_____

_____

_____

_____

3. **Literary Analysis:** Which two words in line 17 of "The Seven Ages of Man" show both **slant rhyme** and **internal rhyme**?

_____

4. **Reading Skill: Paraphrase** lines 3 through 6 of "maggie and milly and molly and may" by rewriting them as a series of sentences.

_____

_____

_____

Writing: Poem

Write a **poem** using the same rhyme scheme as a poem in Poetry Collection 8.
Select a topic for your poem. Then, ask yourself these questions:

- What is the rhyme scheme of the poem from Poetry Collection 8? Use letters to identify the pattern.

  _____

- What feelings about this topic do I want to express?

  _____

  _____

- What images, details, phrases, or words do I want to use to describe this topic?

  _____

  _____

Use these notes to help draft your poem.

Listening and Speaking: Panel Discussion

Create a chart like the following to prepare for your panel discussion on Frost's "Fire and Ice".

Personal Interpretation of Poem's Theme or Main Idea: _____

_____

Support in Text: _____

Panel's Position Statement: _____

Book by Frost	Biographies of Frost	Critical Analyses of Frost's Poetry

Case Study

About Case Studies

A **case study** is a detailed look at a real-life situation. A case study usually features:

- An explanation of what is being studied and why
- Facts, examples, and quotations
- Text written for a specific audience

Reading Skill

The **main, or controlling, idea** of a text is what the text is about—its topic or primary idea. The main idea of a text is supported by a variety of **details.** These details are chosen by the author according to his or her **purpose** for writing.

To understand an expository text, it is important to know the author's purpose for writing. It is also important to recognize the main idea and the details that support it. As you read the case study, use this graphic organizer to explain the main idea, author's purpose, and supporting details.

```
┌─────────────────────────────────┐
│         Controlling Idea        │
│                                 │
└─────────────────────────────────┘
     ┌───────────────────────┐
     │    Author's Purpose   │
     │                       │
     └───────────────────────┘
┌────────┐ ┌────────┐ ┌────────┐ ┌────────┐
│ Detail │ │ Detail │ │ Detail │ │ Detail │
│        │ │        │ │        │ │        │
└────────┘ └────────┘ └────────┘ └────────┘
```

Robotics Education Project

Careers in Robotics: A Case Study

Think you'll never use high school math? Think again . . .

Gil Jones and Matt Zucker may seem like regular guys just out of college—but they have one of the coolest jobs around! They are both software engineers for a company that makes underwater robots, otherwise known as autonomous underwater vehicles (AUVs). AUVs are small, unmanned submarines that use on-board artificial intelligence to complete survey tasks with little or no human supervision.

Although Matt and Gil do the same job now, the difference in how they got there shows there really is no single path to robotics.

Getting There

"I was a classic underachiever in high school," says Matt. "I got into college by the skin of my teeth. Once I got into college, though, I realized I wanted to focus on my interests. Studying something I liked really made it all worthwhile." In college at Vassar, Matt took his interests in biology and computers even further. He took classes in psychology, philosophy, anthropology, human brain and behavior, and artificial intelligence to work his way to a degree in cognitive science. His main interest? Helping robots and computers learn complex behaviors.

Fluency Builder

With a partner, circle the punctuation in the first paragraph of the selection. Then, read the paragraph aloud, smoothly and with expression. Be sure to pause appropriately for each punctuation mark.

Comprehension Builder

After reading the first two paragraphs, identify one similarity and one difference between Matt and Gil.

_____

_____

_____

Vocabulary Builder

Idioms The idiom *by the skin of my teeth* means "barely" or "by only a small amount." Use your knowledge of the idiom to complete the sentence below.

Matt _____
by the skin of his teeth.

TAKE NOTES

Vocabulary Builder

Idioms The idiom *on the other hand* means "in contrast to something else" or "from a different viewpoint." Use your knowledge of the idiom to complete the sentence below.

Matt was not a great student. Gil, *on the other hand,* was

_____.

Cultural Understanding

Vassar and Swarthmore colleges are both small, private liberal arts colleges in the Eastern U.S. Vassar is located in Poughkeepsie, New York. Swarthmore is located in Swarthmore, Pennsylvania.

Vocabulary Builder

Suffixes *Internship* is a noun with two word parts: the base word *intern,* which means "someone who works to gain experience," and the suffix *-ship,* which often means "a particular position or job." What does the word *internship* mean?

_____

_____

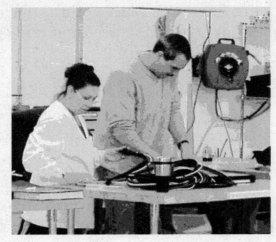

Gil, on the other hand, was a good student in high school, but didn't start out in robotics either—he was more interested in political science. At Swarthmore College, he was inspired by computer science. "I wanted to focus on artificial intelligence. I took an artificial intelligence class where we started playing with toy robots, using Handyboards and sensors." Gil really got interested in robotics through AAAI robotics competitions (imagine creating a robot that can serve hors d'oeuvres!), and when he graduated with a degree in computer science, a lot of his experience was with robots. The bottom line, both Gil and Matt agree, is that you don't have to go to an engineering school. Liberal arts universities and colleges will also give you the skills you need to do robotics. If you're interested in a lot of things—physics, math, science, engineering, communications, and others—you'll do well.

Landing the Job

Both Gil and Matt did summer internships during college that provided them with work experience and an idea of how to get a job in robotics. During one summer, Gil worked for the Naval Research Laboratory doing software artificial intelligence research and then, after graduating, spent the summer preparing for another AAAI competition. When one of his friends got a job at a robotics company, Gil learned about the company and then applied to

© Pearson Education

300 Informational Texts

be a software engineer. Matt got an internship at the same company during the summer between his junior and senior years and was then offered a job following graduation. What's their best advice for getting internships and jobs? Perseverance! "Just find someone who works in robotics and ask them for advice," says Matt. Gil adds, "Sometimes it's difficult to get in, but keep trying. Think about doing an internship for free. Often internships are the first step through the door."

Research, Programming, and . . . Cruising(?)

One of the great things about this job is the variety. Sometimes they spend all day reading up on robotics research, sometimes they spend all day in front of a computer . . . and sometimes they spend all day hanging out on a boat testing the robot in the ocean! "You're making something that has a purpose, something that's part of a bigger project," says Gil. "You get to see if what you did worked. Of course, that means you're entirely responsible." Another perk, according to Matt, is that "you usually get to learn something big and new every few weeks." One warning: Pay attention in high school math classes. "You'll use trigonometry like crazy!"

Next Steps

Both Matt and Gil plan on going back to school sometime to do graduate work. Matt wants to study computer science, focusing on computer graphics and computer-human interfaces. Eventually, he wants to be a professor. Gil plans to go back to school specifically in robotics. He finds underwater robotics exciting because it requires autonomy, but there are a lot of other cool areas of robotics he'd like to explore.

The draw for both of them is that robotics is a quickly changing and very open field. As they point out, "You can do new stuff in any of the related areas and that's exciting!"

Vocabulary Builder

Contractions Instead of writing *it is,* sometimes writers use the contraction *it's.* Find and circle the contraction *it's* in the text at the top of this page.

Comprehension Builder

How might Matt and Gil spend their days at work? On the lines below, write three activities that are mentioned in the bracketed paragraph.

1. _____

2. _____

3. _____

Vocabulary Builder

Adverbs An adverb may describe how, where, or when the action of a verb is performed. In this paragraph, the word *Eventually* is an adverb that means "after a long time." Which verb does this adverb describe?

_____

Thinking About the Case Study

1. Matt and Gil took different paths to their careers in robotics. What is one difference?

   _____

2. Should students who are not interested in robotics read this case study? Explain.

   _____

TALK ABOUT IT **Reading Skill**

3. Review the first two paragraphs of the text. Considering these two paragraphs, explain the main idea of the text.

   _____

   _____

4. Considering the first two paragraphs of the text, explain the author's purpose.

   _____

WRITE ABOUT IT **Timed Writing: Persuasive Essay (30 minutes)**

"Success is the sum of small efforts, repeated day in and day out."—*Robert Collier*

Write a persuasive essay in which you explain whether or notyou agree with this quotation. In your essay, tell why you do or do not agree and give reasons for your response. Consider using quotations from the sections of the case study listed below as support.

First paragraph under "Getting There":

_____

The "Landing the Job" paragraph:

_____

The first paragraph under "Next Steps":

_____

Elements of Drama

A drama, or play, is a story written to be performed by actors. The events of the story revolve around a **conflict**, or struggle, that the **characters** must resolve. The conflict starts the sequence of events called the **plot**. At some point, the conflict reaches the **climax**, or the point of greatest tension. Then, the conflict is resolved. The **dialogue**, or the speeches of the characters, tells the story. The following elements are found in plays:

- Dramas are made up of **acts** and **scenes**. A drama may consist of one or more acts. Each act may contain any number of scenes.

- A **playwright** is the author of a play. The text of the play is called the **script**. The script includes dialogue and stage directions.

- **Stage directions** tell how the play is to be performed, or staged. Stage directions include details about sets, lighting, sound effects, props, and costumes. They may also give the director hints about how the characters should act. Most stage directions are printed in italic type and set off in brackets. Sometimes, a playwright uses abbreviations to add directions about where a speech should be delivered. These include O.S. for offstage and D.S. for downstage. Downstage means the part of the stage that is closer to the audience. U.S. stands for upstage, or the part of the stage that is farther from the audience.

- **Sets** are constructions that show where the drama takes place. Sets could include painted backdrops, wooden frames, or city sidewalks.

- **Props** are movable objects that are used by the actors onstage. Props may include such things as an umbrella, a sword, or a houseplant.

All of the elements of drama combine to produce a **dramatic effect**. Dramatic effect is a vivid illusion of reality. In the dramatic effect, the dramatist, or playwright, explores a **theme**, or an insight into life.

Types of Drama and Dramatic Conventions

Throughout the history of drama, playwrights have used **dramatic conventions,** or methods, to enhance their plays. There are two basic types of drama, and several special types of speeches used by playwrights.

Types of Drama	Definition	Elements
Tragedy	• a sad story that shows the downfall or death of a **tragic hero**, or main character	• Greek tragedy: hero is an outstanding person brought low by a **tragic flaw**, or defect in character • Greek tragedy: included a **chorus**, or group of performers who commented on the action • Modern tragedy: hero can be an ordinary person destroyed by an evil in society
Comedy	• a funny story with a happy ending	• emphasizes the weaknesses of humans and society
Types of Dramatic Speeches	**Definition**	**Elements**
Monologue	• a long, uninterrupted speech	• delivered by a character to other characters who are onstage but who remain silent
Soliloquy	• a short or long uninterrupted speech	• delivered by a character alone onstage • reveals character's thoughts and feelings to the audience
Aside	• a brief remark	• delivered by a character expressing private thoughts to the audience rather than to the other characters

from The Shakespeare Stealer

Gary Blackwood

Summary Fourteen-year-old Widge is an apprentice to Dr. Timothy Bright. He copies the words of other people's sermons for Bright. Then, Widge gets caught. As a result, Bright sells him to another man. His new boss asks him to copy *Hamlet*, one of Shakespeare's plays.

Note-taking Guide

Use the chart to recall the three most important events of the story.

> Bass tells Widge he must copy *Hamlet*, one of Shakespeare's plays.

Activate Prior Knowledge

Are there any situations you can think of in which stealing might be allowable? Explain your reasoning.

_____

_____

_____

Drama

A prologue introduces a literary work. It often sets the scene and introduces the **characters** and their **conflict**, or struggle. What role does the prologue play here?

_____

_____

_____

Drama

The **stage directions** help the audience understand that the play took place in England 400 years ago. Underline words and phrases in the bracketed passage that establish the setting.

Drama

Sets are constructions that show where the drama takes place. Throughout the play, the set on the stage will show three different locations. What three different places will be represented? Circle the sentence that tells the answer.

from The Shakespeare Stealer
Gary Blackwood

Characters

SANDER COOKE
DR. TIMOTHY BRIGHT, 50s or 60s
WIDGE, 14
FALCONER/SIMON BASS (must be played by the same actor), 30s or 40s

THIEF #1, 30s
THIEF #2, 30s
THIEF #3, late teens
LIBBY, 40s–60s

Prologue

SANDER. I bid you welcome. For an hour or so
I ask you to imagine, if you will,
That this poor stage is not a stage at all
But England, some four hundred years ago.
That the actors who—I hope—will soon appear
Are something more than they appear to be,
That they are not mere shadows on a stage
But men and women of another age.

Act I

At the rear of the playing area is a shallow, two-story set with a narrow flight of steps leading to the upper story. In the center of the upper story is a single wide doorway draped with a curtain. The lower story has two smaller openings, one at Left and one at Right, also covered by curtains. At various times, this set will represent DR. TIMOTHY BRIGHT's apothecary, with WIDGE's living quarters upstairs; Simon Bass's house; and the backstage area at the Globe Theatre.

At Lights Up, it is DR. BRIGHT's apothecary in Berwick-in-Elmet, Yorkshire, c. 1601. A table at Center contains glass and earthenware jars and beakers. One of the containers bubbles over a pot filled with burning pitch. WIDGE sits on a stool at the table, copying something from a small bound notebook onto loose sheets of paper, using a plumbago pencil-a stick of graphite wrapped in paper, similar to a grease pencil or charcoal pencil. WIDGE is a slight boy of fourteen with a "pudding basin," or bowl, haircut. He wears a working-class tunic.

All is quiet and peaceful for a long moment. Then the audience is startled by the entrance of DR. TIMOTHY BRIGHT, a florid, overweight man in his forties or fifties, who is slightly deaf. He strides on brandishing a walking stick, and roaring—but he is nearly as comical as he is menacing.

BRIGHT. You! . . . clod-pated drivel! *(WIDGE reacts, knocking a beaker to the floor, where it shatters, enraging BRIGHT even more)* You . . . halfwitted hoddypeak! Do you know what you've done?!

WIDGE. *(Puts the table between himself and BRIGHT)* I— I didn't mean to! I'll clean it up at once!

BRIGHT. Not *that*, you simpleton! This! *(He waves a paper about)* It's from the bishop's secretary. I've been accused of stealing sermons from my fellow rectors! How in heaven's name did the bishop get wind of this? Have you let a hint drop to anyone of what you were up to? Anyone at all?

WIDGE. Nay, I never! So help me God and halidom!

BRIGHT. Has anyone shown any signs of suspecting you?

WIDGE. Nay, no one.

BRIGHT. You're lying. No, don't bother to deny it. I've the proof here. The rector at Leeds caught you red-handed. Isn't that so? Isn't that so?

WIDGE. *(murmurs)* Aye.

BRIGHT. What's that? Speak up, boy!

WIDGE. Aye! It was a fortnight ago. 'A spotted me scribbling away, and afore I could make me escape, 'a collared me and snatched away me table-book!

BRIGHT. Why did you not tell me this sooner?

WIDGE. I was afeared. I kenned you'd be angry.

BRIGHT. You were right. But . . . if he took away your transcription of his sermon, then . . . then whose sermon was it that I . . . *(he doesn't want to say "stole")* . . . used as my model last Sunday?

WIDGE. Well . . . I—I wrote it all out as best I could remember . . .

BRIGHT. *You?* I delivered a sermon composed by my idle-headed apprentice! You deceitful little whelp! When will you learn not to lie to me? Well, by St. Pintle, I'll teach you right from wrong! Come here! *(WIDGE dodges the man's grasp, circling the table, but then he slips on the contents of the broken beaker, and is caught. BRIGHT raises the stick as if to strike; WIDGE cowers and flinches. But then BRIGHT tosses him aside and, puffing with the exertion, plops down on the stool)* Ahh, what's the use of it? If I haven't beaten some sense into you by now, I never will. *(shakes his head)* When I think of all I've done for you, all the years I've invested in you. When I took you in five years ago—

WIDGE. Seven.

BRIGHT. Eh? What's that?

WIDGE. It's been seven years, sir.

Drama

Stage directions tell how the work is to be performed, or staged. Read the first bracketed passage. What role do the stage directions play here for both readers and actors?

_____

_____

_____

_____

Drama

Dialogue is the conversation that occurs between characters. What is the job that dialogue performs in the second bracketed passage?

_____

_____

_____

Underline the words and groups of words that help you determine the dialogue's purpose.

Drama

The **plot** is the sequence of events in a story. Summarize what you have learned about the plot so far.

_____

_____

_____

_____

Drama

Read the first bracketed passage. What does Dr. Bright's **dialogue** tell you about Widge?

_____

_____

_____

_____

_____

Drama

Read the second bracketed passage. From the information in the stage directions, what are your first impressions of Falconer?

_____

_____

_____

_____

Underline the words and groups of words in the text that led to those impressions.

Reading Check

What does Falconer take out from beneath his cloak? Circle the sentence that tells the answer.

BRIGHT. That's beside the point. When I took you in, you were a <u>feckless</u>, illiterate orphan with no prospects whatever in the world. I taught you to read and cipher, taught you about medicine, even taught you my system of swift writing, and this is what I get in return? *(waves the paper)* If someone were to offer it, I'd sell your services for a farthing; it's far more than you're worth. Yes, and I expect you'd jump at the chance to change masters, wouldn't you? Eh? *(The way* WIDGE *hangs his head makes it clear that he would)* Well, all I can say is, be careful what you wish for, boy. There are far worse places than this, believe me, and far worse masters than me.

WIDGE. *(aside)* Aye, the Devil, for one.

BRIGHT. What's that?

WIDGE. Nothing. *(He sets about cleaning up the broken beaker, while* BRIGHT *checks his boiling potion. The silence is broken by the sound of an iron door knocker pounding O.S. Right)*

BRIGHT. Yes, yes, coming. Bloody patients. Why can't they be sick in the daytime? *(He crosses to Left, reaches O.S to open a door, then backs up as* FALCONER *enters, a tall figure in a hooded cloak, looking as grim as Death. Beneath the cloak he carries a rapier. We seldom see his face, but when he does reveal a glimpse of it, we see that he has a bushy, dark beard and a hooked nose. A nasty scar disfigures one side of his face)* G-good evening, sir. How may I serve you?

FALCONER. *(seems to reach for his rapier, but instead takes a leather-bound book from beneath his cloak. In a deep, almost* <u>spectral</u> *voice)* This is yours, is it not?

BRIGHT. *(moves hesitantly closer to the man)* Why, yes. Yes, it is. It's a copy of my book on charactery.

FALCONER. Does it *work?*

BRIGHT. I beg your pardon?

FALCONER. Your system of charactery. Does it work?

BRIGHT. Of course it works. Using my system of swift writing, one may without effort transcribe the written or the spoken word—

FALCONER. How long does it take?

BRIGHT. As I was about to say, one may set down speech as rapidly as it is spoken—

Vocabulary Development

feckless (FEK luhs) *adj.* worthless; irresponsible

spectral (SPEK trahl) *adj.* like a phantom or ghost

FALCONER. *(impatient)* Yes, yes, but how long to learn it?

BRIGHT. Well, that depends upon the aptitude of the—

FALCONER. How *long?*

BRIGHT. *(nervously, stretching the truth)* Oh, two months, perhaps three. Well, let's say four. Five, at the outside.

FALCONER. *(tosses the book rather contemptuously onto the table)* To how many have you taught this system of yours?

BRIGHT. Let me see . . . There's my apprentice, here, and then . . .

FALCONER. How *many?*

BRIGHT. Well . . . one, actually.

FALCONER. And how proficient is he?

BRIGHT. Oh, quite proficient. Extremely. *(WIDGE is surprised to hear this)*

FALCONER. Show me.

BRIGHT. *(to WIDGE)* Are you deaf, boy? The gentleman wishes a demonstration of your skill.

WIDGE. *(picks up notebook and pencil)* What must I write?

FALCONER. Write this: "I hereby convey to the bearer of this paper the services of my former apprentice—"

WIDGE. Go on. I've kept up wi' you.

FALCONER. Your name.

WIDGE. Pardon?

FALCONER. What is your *name?*

BRIGHT. Widge. It's Widge. *(laughs as if to show that he realizes how odd it sounds)*

FALCONER. "—my former apprentice, Widge, in consideration of which I have accepted the amount of ten pounds sterling."

BRIGHT. *(staggered)* Ten p—?!

WIDGE. Is that all, then?

FALCONER. Let me see it. *(WIDGE hands him the notebook. Skeptical)* You've copied down every word?

WIDGE. Aye.

FALCONER. Read it back.

WIDGE. *(takes notebook)* "I hereby convey to the bearer of this paper the services of my former apprentice, Widge, in consideration—*(the meaning of the words finally sinks in)*. Do you— does this mean—?

FALCONER. Copy it out, now, in a normal hand.

BRIGHT. *(when WIDGE hesitates)* Go on. Do as he says! *(While WIDGE copies it out, FALCONER takes out a purse and counts out ten sovereigns onto the table, with BRIGHT watching greedily)*

Drama

Read the first bracketed passage. What do you learn about Bright and Falconer from their **dialogue?** Circle words and phrases that tell the answer.

Stop to Reflect

Read the second bracketed passage. Why do you think Widge is surprised by what Dr. Bright says?

_____

_____

_____

_____

Drama

Read the third bracketed passage. How do the **stage directions** help the actor who is playing Bright?

_____

_____

_____

_____

Drama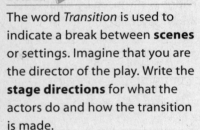

Read the bracketed passage. How does the **set** affect this scene?

_____

_____

_____

Drama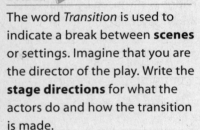

The word _Transition_ is used to indicate a break between **scenes** or settings. Imagine that you are the director of the play. Write the **stage directions** for what the actors do and how the transition is made.

_____

_____

_____

_____

_____

Reading Check

How does Falconer act toward the thieves when they first enter the scene? Is he scared, friendly, or angry? Circle the text that tells the answer.

FALCONER. If there's anything you want to take along, you'd best fetch it now, boy. I'll be outside. _(to_ BRIGHT_)_ Where can I water my horse?

BRIGHT. On the north side of the house, there's a trough. _(to_ WIDGE_)_ Go on, lad. _(through the following_ WIDGE _goes upstairs, collects his meager belongings, including a leather wallet on a strap. To_ FALCONER_)_ I hope you'll keep a close eye on the boy. _(The concern this implies is belied by_ BRIGHT_'s next line)_ He can be sluggish if you don't stir him from time to time with a stick. _(_FALCONER _exits)_ Move your bones, boy, before he changes his mind. _(_WIDGE _descends the stairs reluctantly)_

WIDGE. Must I go with him, then?

BRIGHT. _(busy fondling the sovereigns)_ Eh? Of course you must. He's paid for you, and far more handsomely than I would have dreamed.

WIDGE. Will you not bid me farewell, at least, sir?

BRIGHT. _(perfunctorily)_ Of course, of course. Fair 'chieve you, boy, fair 'chieve you.

Transition

_(_FALCONER _enters at Down Right, looking about warily, trailed by_ WIDGE_, who is rubbing his backside)_

WIDGE. Gog's blood, I'm glad to be off that horse.

FALCONER. It won't be for long. Here. _(Hands_ WIDGE _a journey cake, nibbles at one himself, still looking about alertly. They pass a flask of something back and forth)_

WIDGE. When will we be at our destination?

FALCONER. When we get there.

WIDGE. These woods are much more . . . wild than around Berwick, and more dense. It feels almost as though they're closing in on us. _(shivers)_

FALCONER. Stop your wagging tongue. You'll have every cutpurse within a league down upon us.

WIDGE. Cutpurse? _(looks about even more fearfully)_ You mean . . . there are thieves in these woods? _(realizes he's still talking)_ Sorry.

(Horse whinnies O.S. Right. FALCONER _reacts, abruptly puts away the flask and loosens his rapier in its sheath, looking about and listening intently._ THREE THIEVES _enter at Left, one armed with a pistol, two with swords)_

THIEF #1. Don't move, if you value your life.

FALCONER. _(unexpectedly amiable)_ God rest you, gentlemen.

THIEF #1. God, is it? Don't tell me you're a parson.

FALCONER. No, no. Far from it.

THIEF #1. Good. I don't like doing business with parsons. They're too <u>parsimonious</u>. *(Laughs)* All right, let's have it, then.

FALCONER. Have what?

THIEF #1. *(Laughs again)* Have what, 'a says! Have what? Why, have a pot of ale wi' us, of course. *(More soberly)* Come now, enough pleasantries. Let's have your purse, man.

FALCONER. *(Pulls out his hefty purse. Still amiable)* Ah. Forgive me for not taking your meaning.

THIEF #1. Oh, aye, an you forgive *me* for taking your purse.

(FALCONER steps to the man, who holds out a hand for the purse. Instead of handing it over, FALCONER swings it swiftly upward, catching THIEF #1 alongside the head. The man cries out, crumples to the ground; his pistol goes off wildly. The other thieves spring forward. FALCONER draws his rapier, parries an ineffectual blow, kicks the man in the groin. WIDGE picks up a rock, but has no chance to use it. FALCONER grasps the third man's blade in his cloak-wrapped hand, yanks it away, and slices the man's ribs with his own sword. With the thieves lying about groaning, FALCONER lifts his purse with the point of his sword, flips it in the air, catches it, then shakes a single coin from it and throws it at the men's feet)

FALCONER. If this is a toll road, you might simply have *tolled* me.

THIEF #1. *(laughs, then groans in pain)* Would that you had been a parson after all.

FALCONER. *(to WIDGE)* Come. *(starts Off Right)*

WIDGE. What you did back there—I've never seen the like of it.

FALCONER. Yes, well, you haven't seen much, have you?

Transition

(A bed has been brought on upstairs, and a writing desk and two chairs downstairs. FALCONER and WIDGE enter at Right. WIDGE is walking stiffly, wincing)

WIDGE. Are we in London, then?

FALCONER. *(scoffing)* Hardly. This is Leicester.

(LIBBY, a sympathetic, plain woman in a maid's garb, emerges from one of the downstairs doorways)

LIBBY. Welcome back, sir.

FALCONER. The boy will be staying the night. Show him to the garret. *(Exits upstage)*

© Pearson Education

Vocabulary Development

parsimonious (pahr suh MOH nee uhs) *adj.* miserly; stingy

TAKE NOTES

Drama

Read the **dialogue** in the first bracketed passage. Puns are humorous plays on words that sound alike. Underline the two words that sound alike. What pun is the thief making with these words?

_____

_____

_____

_____

Drama

Read the **stage directions** in the second bracketed passage. What do these stage directions tell you about Falconer?

_____

_____

_____

_____

Stop to Reflect

After Widge sees Falconer take care of the thieves, how do you think Widge feels?

_____

_____

_____

_____

Drama

Read the **dialogue** in the first bracketed passage. What does Libby's comment tell the audience to expect from Falconer?

Drama

Read the second bracketed passage. Why do you think the **stage directions** indicate that Bass and Falconer should be played by the same actor?

_____

_____

_____

Reading Check ✎

In comparison to Falconer, what is Bass's personality like? Underline the sentence that tells the answer.

LIBBY. Yes, sir. *(looking* WIDGE *over)* Where you from, then?

WIDGE. Berwick-in-Elmet.

LIBBY. Where's *that?*

WIDGE. Up Yorkshire way. Near Leeds.

LIBBY. I see. Well, come. We'd best get you to your room. *(Leads him up the steps)* I'll bring you some food up in a bit. Here you are. It's not much.

WIDGE. More than I'm used to. Mind you, it could be a pit of snakes for all I care, I'm that exhausted. *(sinks down on the bed)* You didn't seem surprised at all, that 'a came back wi' me in tow.

LIBBY. Nothing the master does surprises me. Have a good rest.

Transition

*(*WIDGE *wakes up, rubs eyes, looks around at the unfamiliar surroundings then hobbles downstairs.* LIBBY *is at the bottom of the steps)*

LIBBY. I was just coming to wake you. The master said to bring you to him as soon as you were up. I don't think he expected you to sleep so late. *(They cross to where* SIMON BASS *sits at the writing desk. He is played by the same actor who plays* FALCONER, *minus the hooded cloak, the curly black wig, the hooked nose, the swarthy skin, the beard, the scar, and the high boots that make him several inches taller.* BASS *is much more approachable and genial, but a prickliness lurks beneath the surface)*

WIDGE. Will 'a be cross wi' me, do you wis?

LIBBY. I can't say. He's a queer one, the master is. *(sotto voce)* Not to tell him I said so, now. *(Leaning into desk area)* I've brought the boy, sir.

BASS. *(without turning; we still assume it's* FALCONER *sitting there)* Come in, Widge. *(*WIDGE *enters the "room," clearly awed by the furnishings)* Sit down.

WIDGE. Eh? Oh. *(sits)* Sorry. It's just that I've never seen such a grand room, with so many books, not even at Squire Cheyney's.

BASS. Wait until you see the houses in London. *(He turns, rises. We and* WIDGE *get our first good look at him.* WIDGE *is obviously bewildered)*

WIDGE. Who—who are you?

BASS. My name is Simon Bass. I'm your new master.

WIDGE. But—but I thought—

BASS. You thought the one who brought you here was to be your master.

WIDGE. Aye.

BASS. *(shrugs)* Falconer is not the most communicative of men, I warrant, nor the most genial. But he is reliable and effective. I could not go to Yorkshire myself . . . for various reasons. He got you here safe and sound, it appears.

WIDGE. *(squirming on his sore rear end)* Well, *safe*, at any rate.

BASS. Let's get down to business. You'll want to know what's expected of you.

WIDGE. Aye.

BASS. Very well. The first thing I expect is for you to say "yes," rather than "aye." I'd just as soon you did not sound like a complete <u>rustic</u>. Understood?

WIDGE. Aye—I mean, yes.

BASS. Excellent. Now, when you go to London—

WIDGE. London?

BASS. Yes. It's a large city to the south.

WIDGE. I ken that, but—

BASS. Let me finish, then ask questions. You will be attending a play called *The Tragedy of Hamlet, Prince of Denmark.* You will copy down the play, every word of it, in Dr. Bright's charactery, and then you will deliver it to me. *(WIDGE looks uncomfortable)* Do you have some objection to that?

WIDGE. Nay, not especially. It's only words, after all. It's just that—Well, when a wight back home caught me copying his sermons, 'a got very upset wi' me.

BASS. Then you'll have to make certain you don't get caught, won't you? You will use a small tablebook, easily concealed . . . *(rummages through his desk)* You see how easily it's concealed? Even I can't find it. Ah, here it is. *(hands it to WIDGE)* Keep it in your wallet. You have a plumbago pencil?

WIDGE. Ay—Yes. An I might ask—for what purpose am I to do this?

BASS. Does it matter?

WIDGE. Nay; I was only curious. The only plays I've ever seen are the ones the church does at Easter and Yuletide, and those certainly didn't seem worth stealing.

BASS. *(being prickly now)* I would prefer it if you did not use that term. I am not a thief. I am a man of business, and one of my more profitable ventures is

---

Vocabulary Development

rustic (RUS tik) *n.* simple, plain, or artless person; someone from a rural area

---

TAKE NOTES

Stop to Reflect

Read the bracketed passage. Why do you think Bass is concerned about Widge's language?

_____

_____

_____

Drama

Underline words in the **dialogue** on this page that show that the play took place during the seventeenth century.

Drama

Conflict is the struggle that characters have with forces outside or inside of themselves. Which kind of conflict does Widge have when Bass gives him the task of copying *Hamlet*? Why do you think so?

_____

_____

_____

_____

Stop to Reflect

How do Bass's reasons for stealing Shakespeare's works differ from Dr. Bright's reasons for copying other rectors' sermons?

_____

_____

_____

Stop to Reflect

What argument does Bass use to persuade Widge that he is not stealing?

_____

_____

_____

_____

Drama

Now that the **conflict** is established, predict how the play will develop.

_____

_____

_____

Reading Check

Where is Bass sending Widge to copy *Hamlet*? Circle the word that tells the answer.

a company of players. They are not so successful as the Lord Chamberlain's Men or the Admiral's Men, of course, but they draw a sizable audience here in the Midlands. If we could stage a current work, by a well-known poet, we could double our profits. Now, sooner or later someone will pry this *Tragedy of Hamlet* from the grasp of its author, Mr. Shakespeare, just as they have his earlier plays. I would like that someone to be me. If I wait for others to do it, they will do a botched job, cobbled together from various sources, none of them very reliable. Mr. Shakespeare deserves better. He is a poet of quality, perhaps of genius, and if his work is to be borrowed, it should be done properly. That is your mission. If you fulfill it satisfactorily, the reward will be considerable.

WIDGE. And . . . what an I do not?

BASS. Falconer will make certain that you do.

WIDGE. Oh. I didn't ken that 'a would go wi' me.

BASS. Did you suppose I would send you off to London on your own? I might as well send you to Guiana. Go and rest now, or soak your haunches, or whatever you will. You'll be leaving for London early in the morning. (*He exits.* WIDGE *shuffles downstage as* LIBBY *enters at Left*)

Reader's Response: Do you think Bass's assignment to Widge is wrong? Why or why not?

_____

_____

_____

_____

_____

Drama

1. **Infer:** Dr. Bright does not know that Widge has been caught copying a sermon in Leeds. He finds this out only when he receives a letter. What does the episode show about Widge's talent as a writer?

_____

_____

_____

2. **Speculate:** Why does Falconer test Widge when he comes to see Dr. Bright?

_____

_____

3. **Drama:** Give three examples of **dialogue** that show that the play takes place in seventeenth-century England.

_____

_____

_____

4. **Drama:** Use the chart to show how Dr. Bright, Widge, and Falconer use **props** to reveal their personalities.

Prop	How It Is Used	What It Shows

Foreword

Write a **foreword** to a collection of books about Widge's adventures. A foreword is introductory material. Use your notes from the prompts below to write your foreword.

- Read the rest of the play *The Shakespeare Stealer* or the novel of the same name. Gary Blackwood has written two other books in the same series, *Shakespeare's Scribe* and *Shakespeare's Spy*.

  Briefly summarize the plots of these three works.

  _____

  _____

  _____

  _____

  _____

  _____

- Search the Internet for critics' and readers' reviews of these books. Mark key passages to be quoted in your foreword.

  Briefly summarize the ideas that you want to use from the reviews.

  _____

  _____

  _____

  _____

- Watch the video interview with Gary Blackwood. Add what you learn in the interview to the other information you have found. Then, think about what you want readers to know and understand about Gary Blackwood and his Shakespeare works.

  Write the main point of your foreword here:

  _____

  _____

  _____

  _____

The Tragedy of Romeo and Juliet, Act I

Literary Analysis

Dialogue is conversation between characters. In prose, dialogue is usually set off with quotation marks. In drama, the dialogue generally follows the name of the speaker, as in this example:

> **BENVOLIO.** My noble uncle, do you know the cause?

> **MONTAGUE.** I neither know it nor can learn of him.

Dialogue reveals the personalities and relationships of the characters and advances the action of the play.

Stage directions are notes in the text of a play that describe how the work should be performed, or staged. These instructions are usually printed in italics and are sometimes set in brackets or parentheses. They describe scenes, lighting, and sound effects, as well as the appearance and physical actions of characters, as in this example:

> **Scene iii.** FRIAR LAWRENCE's *cell.*
> *(Enter* FRIAR LAWRENCE *alone, with a basket.)*

As you read, notice how the dialogue and stage directions work together to help you "see" and "hear" the play in your mind.

Reading Skill

Summarizing is briefly stating the main points of a piece of writing. Pausing to summarize what you have read helps you check your comprehension before you read further. To be sure that you understand Shakespeare's language before you summarize, **use text aids**—the numbered explanations that appear with the text.

As you read Act I, use the chart below to record a summary of each scene.

Act I	
Scene	Summary of Action

The Tragedy of Romeo and Juliet, Act I

William Shakespeare

Summary As Act I begins, the Montague family and the Capulet family are involved in a long-standing fight. Romeo Montague meets Juliet Capulet at a feast given by Juliet's family. The teens fall in love before discovering what hatred exists between their families.

 Writing About the Big Question

Do our differences define us? In The Tragedy of Romeo and Juliet, two lovers come from families locked in a deadly feud. That difference defines their relationship and forces the plot toward tragic consequences. Use this sentence starter to develop your ideas about the Big Question.

When family differences stand between two people, it can be destructive

because _____.

Note-taking Guide

Use these boxes to record the four most important events in Act I.

Beginning Event

A fight occurs between the Capulets and the Montagues.

Final Outcome

The Tragedy of Romeo and Juliet, Act I

1. **Compare and Contrast:** How are Romeo's and Juliet's personalities similar and different?

_____

_____

2. **Evaluate:** Do you think that Shakespeare's description of Romeo's behavior in Act I accurately portrays a teenager in love? Explain.

_____

_____

3. **Literary Analysis:** Using the chart below, explain what the **dialogue** involving the Nurse, Juliet, and Lady Capulet in Act I, Scene iii reveals about each character.

Character	Dialogue	Reveals

4. **Reading Skill: Use text aids** to restate in your own words Capulet's scolding of Tybalt in Act I, Scene v, lines 77–87.

_____

_____

_____

Writing: Letter to an Advice Columnist

As either Romeo or Juliet, write a **letter to an advice columnist**. Make a list of
questions for the advice columnist. Use the reasons that the love is considered
unacceptable to create your questions. For example, suppose one of the reasons
is "My family refuses to accept our relationship." Your question for the columnist
could be, "How can I get my family to accept the one I love?"

_____

_____

_____

_____

_____

Use your notes to help write your letter.

Listening and Speaking: Staged Performance

Use the following chart to prepare for your staged performance of a scene from
Act I. Make notes critiquing your group's work, and the work of other groups.

Scene: _____

Characters in Scene: _____

Role Assignments: _____

_____

Critique of My Group's Work: _____

_____

Critique of Other Group's Work: _____

_____

The Tragedy of Romeo and Juliet, Act II, Scene ii

Literary Analysis

Blank verse is unrhymed poetry written in a meter called iambic pentameter. A line written in iambic pentameter includes five stressed syllables, each preceded by an unstressed syllable, as in the following example:

> Bût sôft! Whât light thrôugh yônder window breaks?
> Iî is the east, and Júliet is the sun!

Much of *The Tragedy of Romeo and Juliet* is written in blank verse. Shakespeare uses its formal meter to reinforce a character's rank. Important or aristocratic characters typically speak in blank verse. Minor or comic characters often do not speak in verse.

Using your understanding of blank verse, complete the chart below to identify a character's rank in the play. Circle *Formal* or *Informal* to describe the character's speech. Write in an action that tells you about his or her rank. Then, check the box that indicates what his or her rank is.

Character's Speech	Character's Action	Character's Rank
• Formal • Informal		☐ Important ☐ Minor ☐ Aristocrat ☐ Commoner

Reading Skill

Summarizing is briefly stating the main points of a piece of writing. Stopping periodically to summarize what you have read helps you check your comprehension before you read further.

Summarizing is especially useful when reading a play that has long passages of blank verse. When you encounter one of these passages, **read in sentences**—just as if you were reading a poem. Pause according to punctuation instead of at the end of each line. As you become more accustomed to the form, you will be able to increase your speed.

Once you have grasped the meanings of individual sentences in blank verse, you can more easily and more accurately summarize long passages.

The Tragedy of Romeo and Juliet, Act II, Scene ii

William Shakespeare

Summary Romeo visits Juliet at night. He calls to Juliet from below her window and speaks of his love for her. They agree that their love is stronger than the hatred between their families. Juliet wants proof that Romeo's love will last. Romeo promises that he will send word the next day about his plans to marry her.

Note-taking Guide

Use this chart to record the causes and effects of events in Act II, Scene ii.

Cause	→	Effect/Cause	→	Effect/Cause
Juliet wants proof that Romeo's love for her will last.				

The Tragedy of Romeo and Juliet, Act II, Scene ii

William Shakespeare

A feud is a bitter hatred between two families. Romeo and Juliet may come from feuding families, but they are determined to be together. In the previous act, Romeo met Juliet in disguise at a costume ball and they fell in love. In this scene he makes the risky journey in the dark of night to proclaim his love for Juliet.

Scene ii. CAPULET's orchard.

> **ROMEO.** (*Coming forward*) He jests at scars that
> never felt a wound.

(Enters JULIET *at a window.*)

> But soft! What light through yonder window breaks?
> It is the East, and Juliet is the sun!
> Arise, fair sun, and kill the envious moon,
> 5 Who is already sick and pale with grief
> That thou her maid art far more fair than she.
> Be not her maid, since she is envious.
> Her vestal <u>livery1</u> is but sick and green,
> And none but fools do wear it. Cast it off.
> 10 It is my lady! O, it is my love!
> O, that she knew she were!
> She speaks, yet she says nothing. What of that?
> Her eye discourses; I will answer it.
> I am too bold; 'tis not to me she speaks.
> 15 Two of the fairest stars in all the heaven,
> Having some business, do entreat her eyes
> To twinkle in their spheres² till they return.
> What if her eyes were there, they in her head?
> The brightness of her cheek would shame those stars
> 20 As daylight doth a lamp; her eyes in heaven
> Would through the airy region stream so bright
> That birds would sing and think it were not night.
> See how she leans her cheek upon that hand,
> O, that I were a glove upon that hand,
> That I might touch that cheek!

> **JULIET.**   Ay me!

> 25 **ROMEO.**   She speaks.
> O, speak again, bright angel, for thou art
> As glorious to this night, being o'er my head,

---

1. **livery** clothing or costume worn by a servant.

2. **spheres** orbits.

Activate Prior Knowledge

This scene is taken from a famous play. What do you know about the characters Romeo and Juliet?

_____

_____

_____

_____

_____

Literary Analysis

In most of this scene, the characters speak in **blank verse.** Blank verse consists of unrhymed lines with ten syllables per line: five stressed and five unstressed. Underline the line in the first bracketed passage that breaks the ten-syllable pattern.

Reading Skill

The key to reading **blank verse** is **reading in sentences.** A sentence ends only where a period, a question mark, or an exclamation point appears. The end of a line is not necessarily the end of a sentence. In the second bracketed passage, circle the beginning and end of the sentence.

Reading Check

Whom does Romeo see at the window? Circle the text that tells you.

TAKE NOTES

Stop to Reflect

Why are Romeo and Juliet concerned about their families' names?

_____

_____

_____

Reading Skill

Summarizing is briefly stating the main points of a piece of writing. You can summarize to make sure that you understand what you have read. Summarize the underlined text in which Juliet talks about Romeo's name.

_____

_____

_____

_____

Literary Analysis 🔍

Read line 57. How do the stressed syllables of the **blank verse** reinforce Romeo's meaning?

_____

_____

_____

Reading Check

Why is Romeo's name hateful to him? Underline the sentence that tells you.

_____

As is a wingèd messenger of heaven
Unto the white-upturnèd wond'ring eyes
30 Of mortals that fall back to gaze on him
When he bestrides the lazy puffing clouds
And sails upon the bosom of the air.

JULIET. O Romeo, Romeo! Wherefore art thou Romeo?[3]
Deny thy father and refuse thy name;
35 Or, if thou wilt not, be but sworn my love,
And I'll no longer be a Capulet.

ROMEO. *(Aside)* Shall I hear more, or shall I speak
at this?

JULIET. 'Tis but thy name that is my enemy.
Thou art thyself, though not[4] a Montague.
40 What's Montague? It is nor hand, nor foot,
Nor arm, nor face, nor any other part
Belonging to a man. O, be some other name!
What's in a name? That which we call a rose
By any other name would smell as sweet.
45 So Romeo would, were he not Romeo called,
Retain that dear perfection which he owes[5]
Without that title. Romeo, doff[6] thy name;
And for thy name, which is no part of thee,
Take all myself.

ROMEO.   I take thee at thy word.
50 Call me but love, and I'll be new baptized;
Henceforth I never will be Romeo.

JULIET. What man art thou, thus bescreened in night,
So stumblest on my counsel?[7]

ROMEO.   By a name
I know not how to tell thee who I am.
55 My name, dear saint, is hateful to myself
Because it is an enemy to thee.
Had I it written, I would tear the word.

JULIET. My ears have yet not drunk a hundred words
Of thy tongue's uttering, yet I know the sound.
60 Art thou not Romeo, and a Montague?

ROMEO. Neither, fair maid, if either thee dislike.

JULIET. How camest thou hither, tell me, and
wherefore?
The orchard walls are high and hard to climb,

---

3. **Wherefore ... Romeo?** Why are you Romeo—a Montague?

4. **though not** even if you were not.

5. **owes** owns; possesses.

6. **doff** remove.

7. **counsel** secret thoughts.

And the place death, considering who thou art,
65   If any of my kinsmen find thee here.

ROMEO. With love's light wings did I o'erperch[8] these
          walls;
      For stony limits cannot hold love out,
      And what love can do, that dares love attempt.
      Therefore thy kinsmen are no stop to me.

70 JULIET. If they do see thee, they will murder thee.

ROMEO. Alack, there lies more peril in thine eye
      Than twenty of their swords! Look thou but sweet,
      And I am proof[9] against their enmity.

JULIET. I would not for the world they saw thee here.

75 ROMEO. I have night's cloak to hide me from their
          eyes;
      And but[10] thou love me, let them find me here.
      My life were better ended by their hate
      Than death prorogued,[11] wanting of thy love.

JULIET. By whose direction found'st thou out this
          place?

80 ROMEO. By love, that first did prompt me to inquire.
      He lent me counsel, and I lent him eyes.
      I am no pilot; yet, wert thou as far
      As that vast shore washed with the farthest sea,
      I should adventure[12] for such merchandise.

85 JULIET. Thou knowest the mask of night is on my face;
      Else would a maiden blush bepaint my cheek
      For that which thou hast heard me speak tonight.
      Fain would I dwell on form[13]—fain, fain deny
      What I have spoke; but farewell compliment![14]
90   Dost thou love me? I know thou wilt say "Ay";
      And I will take thy word. Yet, if thou swear'st,
      Thou mayst prove false. At lovers' perjuries,
      They say Jove laughs. O gentle Romeo,
      If thou dost love, pronounce it faithfully.
95   Or if thou thinkest I am too quickly won,
      I'll frown and be perverse[15] and say thee nay,
      So thou wilt woo; but else, not for the world.
      In truth, fair Montague, I am too fond,[16]

Reading Check

What is Juliet unsure about? Circle the lines in which Juliet expresses doubt.

Literary Analysis

Read lines 80–84, stressing every second syllable. Place an accent mark (') above each stressed syllable. **Blank verse** has a formal, impressive sound. Why do you think Shakespeare uses this type of verse for important, noble characters?

_____

_____

_____

Stop to Reflect

Is Juliet's concern about how Romeo thinks of her similar to concerns voiced by couples today? Explain.

_____

_____

_____

_____

8. **o'erperch** fly over.

9. **proof** protected, as by armor.

10. **And but** unless

11. **prorogued** postponed.

12. **adventure** risk a long journey, like a sea adventurer.

13. **Fain . . . form** eagerly would I follow convention (by acting reserved).

14. **compliment** conventional behavior.

15. **be perverse** act contrary to my true feelings.

16. **fond** affectionate.

© Pearson Education

Literary Analysis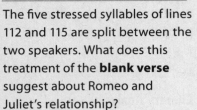

The five stressed syllables of lines 112 and 115 are split between the two speakers. What does this treatment of the **blank verse** suggest about Romeo and Juliet's relationship?

_____

_____

_____

Reading Skill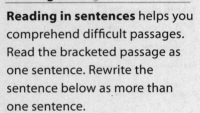

Reading in sentences helps you comprehend difficult passages. Read the bracketed passage as one sentence. Rewrite the sentence below as more than one sentence.

_____

_____

Reading Check

Why doesn't Juliet want Romeo to swear by the moon? Circle the text that tells you.

And therefore thou mayst think my havior light;[17]

100 But trust me, gentleman, I'll prove more true
Than those that have more cunning to be strange.[18]
I should have been more strange, I must confess,
But that thou overheard'st, ere I was ware,
My truelove passion. Therefore pardon me,

105 And not impute this yielding to light love,
Which the dark night hath so discoverèd.[19]

ROMEO. Lady, by yonder blessèd moon I vow,
That tips with silver all these fruit-tree tops—

JULIET. O, swear not by the moon, th' inconstant moon,

110 That monthly changes in her circle orb,
Lest that thy love prove likewise variable.

ROMEO. What shall I swear by?

JULIET. Do not swear at all;
Or if thou wilt, swear by thy gracious self,
Which is the god of my idolatry,
And I'll believe thee.

115 **ROMEO.** If my heart's dear love—

JULIET. Well, do not swear. Although I joy in thee,
I have no joy of this contract[20] tonight.
It is too rash, too unadvised, too sudden;
Too like the lightning, which doth cease to be

120 Ere one can say it lightens. Sweet, good night!
This bud of love, by summer's ripening breath,
May prove a beauteous flow'r when next we meet.
Good night, good night! As sweet repose and rest
Come to thy heart as that within my breast!

125 **ROMEO.** O, wilt thou leave me so unsatisfied?

JULIET. What satisfaction canst thou have tonight?

ROMEO. Th'exchange of thy love's faithful vow for mine.

JULIET. I gave thee mine before thou didst request it;
And yet I would it were to give again.

130 **ROMEO.** Wouldst thou withdraw it? For what purpose, love?

Vocabulary Development

cunning (KUN ing) *n.* cleverness; slyness

17. **my havior light** my behavior immodest or unserious.

18. **strange** distant and cold.

19. **discoverèd** revealed.

20. **contract** betrothal.

JULIET. But to be frank[21] and give it thee again.
And yet I wish but for the thing I have.
My bounty[22] is as boundless as the sea,
My love as deep; the more I give to thee,
135   The more I have, for both are infinite,
I hear some noise within. Dear love, adieu!

(NURSE calls within.)

Anon, good nurse! Sweet Montague, be true.
Stay but a little, I will come again.   *(Exit.)*

ROMEO. O blessèd, blessèd night! I am afeard,
140   Being in night, all this is but a dream,
Too flattering-sweet to be substantial.[23]

(Enter JULIET again.)

JULIET. Three words, dear Romeo, and good night
    indeed.
If that thy bent[24] of love be honorable,
Thy purpose marriage, send me word tomorrow,
145   By one that I'll procure to come to thee,
Where and what time thou wilt perform the rite;
And all my fortunes at thy foot I'll lay
And follow thee my lord throughout the world.

NURSE. *(Within)* Madam!

150 **JULIET.** I come anon.—But if thou meanest not well,
I do beseech thee—

NURSE.   *(Within)* Madam!

JULIET.   By and by[25] I come.—
To cease thy strife[26] and leave me to my grief.
Tomorrow will I send.

ROMEO.   So thrive my soul—

JULIET. A thousand times good night!   *(Exit.)*

155 **ROMEO.** A thousand times the worse, to want thy
    light!
Love goes toward love as schoolboys from their
    books;
But love from love, toward school with heavy looks.

---

21. **frank** generous.

22. **bounty** what I have to give.

23. **substantial** real.

24. **bent** purpose; intention.

25. **By and by** at once.

26. **strife** efforts.

Literary Analysis

Two speakers share the rhythm of line 151. Does the Nurse's interruption complete or break the **blank verse**? Explain.

_____

_____

_____

_____

Stop to Reflect 📖

Romeo is expressing his love for Juliet in lines 155–157. What expressions do modern lovers use to show love for one another?

_____

_____

_____

_____

Reading Check

What plans do Romeo and Juliet make for the next day? Circle the text that tells you.

Literary Analysis

Given that Romeo and Juliet speak in **blank verse,** what can you conclude about their position in society?

_____

_____

_____

Reading Skill

For the bracketed lines, **read in sentences.** Underline the words that you think are the most important.

Stop to Reflect 📖

This scene is a very famous love scene. What other love scenes can you think of from movies and books? What do those scenes have in common with this one?

_____

_____

_____

_____

(Enter JULIET again.)

JULIET. Hist! Romeo, hist! O for a falc'ner's voice
   To lure this tassel gentle[27] back again!
160 Bondage is hoarse[28] and may not speak aloud,
   Else would I tear the cave where Echo[29] lies
   And make her airy tongue more hoarse than mine
   With repetition of "My Romeo!"

ROMEO. It is my soul that calls upon my name.
165 How silver-sweet sound lovers' tongues by night,
   Like softest music to attending ears!

JULIET. Romeo!

ROMEO.   My sweet?

JULIET.   What o'clock tomorrow
   Shall I send to thee?

ROMEO.   By the hour of nine.

JULIET. I will not fail. 'Tis twenty year till then.
170 I have forgot why I did call thee back.

ROMEO. Let me stand here till thou remember it.

JULIET. I shall forget, to have thee still stand there,
   Rememb'ring how I love thy company.

ROMEO. And I'll stay, to have thee still forget,
175 Forgetting any other home but this.

JULIET. 'Tis almost morning. I would have thee gone—
   And yet no farther than a wanton's[30] bird,
   That lets it hop a little from his hand,
   Like a poor prisoner in his twisted gyves,[31]
180 And with a silken thread plucks it back again,
   So loving-jealous of his liberty.

ROMEO. I would I were thy bird.

JULIET.   Sweet, so would I.
   Yet I should kill thee with much cherishing.
   Good night, good night! Parting is such sweet
      sorrow
185 That I shall say good night till it be morrow.   *(Exit.)*

27. **tassel gentle** male falcon.

28. **Bondage is hoarse** being bound in by my family restricts my speech.

29. **Echo** In classical mythology, the nymph Echo, unable to win the love of Narcissus, wasted away in a cave until nothing was left of her but her voice.

30. **wanton's** spoiled, playful child's.

31. **gyves** (jīvz) chains.

ROMEO. Sleep dwell upon thine eyes, peace in thy
     breast!
  Would I were sleep and peace, so sweet to rest!
  Hence will I to my ghostly friar's[32] close cell,[33]
  His help to crave and my dear hap[34] to tell.   *(Exit.)*

Reader's Response: Did you like the characters of Romeo and
Juliet? Why or why not?

_____

_____

_____

_____

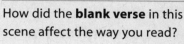

Literary Analysis

How did the **blank verse** in this
scene affect the way you read?

_____

_____

_____

_____

Reading Check

Where is Romeo going at the end
of the scene? Circle the text that
tells you.

---

32. **ghostly friar's** spiritual father's.

33. **close cell** small room.

34. **dear hap** good fortune.

The Tragedy of Romeo and Juliet, Act II, Scene ii

1. **Interpret:** What role does darkness play in this scene?

_____

_____

_____

2. **Evaluate:** Why do you think this love scene is one of the most famous dramatic scenes in literature?

_____

_____

_____

3. **Literary Analysis:** Using the chart below, rewrite the following line, marking stressed and unstressed syllables. Then, identify the key words stressed in the line. Explain why those words are significant to the meaning of the line.

   JULIET. Three words dear Romeo and good night indeed.

Blank Verse Pattern	Key Words	Why are the stressed words important ones?

4. **Reading Skill:** How many sentences are in lines 1–25, Romeo's first speech of Act II, Scene ii?

_____

Writing: Parody

A parody uses humor to mock the characteristics of a piece of writing. Write a **parody** of the famous balcony scene in Romeo and Juliet. The following chart will help you decide what elements of the scene you could make light of.

Parody of the Balcony Scene	
Original Element	How can I make light of this element?
Setting	
Characters	
Dialogue	
Outcome of the scene	

Use the information from the graphic organizer to determine what the main focus of your parody will be.

Research and Technology: Annotated Flowchart

Create an **annotated flowchart** that shows and explains the structure of the nobility in sixteenth-century Verona. Use text and images to show the relative rank of the Prince, Count Paris, the Montagues, and the Capulets. Use library and Internet resources to do your research.

Prince Escalus: _____

Count Paris: _____

Capulets: _____

_____

Montagues: _____

_____

Friar Lawrence: _____

The Tragedy of Romeo and Juliet, Act III

Literary Analysis

Plays often include these types of **dramatic speeches:**

- **Soliloquy:** a lengthy speech in which a character—usually alone on stage—expresses his or her true thoughts or feelings. Soliloquies are unheard by other characters.

- **Aside:** a character's revealing of his or her true thoughts or feelings in a remark that is unheard by other characters.

- **Monologue:** a lengthy speech by one person. Unlike a soliloquy, a monologue is addressed to other characters.

Dramatic speeches often include **allusions**. Allusions are references to well-known people, places, or events from mythology or literature. An example is found in Act II. Mercutio insultingly calls Tybalt "Prince of Cats." He is alluding to a cat named Tybalt in French fables.

Consider what each type of speech reveals about the speaker and his or her relationships with other characters. Use the chart below to note the effect of any allusions you find.

Reading Skill

Summarizing is briefly stating the main points in a piece of writing. You should **paraphrase** a long passage of a play before summarizing it. To **paraphrase** means to restate the lines in your own words. For example, compare these two versions of a speech by Romeo:

Shakespeare's version: "This gentleman, the prince's near ally / My very friend hath got his mortal hurt / In my behalf . . . ."

Paraphrase: My good friend is a close relative of the prince. He has been fatally wounded defending me.

You can more easily and accurately summarize an entire passage after you have paraphrased small portions of text.

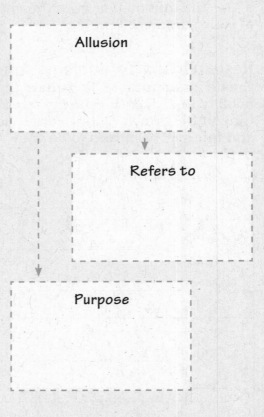

Allusion

↓

Refers to

↓

Purpose

The Tragedy of Romeo and Juliet, Act III

William Shakespeare

Summary Romeo and Juliet are secretly married. They spend one night together before Romeo must leave. Juliet's cousin Tybalt kills Mercutio. Romeo kills Tybalt and is not allowed to return to Verona. The Capulets plan to marry Juliet to Paris.

Note-taking Guide

Use this flowchart to describe the connections between events in Act III.

Cause	→	Effect/Cause	→	Effect
Tybalt kills Mercutio.				

The Tragedy of Romeo and Juliet, Act III

1. **Infer:** Look at the chart below. The first column contains one of Mercutio's dying remarks regarding the Montagues and Capulets. Mercutio repeats this remark three times. Explain what Mercutio means by this exclamation in the second column.

Mercutio's Dying Remark	
What Does He Say?	What Does It Mean?
"A plague on both your houses."	

2. **Interpret:** Romeo kills Tybalt. What does Romeo mean when he says "I am fortune's fool"?

_____

_____

_____

3. **Literary Analysis:** What thoughts and feelings does Juliet express in the **soliloquy** that opens Scene ii of Act III?

_____

_____

_____

4. **Reading Skill: Paraphrase** lines 29–51 in Act III, Scene iii.

_____

_____

_____

_____

Writing: Editorial

Write an **editorial** that addresses the Prince's response to the deaths of Tybalt and Mercutio.

- Summarize the Prince's response.

  _____

  _____

- Was Romeo's punishment fair? Why or why not?

  _____

  _____

- Would a different punishment have been more appropriate?

  _____

  _____

Include the answers in your editorial.

Research and Technology: Film Review

Present a **film review** of Prokofiev's ballet for your classmates. Your review of the film should say more than "It was good," or "It was bad." Be specific and use strong supporting details when you state your opinion. With your group, use the following chart to develop notes for your film review.

Dancing	Music	Camera Angles
_____	_____	_____
_____	_____	_____
_____	_____	_____

Our Opinion of the Film: _____

Support for Our Opinion: _____

_____

The Tragedy of Romeo and Juliet, Act IV

Literary Analysis

Dramatic irony is a contradiction between what a character thinks and says and what the audience or reader knows is true. Dramatic irony involves the audience emotionally in the story.

Shakespeare knew his audience could become *too* involved in the intense emotion of *Romeo and Juliet*. He made sure to include the following elements to lighten the play's mood:

- **Comic relief:** a technique used to interrupt a serious scene by introducing a humorous character or situation
- **Puns:** plays on words involving a word with multiple meanings or two words that sound alike but have different meanings.

Notice how Shakespeare uses dramatic irony, comic relief, and puns to balance emotional suspense with laughter and wit.

Reading Skill

Summarizing is briefly stating the main points in a piece of writing. Stopping periodically to summarize what you have read helps you check your comprehension before you read further.

You should **break down long sentences** before you summarize a long passage of Shakespearean dialogue.

- Separate sentences that have multiple subjects and verbs into smaller sentences with one subject and one verb.
- Treat colons, semicolons, and dashes as periods.

Use the chart below to help you break down long sentences.

Line of Dialogue	Line in Smaller Sentences	Summary of Line

The Tragedy of Romeo and Juliet, Act IV
William Shakespeare

Summary Juliet promises her parents that she will marry Paris. She then drinks a potion that makes her appear lifeless. The Capulets find Juliet and mourn, thinking that their daughter is dead.

Note-taking Guide
Use this character wheel to record details about Juliet and her actions in Act IV.

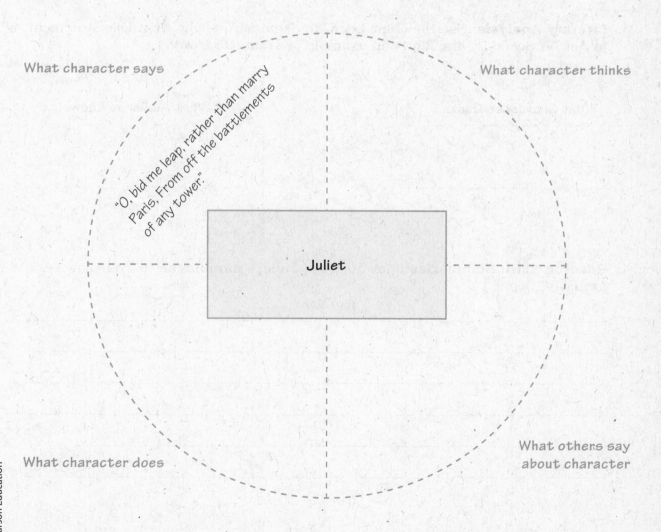

What character says

What character thinks

"O, bid me leap, rather than marry Paris, From off the battlements of any tower."

Juliet

What character does

What others say about character

The Tragedy of Romeo and Juliet, Act IV

1. **Respond:** Should Romeo and Juliet have followed Friar Lawrence's advice? Why or why not?

   _____

   _____

2. **Interpret:** What does Juliet's **soliloquy** in Act IV, Scene iii reveal about her personality?

   _____

   _____

3. **Literary Analysis:** Use the chart below to demonstrate why Capulet's statement in Act IV, Scene iv, line 25, is an example of **dramatic irony**.

   What Character Thinks   **What Audience Knows**

4. **Reading Skill: Summarize** lines 50–54 of Juliet's **monologue** to Friar Lawrence in Act IV, Scene i.

   _____

   _____

   _____

   _____

   _____

Writing: Abstract

Write an **abstract,** or summary, of what has happened so far in *Romeo and Juliet.*

Review Acts I–IV. Choose two major events in each act for your abstract. Ask yourself these questions to determine whether an event is important.

- How does this event move the plot forward?

  _____

  _____

  _____

- How does this event add to the larger meaning of the play?

  _____

  _____

  _____

The mood can often be described in one word, such as *frightening, serious,* or *funny.*

- What are four adjectives that could describe the mood of the play?

  _____

  _____

Use the answers to these questions to write your abstract.

Research and Technology: Multimedia Presentation

With your partner, use a chart to take notes for your multimedia presentation on Renaissance music.

Notes on Act IV, Scene V: _____

Styles/Types of Renaissance Music: _____

_____

Renaissance Musical Instruments: _____

Sources I Used for Information: _____

_____

© Pearson Education

The Tragedy of Romeo and Juliet, Act V

Literary Analysis

A **tragedy** is a drama in which the central character, who is of noble stature, meets with disaster or great misfortune. The tragic hero's downfall is usually the result of one of the following:

- *fate*, or the idea of a preplanned destiny

- a serious character flaw

- some combination of both

Motive is an important element of a tragic hero's character. A character's motive is the reason for his or her thoughts or actions. The hero's motives are basically good in many of Shakespeare's tragedies. The hero suffers a tragic fate that may seem undeserved.

Tragedies are sad. They can also be uplifting. They show the greatness and nobility of the human spirit when faced with grave challenges. Consider what positive message might be conveyed by the play's tragic events as you read the conclusion of *Romeo and Juliet*.

Reading Skill

Summarizing is briefly stating the main points in a piece of writing. In summarizing the action, it is useful to first **identify causes and effects**.

- A *cause* is an event, action, or emotion that produces a result.

- An *effect* is the result produced by the cause.

Tragedies often involve a chain of events that advance the plot and lead to the final tragic outcome. Understanding the sequence of causes and effects will help you summarize complicated plots like the one in *Romeo and Juliet*. Use the chart below to record causes and effects as you read Act V.

Cause	Effect/Cause	Effect

The Tragedy of Romeo and Juliet, Act V

William Shakespeare

Summary Romeo learns of Juliet's death. He buys poison and goes to her tomb. He kills Paris. Romeo finds Juliet's seemingly lifeless body. He drinks the poison and dies. Juliet wakes up. She sees Romeo and stabs herself. The Montagues and the Capulets agree to end their fighting.

Note-taking Guide

Use this timeline to record the most important events in Act V.

Beginning Event
Romeo hears of Juliet's death.

Final Event

The Tragedy of Romeo and Juliet, Act V

1. **Respond:** Were you surprised by the way in which this play ends? Why or why not?

   _____

   _____

2. **Make a Judgment:** Is the end of long-term violence between their families a fair exchange for the deaths of Romeo and Juliet? Explain.

   _____

   _____

   _____

3. **Literary Analysis:** Use the chart below to identify details of the elements that contribute to the **tragedy** in the play.

Romeo's and Juliet's Personalities	Fate or Chance	Other Causes

4. **Reading Skill: Summarize** the events that occur at the tomb.

   _____

   _____

   _____

   _____

Writing: Persuasive Letter

Imagine that you are Friar Lawrence. Write a **persuasive letter** to Lord Capulet and to Lord Montague, urging them to end their feud.

- Fill in the chart below with three persuasive reasons for ending the feud.

Why the Capulets and Montagues Should End Their Feud		
First Reason:	Second Reason:	Third Reason:

- Rank your reasons in order of importance: most important, second, third.

  Use your notes to write your persuasive letter.

Listening and Speaking: Mock Trial

With your group, make notes to prepare for your mock trial.

Role Assignments: _____

_____

Depositions/Statements: _____

_____

_____

_____

Questioning/Cross-Examination of Witnesses: _____

_____

_____

_____

_____

Expository Texts

About Expository Texts

The purpose of an **expository text** is to convey information to the reader on a particular topic. There are many types of expository texts. Some examples include

- **a Web site**—a group of Internet pages written and published for a particular reason. Not all Web sites are expository.

- **a newspaper article**—a short online or printed text that provides facts, details, and quotations

Reading Skill

Media are the different sources that report on subjects and events. There are many types of media, including newspapers, magazines, television broadcasts, and Web sites. When you read about an event, carefully evaluate the way the event is reported.

Analyze media coverage by considering the audience and purpose of the report. Then, think about how these may affect the text. For example, a newspaper article written for second grade students would probably be very different from one written for ninth grade students. Use this chart to **compare and contrast coverage** of "The Big Event" on the Web site and in the newspaper article.

	Web Site	Newspaper Article
Content		
Audience		
Purpose		
Visuals (photos and graphics)		

THE BIG EVENT

TEXAS A&M
UNIVERSITY

Home
About the Event
For Participants
For Community Residents
Conference
Expansion
Contact

Features:
- headings and sub-headings
- links to further information
- visuals that support the information

ABOUT THE EVENT

In 1982 Joe Nussbaum, then Vice President of the Student Government Association at Texas A&M University, started The BIG Event as a way for students to say "Thank You" to the surrounding community. Nussbaum envisioned a one-day service project where residents of Bryan and College Station would be shown appreciation for their continued support of Texas A&M University students during their college careers. Mr. Nussbaum viewed The BIG Event as a means for students to show their gratitude by completing various tasks at area residents' homes. Joe believed that it was the least the students could do to give one big thanks to their community on one big day each year.

The photographs give information about The BIG Event. **Compare and contrast what you learn from the photographs with what you learn from the text.**

Mission Statement

Through service-oriented activities, The BIG Event promotes campus and community unity as students come together for one day to express their gratitude for the support from the surrounding community.

Core Values

The BIG Event at Texas A&M University is an organization which strives to uphold the ideals of unity and service. This one-day event is not based on socioeconomic need, but rather a way for the student body to express their gratitude to the entire community which supports Texas A&M. It is important to remember The BIG Event is not about the number of jobs completed or the number of students who participate each year. Instead, it is the interaction between students and residents, and the unity that results throughout the community that makes The BIG Event such a unique project.

The BIG Event is the largest, one-day, student-run service project in the nation where students of Texas A&M University come together to say 'thank you' to the residents of Bryan and College Station. For the past 26 years, Aggie students have participated in this annual event to show their appreciation to the surrounding community by completing service projects such as yard work, window washing, and painting for community members. Although The BIG Event has become the largest one-day, student-run service project in the nation, our message and our mission remains the same—to simply say "thank you."

The BIG Event is a proud member of the Student Government Association at Texas A&M and a recognized student organization of Texas A&M University.

The Mission Statement tells the goal of The BIG Event. These sections of the text give specific details about the event.

THE BIG

Do our differences define us?
How does The BIG Event work to support unity within the community?

Features:

- attention-grabbing title
- facts and details
- quotations from witnesses or participants

A&M students help out in 'big' way

By JOHN BRADEN
Eagle Staff Writer

With 10,600 students signed up for 1,000 jobs Saturday, Texas A&M University's Big Event was the largest in the program's history.

Big Event director Anna Rash said she was proud of everybody for reaching that milestone.

"This was the first time we were able to break 1,000 jobs," Rash said.

Since the Big Event began in 1982, student volunteers have logged more than 500,000 hours of community service, making it the largest one-day collegiate community service project in the nation, according to the Texas A&M Student Government Association.

College Station resident Poppy Capehart, who graduated from Texas A&M in 1975, and his wife, Tracey, class of 2005, said this was the first time the Big Event had come to their home.

The writer quotes participants in order to present a personal view of the Big Event.

"It's a great chance for us to meet students, and I thought I could make a great contribution," Poppy Capehart said. "My daughter, class of 2006, was in the Aggie Band and participated in Big Event every year she was a student, and I'm glad that we get to participate now also."

Senior Kajay Rainey, site leader for Delta Zeta at the Capehart residence, said the main goal of the Big Event was to better the community in any way possible.

"This is just a great way for us to show everyone that we, as a Greek organization, do other things besides stereotypical Greek life," Rainey said. "It helps give A&M a good name and shows that the students care about this city and want to help out."

Meghan LePage was the freshman Delta Zeta job site leader at the Wellborn Cemetery, where the teams were responsible for cleaning up and pulling weeds around the graves.

"Everybody needs help of some kind, no matter what they do or where they work," LePage said.

Fellow Delta Zeta freshman Hanna Skinner said her interest in the volunteer project started when she came to visit A&M on Big Event weekend last year.

"My friends at other schools wouldn't believe we are doing stuff like this, and my parents loved the idea of me getting out and volunteering," Skinner said. "I think they got a kick out of me doing manual labor."

Andrew Garcia, sophomore Pi Kappa Phi site leader at the Wellborn Cemetery, said it was an interesting place to work.

"It's different, and a little creepy, but it works," Garcia said. "Even though all the work may seem hard and waking up early on a Saturday may be hard to do, it's worth it in the end. Just knowing that a whole bunch of people got together on one day and were able to accomplish something this huge is a moving experience, even if your job is cleaning a graveyard."

Teams spent all morning and most of the afternoon volunteering at locations all over Bryan, College Station, and neighboring communities.

Members of the coed service fraternity Alpha Pi Omega spent the day working at a daycare center in a Bryan home.

Marsha Mason, the owner of Precious Moments Daycare, expressed appreciation for the hard work A&M students do for the community.

"I have had Big Event students help me for three years, and the thing I like is that they are all volunteers," Mason said. "It is important to have this effort in the community, because a lot of residents can't get out and do the yard work themselves. Our society really appreciates the hard work they do."

Sophomore Stephanie Taylor said that with 50,000 college students in the Bryan-College Station area, it's great that they get to give back at least once a year by doing good for the community.

The writer gives a volunteer's perspective of the event's effects.

"I would tell anybody considering to participate next year that it is definitely worth it," Taylor said. "When you walk out to start your day and there's 10,000 people standing there, ready to work, you just kind of get it. It's an overwhelming sight."

? Do our differences define us?

According to a volunteer, "Everybody needs help . . . no matter what they do or where they work." How does this statement show that perhaps it is our similarities, not our differences, that define us?

Thinking About the Expository Texts

1. What is The Big Event?

   _____

2. Who benefits from The Big Event?

   _____

TALK ABOUT IT **Reading Skill**

3. Explain one similarity between the Web site's and the newspaper's coverage of The Big Event.

   _____

   _____

4. Explain one difference between the Web site's and the newspaper's coverage of The Big Event.

   _____

   _____

WRITE ABOUT IT **Timed Writing: Proposal (20 minutes)**

Write a proposal—a suggestion—to your school's principal. Identify a way to improve your school or community. Then, offer a plan for a way that students can help make the improvement. Support your ideas with facts and examples. Use the following chart to decide on a topic:

Issue	Students could help by	Do I have strong feelings about this issue?

The Inspector-General

Literary Analysis

Comedy is a form of drama that is lighter in mood than tragedy, ends happily, and aims primarily to amuse. The humor in comic plays may arise from one or more of the following elements:

- funny names
- witty dialogue
- comic situations, such as deception by a character, misunderstandings, or mistaken identities

The humor of comic situations often relies on **dramatic irony**. This is a contradiction between what a character thinks and says and what the audience knows to be true. In comedies, the audience often knows the truth about a situation in the play while the characters remain unaware. As a result, the characters' statements and behavior may seem funny to the audience.

Reading Skill

A **conclusion** is a decision or an opinion that you reach based on details in a text. You consider both stated and implied information when you draw conclusions. **Use both dialogue and stage directions** to find meaningful information. This will help you draw conclusions about characters in a play.

- Consider what characters' words suggest about their personalities and circumstances.

- Read stage directions closely for details about the scene, characters' appearances, and characters' behavior. Take note of other information that could prove essential to the plot or ideas expressed in the play.

As you read, use this chart to record conclusions you draw about characters.

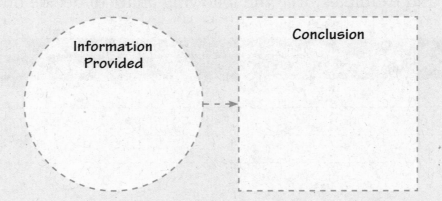

Information Provided

Conclusion

The Inspector-General
Anton Chekhov

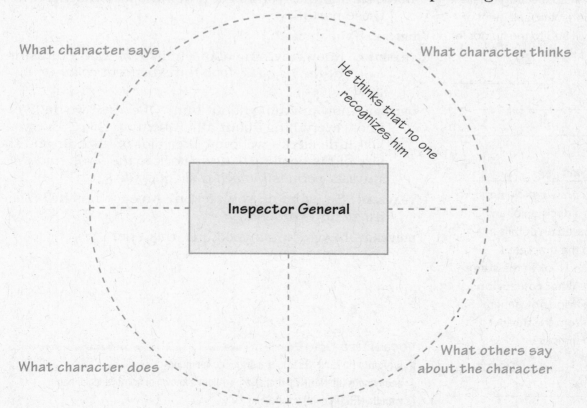

Summary The new inspector-general rides to town in disguise. He has a conversation with the driver. He quickly discovers that his identity is not as secret as he thinks.

Writing About the Big Question

Do our differences define us? In The Inspector-General, the Inspector-General dresses in disguise so people won't know he's on official business. He is different from those around him, though, and the truth is hard to conceal.

A person's background may be difficult to conceal because _____

_____.

Note-taking Guide

Use this character wheel to record details about the inspector-general.

What character says

What character thinks

He thinks that no one recognizes him

Inspector General

What character does

What others say about the character

Activate Prior Knowledge

Think about how you might feel if someone tried to "check up" on you. Perhaps an older brother or sister would try to find out whether you were keeping up with your homework. Describe what your feelings might be.

_____

_____

_____

_____

Literary Analysis 🔍

The humor in **comedy** often comes from comic situations, such as deception by a character, misunderstandings, or mistaken identities. Read the Storyteller's introduction. Which element of comedy will add to the humor in this play? Explain.

_____

_____

_____

Reading Skill

When you draw **conclusions,** you reach a decision or an opinion based on details in a text. Read the bracketed passage, and look at the **stage direction. What conclusion** about the inspector-general can you draw from the traveler smiling to himself?

_____

_____

_____

_____

The Inspector-General
Anton Chekhov
Adapted by Michael Frayn

The curtain goes up to reveal falling snow and a cart facing away from us. Enter the STORYTELLER, *who begins to read the story. Meanwhile, the* TRAVELER *enters. He is a middle-aged man of urban appearance, wearing dark glasses and a long overcoat with its collar turned up. He is carrying a small traveling bag. He climbs into the cart and sits facing us.*

STORYTELLER. The Inspector-General. In deepest incognito, first by express train, then along back roads, Pyotr Pavlovich Posudin[1] was hastening toward the little town of N, to which he had been summoned by an anonymous letter. "I'll take them by surprise," he thought to himself. "I'll come down on them like a thunderbolt out of the blue. I can just imagine their faces when they hear who I am . . ." *[Enter the* DRIVER, *a peasant, who climbs onto the cart, so that he is sitting with his back to us, and the cart begins to trundle slowly away from us.]* And when he'd thought to himself for long enough, he fell into conversation with the driver of the cart. What did he talk about? About himself, of course. *[Exit the* STORYTELLER.*]*

TRAVELER. I gather you've got a new Inspector-General in these parts.

DRIVER. True enough.

TRAVELER. Know anything about him? *[The* DRIVER *turns and looks at the* TRAVELER, *who turns his coat collar up a little higher.]*

DRIVER. Know anything about him? Of course we do! We know everything about all of them up there! Every last little clerk—we know the color of his hair and the size of his boots! *[He turns back to the front, and the* TRAVELER *permits himself a slight smile.]*

TRAVELER. So, what do you reckon? Any good, is he? *[The* DRIVER *turns around.]*

DRIVER. Oh, yes, he's a good one, this one.

Vocabulary Development

incognito (in kahg NEE toh) *n.* a disguised condition
anonymous (uh NAHN uh muhs) *adj.* without a known or acknowledged name
trundle (TRUHN duhl) *v.* roll along

1. **Pyotr Pavlovich Posudin** (PYOH tuhr pahv LOH vich poh SYOO duhn)

TRAVELER. Really?

DRIVER. Did one good thing straight off.

TRAVELER. What was that?

DRIVER. He got rid of the last one. Holy terror he was! Hear him coming five miles off! Say he's going to this little town. Somewhere like we're going, say. He'd let all the world know about it a month before. So now he's on his way, say, and it's like thunder and lightning coming down the road. And when he gets where he's going he has a good sleep, he has a good eat and drink—and then he starts. Stamps his feet, shouts his head off. Then he has another good sleep, and off he goes.

TRAVELER. But the new one's not like that?

DRIVER. Oh, no, the new one goes everywhere on the quiet, like. Creeps around like a cat. Don't want no one to see him, don't want no one to know who he is. Say he's going to this town down the road here. Someone there sent him a letter on the sly, let's say. "Things going on here you should know about." Something of that kind. Well, now, he creeps out of his office, so none of them up there see him go. He hops on a train just like anyone else, just like you or me. Then when he gets off he don't go jumping into a cab or nothing fancy. Oh, no. He wraps himself up from head to toe so you can't see his face, and he wheezes away like an old dog so no one can recognize his voice.

TRAVELER. Wheezes? That's not wheezing! That's the way he talks! So I gather.

DRIVER. Oh, is it? But the tales they tell about him. You'd laugh till you burst your tripes![2]

TRAVELER. *[sourly.]* I'm sure I would.

DRIVER. He drinks, mind!

TRAVELER. *[startled.]* Drinks?

DRIVER. Oh, like a hole in the ground. Famous for it.

TRAVELER. He's never touched a drop! I mean, from what I've heard.

DRIVER. Oh, not in public, no. Goes to some great ball— "No thank you, not for me." Oh, no, he puts it away at home! Wakes up in the morning, rubs his eyes, and the first thing he does, he shouts, "Vodka!" So in runs his valet with a glass. Fixed himself up a tube behind his desk, he has. Leans down, takes a pull on it, no one the wiser.

TRAVELER. *[offended.]* How do you know all this, may I ask?

Reading Skill

Read the first bracketed passage. Underline three details that tell how the driver thinks the new inspector will act. What **conclusion** can you draw about what the driver knows about the traveler?

_____

_____

_____

_____

Literary Analysis

Comedy is a form of drama that ends happily and is meant to amuse. **Dramatic irony** happens when a character thinks and says one thing and the audience knows something else is true. Read the second bracketed passage. How does your knowledge of the traveler's identity make this dialogue humorous?

_____

_____

_____

_____

_____

_____

Reading Check ✏

Why was the previous inspector not good at his job? Underline two details that tell you.

© Pearson Education

Reading Skill

Underline the **stage direction** that tells what the traveler does when the driver mentions the inspector-general's bottle of vodka. Based on this action, what **conclusion** do you draw about the traveler?

_____

_____

_____

_____

Literary Analysis

Comedy can be based on comic situations in which a character tries to fool or trick another character. How is the traveler trying to fool the driver? How is the driver trying to trick the traveler?

_____

_____

_____

_____

Stop to Reflect

Who do you think is the wiser and cleverer man, the driver or the traveler? Explain.

_____

_____

_____

_____

_____

DRIVER. Can't hide it from the servants, can you? The valet and the coachman have got tongues in their heads. Then again, he's on the road, say, going about his business, and he keeps the bottle in his little bag. [*The* TRAVELER *discreetly pushes the traveling bag out of the* DRIVER'*s sight.*] And his housekeeper . . .

TRAVELER. What about her?

DRIVER. Runs circles around him, she does, like a fox round his tail. She's the one who wears the trousers.[3] The people aren't half so frightened of him as they are of her.

TRAVELER. But at least he's good at his job, you say?

DRIVER. Oh, he's a blessing from heaven, I'll grant him that.

TRAVELER. Very <u>cunning</u>—you were saying.

DRIVER. Oh, he creeps around all right.

TRAVELER. And then he pounces, yes? I should think some people must get the surprise of their life, mustn't they?

DRIVER. No, no—let's be fair, now. Give him his due. He don't make no trouble.

TRAVELER. No, I mean, if no one knows he's coming . . .

DRIVER. Oh, that's what he thinks, but we all know.

TRAVELER. You know?

DRIVER. Oh, some gentleman gets off the train at the station back there with his greatcoat up to his eyebrows and says, "No, I don't want a cab, thank you, just an ordinary horse and cart for me." Well, we'd put two and two together, wouldn't we! Say it was you, now, creeping along down the road here. The lads would be down there in a cab by now! By the time you got there the whole town would be as regular as clockwork! And you'd think to yourself, "Oh, look at that! As clean as a whistle! And they didn't know I was coming!" No, that's why he's such a blessing after the other one. This one believes it!

TRAVELER. Oh, I see.

DRIVER. What, you thought we wouldn't know him? Why, we've got the electric telegraph these days!

Vocabulary Development

discreetly (di SKREET lee) *adv.* without drawing attention
cunning (KUN ing) *adj.* skilled in deception

3. **wears the trousers** has the greatest authority; is really in charge.

Take today, now. I'm going past the station back there this morning, and the fellow who runs the buffet comes out like a bolt of lightning. Arms full of baskets and bottles. "Where are you off to?" I say. "Doing drinks and refreshments for the Inspector-General!" he says, and he jumps into a carriage and goes flying off down the road here. So there's the old Inspector-General, all muffled up like a roll of carpet, going secretly along in a cart somewhere—and when he gets there, nothing to be seen but vodka and cold salmon!

TRAVELER. *[shouts].* Right—turn around, then . . . !

DRIVER. *[to the horse].* Whoa, boy! Whoa! *[To the* TRAVELER.*]* Oh, so what's this, then? Don't want to go running into the Inspector-General, is that it? *[The* TRAVELER *gestures impatiently for the* DRIVER *to turn the cart around.* DRIVER *to the horse.]* Back we go, then, boy. Home we go. *[He turns the cart around, and the* TRAVELER *takes a swig from his traveling bag.]* Though if I know the old devil, he's like as not turned around and gone home again himself. *[Blackout.]*

Reader's Response: Think of the last time you caught someone trying to fool or deceive you. How did you feel when you realized what was happening?

_____

_____

_____

_____

Literary Analysis

Underline one sentence in the bracketed passage that is an example of **dramatic irony**. Explain why you chose this sentence.

_____

_____

_____

_____

Reading Skill 📖

At the very end of the play, the stage directions say that the traveler "takes a swig from his traveling bag." What **conclusion** can you draw from the traveler's action?

_____

_____

_____

_____

Reading Check

How do you know that the town expects the inspector-general's arrival? Underline the sentence that tells you.

The Inspector-General

1. **Interpret:** The driver tells the traveler that the town is preparing for the inspector-general's arrival. Why does the driver's account provoke the traveler's demand to turn the cart around?

_____

_____

2. **Respond:** Use the chart below to gain a better understanding of "The Inspector-General." In the first column, write questions you still have about the play after you have read it. Find details in the play that could help you answer each question. The details you find may tell you about the characters, the place, or the events. Use the details you find to help answer your questions. For each question, write your answer in the third column.

Questions	Details	Understanding of the Play

3. **Literary Analysis:** Note specific ways in which "The Inspector-General" does or does not meet these criteria for **comedy:** it ends happily; it uses witty dialogue; it presents a comic situation; it seeks to amuse.

_____

_____

_____

4. **Reading Skill:** What **conclusions** can you draw about the character of the Driver based on his dialogue with the Traveler? Explain your answer.

_____

_____

Writing: Play

Write a short **play** in which a bully is outsmarted by his or her classmates. Answer the following prompts. Use your notes to write your play.

- Describe a realistic school setting.

_____

_____

- Describe a scene in which the audience knows something that the bully does not know.

_____

_____

_____

_____

- Write some examples of realistic dialogue.

_____

_____

_____

Research and Technology: Informational Chart

Use the chart below to record notes for your informational chart about life in Russia during the rule of the czars.

Facts About Peasant Life: _____

_____

Facts About the Nobility: _____

_____

Facts About Inspector-General: _____

_____

My Sources of Information: _____

_____

Web Sites

About Web Sites

A **Web site** is a collection of information found at a given address on the World Wide Web. A **browser** is a piece of software that you can use to go to a Web site on the Internet. Type a Web address (also called a URL) or click on a link. Usually, you will come to a **home page**. Web sites often have these parts:

- A place to type in a **keyword** so that the browser will search the site for the information you want. A pull-down search gives a list of choices.
- A bulletin board that lists news or questions about the site
- An **e-mail address**

Reading Skill

Some Web sites give true information. Others do not. You do not want to be misled. It is always important to **evaluate sources.** Find the sponsor of the Web site. Decide whether you can trust the sponsor.

Look at the URL ending. It tells you what kind of organization is sponsoring the Web site.

Evaluating Sources

- Is the main idea fully supported by the evidence?
- Are the author's arguments logical and valid?
- Does support consist of specific facts?
- Can the evidence presented be verified?
- Is the material presented in an impartial way?
- Who is the author or sponsor of the site?
  - For Web sites, what is the URL ending? (e.g., ".edu" and ".gov" tend to be the most reliable sites)
  - Is the source current?

Home Page Menu ⬍

National Oceanic and Atmosphere Administration

| Home | Contacts | Media | Disclaimer | Search | People Locator |

Weather Page

**Fujita Tornado
Damage Scale**

Category F0: Light Damage (<73 mph); Some damage to chimneys and sign boards, branches broken off trees, shallow-rooted trees pushed over.

Category F1: Moderate Damage (73-112 mph); Peels surface off roofs; mobile homes pushed off foundations or overturned; moving autos blown off road.

Category F2: Considerable Damage (113-157 mph); Roofs torn off frame houses; mobile homes demolished; boxcars overturned; large trees snapped or uprooted; light-object missiles generated; cars lifted off ground.

Category F3: Severe Damage (158-206 mph); Roofs and some walls torn off well-constructed houses, trains overturned; most trees in forest uprooted; heavy cars lifted off ground and thrown.

Category F4: Devastating Damage (207-260 mph); Well-constructed houses leveled; structure with weak foundations blown off some distance; cars thrown and large missiles generated.

Category F5: Incredible Damage (261-318 mph); Strong frame houses lifted off foundations and swept away; automobile sized missiles fly through the air in excess of 100 meters (109 yards); trees debarked.

Tornadoes

Tornadoes are one of nature's most violent storms. In an average year, about 1,000 tornadoes are reported across the United States, resulting in 80 deaths and over 1,500 injuries. A tornado is a violently rotating column of air extending from a thunderstorm to the ground. The most violent tornadoes are capable of tremendous destruction with wind speeds of 250 mph or more. Damage paths can be in excess of one mile wide and 50 miles long.

Tornadoes come in all shapes and sizes and can occur anywhere in the U.S. at any time of the year. In the southern states, peak tornado season is March through May, while peak months in the northern states are during the summer.

Preparedness Guides

- Are you prepared for Nature's Most Violent Storms?. A preparedness guide including safety information for schools prepared by the National Weather Service, FEMA and the American Red Cross.

- Thunderstorms and Camping Safety

- Weather Safety for Kids - Owlie Skywarn's Weather Book about Tornadoes

More Info . . .
- Weather Glossary for Storm Spotters

- Storm Reports - includes monthly tornado statistics, deadly tornadoes, current severe weather reports and more from the National Weather Service's Storm Prediction Center.

- Tornadoes of the 20th Century - a list of the more notable tornado out-breaks that occurred in the U.S. during the 20th century.

National Weather Service
Owlie Skywarn's Weather Book
Watch Out...Storms Ahead!

Owlie's Front Page

View My Safety
Tips About...
Tornadoes
  Watches
  Warnings
Lightning
Flash Floods
Hurricanes
Winter Weather
Carbon Monoxide

TORNADO!

If you ever see a big black cloud with a funnel-like extension beneath it, watch out. It could be a tornado.

A tornado looks like a funnel with the fat part at the top. Inside it winds may be swirling around at 300 miles an hour. If it goes through a town, the tornado could flatten houses and buildings, lift up cars and trucks, shatter mobile homes into splinters. Sometimes the path is narrow but everything in the path gets wrecked. But you don't always see the funnel. It may be raining too hard. Or the tornado may come at night. Listen for the tornado's roar. Some people say it sounds like a thousand trains.

What to do if...

| You are in your house | You are downtown or in a shopping mall | You are outside |
| You are in school | You are in a mobile home | In Conclusion... |

Last updated June 22, 20__
URL: http://www.crh.noaa.gov/mkx/owlie/tornado1.htm

Educators and students should send their questions to the NOAA outreach team at noaa-outreach@noaa.gov.

Thinking About the Web Site

1. What links have information on how schools can keep students safe during a storm?

_____

_____

2. Describe Category F5 on the Fujita Tornado Damage Scale.

_____

_____

TALK ABOUT IT **Reading Skill**

3. Which link has true information on storms in your area today?

_____

_____

4. How do you know the information on this site is true?

_____

_____

WRITE ABOUT IT **Timed Writing: Evaluation (35 minutes)**

Write an **evaluation** of this Web site. Answer the questions below in your evaluation.

What parts do you think are helpful?	
Who might use this site?	
What should be added to this site?	
Should someone researching bad weather use this site?	

Universal Themes in the Oral Tradition

Written literature grew out of the **oral tradition**. The oral tradition is the passing of people's poems, tales, and sayings by word of mouth. Around campfires and at other gatherings, people would tell stories. These stories featured **universal themes** and offered insights into life that are true for many different times and cultures. Here are some of the most common universal themes:

- the importance of heroism
- the power of love
- the strength of loyalty
- the dangers of greed

Storytellers explore these themes by using **archetypes**. Archetypes are situations, characters, images, and symbols that appear in the tales of various cultures. Here are some important archetypes:

- the **hero's quest**, in which a brave or clever person is tested while searching for something valuable
- the struggle between the **protagonist**, the main character, and the **antagonist**, a person or force that opposes the main character
- the **monster**, a nonhuman or semihuman creature that threatens human society and must be destroyed by the hero
- the **trickster**, a clever character who can fool others but often gets into trouble through curiosity
- the **circle** as a symbol of loyalty, completion, or protection

The **historical and cultural setting** is the social and cultural background of a certain tale. This context affects the presentation of archetypes. One can still recognize archetypes across time and culture. One can do this even when there are cultural variations.

Forms That Express Universal Themes

Anonymous storytellers developed different forms to express universal themes and archetypes. Tales might change with every telling because these early forms were oral. **Traditional literature** developed as stories were written down later in history. Individual authors emerged. Here are some of the most common forms that express universal themes and archetypes.

Form	Definition	Example
myth	• A story that explains the actions of gods and humans or the causes of natural phenomona	• creation myths • flood myths
folk tale	• A story that tells the adventures of human or animal heroes • Not concerned with gods or creation	• Brer Rabbit • Tar Man
legend	• A story that tells the adventures of a human hero • Based on fact • A **tall tale** is a legend told in an exaggerated way.	• Davy Crockett • Johnny Appleseed
epic	• A long narrative poem that describes the adventures of a larger-than-life hero • Tells of a dangerous journey or quest that is important to the history of a group or a culture	• The *Iliad* • The *Odyssey*

Myths, legends, folk tales, and epics express the **values**, ideals, and behaviors that a culture considers important. **Shared values** are held in common by people in different cultures. **Culturally distinct values** are specific to a group. In a literary work, **cultural details** are the beliefs, traditions, and customs that reflect the life of a particular society. In many cases, these beliefs are embodied in that society's **classical literature**—works recognized as enduring and masterful.

Play Hard; Play Together; Play Smart
from The Carolina Way
Dean Smith with John Kilgo

Summary Coach Dean Smith offers his simple program for building and keeping a winning basketball team: Play hard; play together; play smart. Smith shows how this philosophy influenced his players both on and off the court.

Note-taking Guide

Use this diagram to keep track of the main ideas of Coach Smith's winning program.

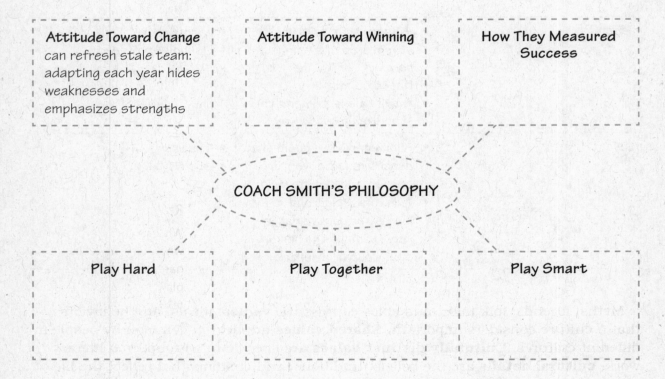

| Attitude Toward Change can refresh stale team: adapting each year hides weaknesses and emphasizes strengths | Attitude Toward Winning | How They Measured Success |

COACH SMITH'S PHILOSOPHY

| Play Hard | Play Together | Play Smart |

Play Hard; Play Together; Play Smart from The Carolina Way

Dean Smith with John Kilgo

I never went into a season as North Carolina's head coach thinking we'd just plug things into the previous year's plan and duplicate ourselves. As I said, we never had the same team return, and there were any number of other variables from one year to the next. We couldn't have had the long run of success that we enjoyed if we'd been too stubborn to change and come up with new ideas and different ways to play the game.

I will repeat this several times in this book: Don't fear change. Sometimes change can refresh a stale team; sometimes it's mandated by changing personnel; sometimes the rules of the game change. We adapted each year to hide our weaknesses and accentuate our strengths.

Although we didn't have a system at North Carolina, we certainly had a philosophy. We believed in it strongly and didn't stray very far from it. It pretty much stayed the same from my first year as head coach. It was our mission statement; our strategic plan, our entire approach in a nutshell: Play hard; play smart; play together.

Hard meant with effort, determination, and courage; *together* meant unselfishly, trusting your teammates, and doing everything possible not to let them down; *smart* meant with good execution and <u>poise</u>, treating each possession as if it were the only one in the game.

That was our philosophy; we believed that if we kept our focus on those <u>tenets</u>, success would follow. Our North Carolina players seldom heard me or my assistants talk about winning. Winning would be the by-product of the process. There could be no shortcuts.

Making winning the ultimate goal usually isn't good teaching. Tom Osborne, the great former football coach of the University of Nebraska, said that making winning the goal can actually get in the way of winning. I agree. So many things happened in games that were beyond our control: the talent and experience of the teams; bad calls by officials; injuries; bad luck.

By sticking to our philosophy, we asked realistic things from our players. A player could play hard. He could play unselfishly and do things to help his teammates succeed.

TAKE NOTES

Activate Prior Knowledge

What might playing a team or individual sport teach you?

_____

_____

_____

_____

Themes in Literature

Did it surprise you to learn that winning is not part of Coach Smith's philosophy? Explain.

_____

_____

Universal themes apply to many different times and cultures. Does Coach Smith's philosophy have any universal themes?

_____

_____

_____

Reading Check

What does Coach Smith mean when he talks about playing hard, playing together, and playing smart? Underline the text that tells you.

Vocabulary Development

poise (poyz) *n.* balance

tenets (TEHN ehts) *n.* principles or beliefs

Stop to Reflect

Which of Coach Smith's principles can best be applied to life in general? Explain why.

_____

_____

_____

_____

_____

Themes in Literature

Leadership is a **universal theme** found in literature. What is your reaction to the leadership strategy in the underlined text? Would this strategy work if it were applied to you? Why or why not?

_____

_____

_____

Reading Check

According to Coach Smith, what can a player always control? Underline the text that tells you.

Themes in Literature

Coach Smith says that basketball "counts on togetherness." Is working together a **shared value** or a **culturally distinct value**? Explain.

_____

_____

_____

He could play intelligently if we did the job in practice as coaches. We measured our success by how we did in those areas.

When we put these elements together, the players had fun, one of my goals as their coach. I wanted our players to enjoy the experience of playing basketball for North Carolina. Each player on our team knew he was important. Each did a terrific job of sharing the ball, which also made the game enjoyable for more players. All won and lost as a team.

Of course it is easier to talk about playing hard, playing smart, and playing together than it is to do all three. It begins by the recruiting of unselfish players, who subscribe to the philosophy of team over individual. In a summer physical education class I once taught at the Air Force Academy there was one young man who shot every time he touched the ball. Exasperated from watching him, I pulled his four teammates off the court. He asked who would throw the ball inbounds to him. "You understand that it takes at least one more player," I said to him.

Playing Hard

Maybe a player wasn't the fastest, the tallest, or the most athletic person on the court. In the course of any given game that was out of his control. But each of them could control the effort with which he played. "Never let anyone play harder than you," I told them. "That is part of the game you can control." If another team played harder than we did, we had no excuse for it. None. We worked on it in every practice. If a player didn't give maximum effort, we dealt with it right then. We stopped practice and had the entire team run sprints for the offending player. We played a style of basketball that was physically exhausting and made it impossible for a player to go full throttle for forty minutes. When he got tired, he flashed the tired signal, a raised fist, and we substituted for him. He could put himself back in the game once he had rested. We didn't want tired players on the court because they usually tried to rest on defense. That wouldn't work in our plan. Therefore we watched closely in practice and in games to make sure players played hard. If they slacked off, it was important to catch them and get them out of the game, or if it occurred in practice, to have the entire team run.

Playing Together

One of the first things I did at the beginning of preseason practice was to spell out for our players the importance of team play. Basketball is a game that counts on togetherness. I pointed out that seldom, if ever, did the nation's leading scorer play on a ranked team. He certainly didn't play on a championship team. I made them understand that our plan would fall apart if they didn't take care of one another: set screens; play team defense; box out; pass to the open man. One man who failed to do his job unselfishly could undermine the efforts of the four other players on the court.

Playing Smart

We taught and drilled until we made the things we wanted to see become habits. The only way to have a smart team is to have one that is fundamentally sound. We didn't skimp on fundamentals. We worked on them hard in practice and repeated them until they were down cold. We didn't introduce something and then move away from it before we had nailed it. Our entire program was built around practice, which we will talk more about in a later chapter. Practice, competitive games, late-game situations, and my relationship with our players are what I've missed most since I retired from coaching. We expected our team to execute well and with precision. If we practiced well and learned, we could play smart. It was another thing we could control . . .

I stay in touch with many members of my extended family, former Carolina basketball players. These men have brought great happiness to my life. Ninety-six percent of them earned their college degrees, and one-third of those continued their studies at graduate and professional schools. It's the way a teacher's career should be judged. Our former players are doing great things for people in all walks of life.

The Carolina Way isn't the only way, that's for certain. But playing hard, playing smart, playing together certainly worked well for us.

Our trophy case is full, but far more important, our Museum of Good Memories runneth over.

Reader's Response: Do you agree that playing a sport the right way is more important than winning? Explain.

_____

_____

_____

TAKE NOTES

Stop to Reflect

Read the bracketed text. How might the behaviors and values that Coach Smith talks about be applied in other situations, such as in a business or even in a school?

_____

_____

_____

Themes in Literature

Cultural details are the beliefs, traditions, and customs that reflect the way of life of a particular society. Do you think Coach Smith's philosophy reflects the cultural details of the United States? Explain.

_____

_____

_____

Reading Check

How does Coach Smith judge his career as a teacher? Underline the text that tells you.

Themes in Literature

1. **Draw Conclusions:** Smith talks about things that a coach or a team cannot control. How does his philosophy help his players deal with the unexpected as they play?

   _____

   _____

2. **Evaluate:** Smith believes that a teacher's career should be judged by how students succeed in the rest of their lives. By his standards, is Smith's career meaningful because he was a teacher or because he was a coach? Explain.

   _____

   _____

3. Use the chart to analyze the **values** that Coach Smith emphasized with his players. In the first column, list the three values or goals that Smith taught. In the second column, give a specific example of how Smith encouraged each value among his players. In the third column, suggest ways in which Smith's values can be applied to people in any group or situation.

Value	Specific Examples	Application to Life

4. Do you think sports are an important part of the **cultural context** of the United States? Use details from Smith's essay to support your answer.

   _____

   _____

   _____

Testimonial Poster

Create a **testimonial poster** that shows the positive results of Smith's coaching beliefs. Use the following tips to research your poster.

- Search the Internet and library for information about famous athletes, coaches, and leaders who have played for Dean Smith.

  What I learned about Dean Smith:

  _____

  _____

  _____

  _____

- Collect comments about Smith made by his former players. Focus on statements relating to the values that Coach Smith taught them.

  Comments made by Smith's former players:

  _____

  _____

  _____

  _____

  _____

- Watch the video interview with Dean Smith. Add what you learn from the video to what you have already learned about the author.

  Additional information learned about the author:

  _____

  _____

  _____

  _____

Use your notes to create your testimonial poster. Remember to include pictures of Smith and the people you quote.

from the Odyssey, Part 1, The Cyclops

Literary Analysis

An **epic hero** is the central character in an **epic**—a long narrative poem about important events in the history or folklore of a culture. The epic hero demonstrates traits that are valued by that culture.

Many epics began *in media res* ("in the middle of things"), meaning that much of the important action in the story occurred before the point at which the poem begins. The epic hero's adventures are often recounted in a **flashback**, a scene that interrupts the sequence of events in a narrative to relate earlier events.

Reading Skill

The **historical and cultural context** of a work is the backdrop of details of the time and place in which the work is set or was written. When you read a work from another time and culture, **use background and prior knowledge** to analyze the influence of the historical and cultural context.

- Read the author biography, footnotes, and other text aids.
- Note how characters' behavior and attitudes reflect the context.

Use the chart to note the influence of Greek culture in Homer's *Odyssey*.

Historical/Cultural Detail	Background	Cause/Effect

from the Odyssey, Part 1, The Cyclops
Homer

Summary The Greek hero Odysseus and his men arrive at the land of the Cyclopes, a race of one-eyed giants. A Cyclops named Polyphemus eats two of Odysseus' men. The hero and his men blind him. Polyphemus asks the god Poseidon to curse the hero.

Writing About the Big Question

Do heroes have responsibilities? In Part 1 of the Odyssey, Homer describes the hero Odysseus' long and dangerous journey home. Complete this sentence:

A hero has an obligation to _____

because _____.

Note-taking Guide

Use this chart to record how the five most important events in this selection lead to the final outcome.

Event 1	
Event 2	
Event 3	
Event 4	
Event 5	
Final Outcome	Odysseus and his men leave the land of the Cyclopes.

Activate Prior Knowledge

What types of characters do you usually find in adventure stories?

_____

_____

Reading Skill

The **historical and cultural context** of a work is the backdrop of details of the time and place in which the work is set or was written. Underline Odysseus' criticism of the Cyclopes. Given this criticism, what kind of society do you think the Greeks valued?

_____

_____

_____

_____

Literary Analysis

An **epic hero** is the larger-than-life central character in an **epic**—a long narrative poem about important events in the history or folklore of a culture. Odysseus leaves his ship to investigate the island. How does this action show that he is an epic hero?

_____

_____

_____

_____

from the Odyssey, Part 1
The Cyclops
Homer
Translated by Robert Fitzgerald

In the next land we found were Cyclopes,[1]
110   giants, louts, without a law to bless them.
In ignorance leaving the fruitage of the earth
   in mystery
to the immortal gods, they neither plow
nor sow by hand, nor till the ground, though grain—
wild wheat and barley—grows untended, and
115   wine-grapes, in clusters, ripen in heaven's rains.
Cyclopes have no muster and no meeting,
no consultation or old tribal ways,
but each one dwells in his own mountain cave
dealing out rough justice to wife and child,
120   indifferent to what the others do. . . .

As we rowed on, and nearer to the mainland,
at one end of the bay, we saw a cavern
yawning above the water, screened with laurel,
and many rams and goats about the place
125   inside a sheepfold—made from slabs of stone
earthfast between tall trunks of pine and rugged
towering oak trees.

                  A prodigious[2] man
slept in this cave alone, and took his flocks
to graze afield—remote from all companions,
130   knowing none but savage ways, a brute
so huge, he seemed no man at all of those
who eat good wheaten bread; but he seemed rather
a shaggy mountain reared in solitude.
We beached there, and I told the crew
135   to stand by and keep watch over the ship:
as for myself I took my twelve best fighters
and went ahead. I had a goatskin full
of that sweet liquor that Euanthes' son,
Maron, had given me. He kept Apollo's[3]
140   holy grove at Ismarus; for kindness
we showed him there, and showed his wife and child,
he gave me seven shining golden talents[4]
perfectly formed, a solid silver winebowl,
and then this liquor—twelve two-handled jars

1. **Cyclopes** (sy KLOH peez) *n.* plural form of **Cyclops** (SY klahps), race of giants with one eye in the middle of the forehead.
2. **prodigious** (proh DIHJ uhs) *adj.* enormous.
3. **Apollo** (uh PAHL oh) god of music, poetry, prophecy, and medicine.
4. **talents** (TAL ents) *n.* units of money in ancient Greece.

145 of brandy, pure and fiery. Not a slave
in Maron's household knew this drink; only
he, his wife and the storeroom mistress knew;
and they would put one cupful—ruby-colored,
honey-smooth—in twenty more of water,
150 but still the sweet scent hovered like a fume
over the winebowl. No man turned away
when cups of this came round.

                        A wineskin full
I brought along, and victuals[5] in a bag,
for in my bones I knew some towering brute
155 would be upon us soon—all outward power,
a wild man, ignorant of civility.

We climbed, then, briskly to the cave. But Cyclops
had gone afield, to pasture his fat sheep,
so we looked round at everything inside:
160 a drying rack that sagged with cheeses, pens
crowded with lambs and kids,[6] each in its class:
firstlings apart from middlings, and the 'dewdrops,'
or newborn lambkins, penned apart from both.
And vessels full of whey[7] were brimming there—
165 bowls of earthenware and pails for milking.
My men came pressing round me, pleading:

                              'Why not
take these cheeses, get them stowed, come back,
throw open all the pens, and make a run for it?
We'll drive the kids and lambs aboard. We say
170 put out again on good salt water!'

                          Ah,
how sound that was! Yet I refused. I wished
to see the cave man, what he had to offer—
no pretty sight, it turned out, for my friends.
We lit a fire, burnt an offering,
175 and took some cheese to eat; then sat in silence
around the embers, waiting. When he came
he had a load of dry boughs[8] on his shoulder
to stoke his fire at suppertime. He dumped it
with a great crash into that hollow cave,
180 and we all scattered fast to the far wall.
Then over the broad cavern floor he ushered
the ewes he meant to milk. He left his rams
and he-goats in the yard outside, and swung
high overhead a slab of solid rock

---

5. **vi uals** (VIT uhlz) *n.* food or other provisions.

6. **kids** (kidz) *n.* young goats.

7. **whey** (hway) *n.* thin, watery part of milk separated from the thicker curds.

8. **b ughs** (bowz) *n.* tree branches.

Reading Skill

Use ba kgr und and pri r kn wledge to analyze the influence of the **his ri al and ul ural n ex**. Odysseus describes Maron's gift of the wine in great detail. What does this description tell you about Greek attitudes toward the importance of gift giving?

_____

_____

_____

_____

Literary Analysis

An **epi her 's** adventures are often recounted in a **flashba k**. A flashback is a scene that interrupts the sequence of events in a narrative to relate earlier events. Read the underlined passage. Circle words or phrases in this passage that prove this scene is a flashback.

Reading Check

Circle the lines that tell where the Cyclops is when Odysseus and his men enter the cave.

Literary Analysis

Epic heroes like Odysseus face dangerous situations from which escape seems impossible. Read the Cyclops' speech in lines 197–200. What danger do Odysseus and his men now face? Explain. Underline the words that suggest they might be in danger.

_____

_____

_____

Reading Skill 📖

Read the bracketed passage. **Use background and prior knowledge** to analyze the influence of the **historical and cultural context**. What ancient Greek beliefs does Odysseus express in his words to the Cyclops?

_____

_____

_____

Reading Check

How do Odysseus and his men feel when the Cyclops first speaks to them? Underline the lines that tell you the answer.

185   to close the cave. Two dozen four-wheeled wagons,
      with heaving wagon teams, could not have stirred
      the tonnage of that rock from where he wedged it
      over the doorsill. Next he took his seat
      and milked his bleating ewes. A practiced job
190   he made of it, giving each ewe her suckling;
      thickened his milk, then, into curds and whey,
      sieved out the curds to drip in withy[9] baskets,
      and poured the whey to stand in bowls
      cooling until he drank it for his supper.
195   When all these chores were done, he poked the fire,
      heaping on brushwood. In the glare he saw us.

      'Strangers,' he said, 'who are you? And where from?
      What brings you here by seaways—a fair traffic?
      Or are you wandering rogues, who cast your lives
200   like dice, and ravage other folk by sea?'

      We felt a pressure on our hearts, in dread
      of that deep rumble and that mighty man.
      But all the same I spoke up in reply:

      'We are from Troy, Achaeans, blown off course
205   by shifting gales on the Great South Sea;
      homeward bound, but taking routes and ways
      uncommon; so the will of Zeus would have it.
      We served under Agamemnon,[10] son of Atreus—
      the whole world knows what city
210   he laid waste, what armies he destroyed.
      It was our luck to come here; here we stand,
      beholden for your help, or any gifts
      you give—as custom is to honor strangers.
      We would entreat you, great Sir, have a care
215   for the gods' courtesy; Zeus will avenge
      the unoffending guest.'

                          He answered this
      from his brute chest, unmoved:

                                  You are a ninny,
      or else you come from the other end of nowhere,
      telling me, mind the gods! We Cyclopes
220   care not a whistle for your thundering Zeus
      or all the gods in bliss; we have more force by far.
      I would not let you go for fear of Zeus—
      you or your friends—unless I had a whim[11] to.
      Tell me, where was it, now, you left your ship—
225   around the point, or down the shore, I wonder?'

---

9. **withy** (WITH ee) _adj._ made from tough, flexible twigs.

10. **Agamemnon** (ag uh MEHM nahn) king who led the Greek army during the Trojan War.

11. **whim** (hwim) _n._ sudden thought or wish to do something.

He thought he'd find out, but I saw through this,
and answered with a ready lie:

                               'My ship?
Poseidon[12] Lord, who sets the earth a-tremble,
broke it up on the rocks at your land's end.

230 A wind from seaward served him, drove us there.
We are survivors, these good men and I.'

Neither reply nor pity came from him,
but in one stride he clutched at my companions
and caught two in his hands like squirming puppies

235 to beat their brains out, spattering the floor.
Then he dismembered them and made his meal,
gaping and crunching like a mountain lion—
everything: innards, flesh, and marrow bones.
We cried aloud, lifting our hands to Zeus,

240 powerless, looking on at this, appalled;
but Cyclops went on filling up his belly
with manflesh and great gulps of whey,
then lay down like a mast among his sheep.
My heart beat high now at the chance of action,

245 and drawing the sharp sword from my hip I went
along his flank to stab him where the midriff
holds the liver. I had touched the spot
when sudden fear stayed me: if I killed him
we perished there as well, for we could never

250 move his ponderous doorway slab aside.
So we were left to groan and wait for morning.

When the young Dawn with fingertips of rose
lit up the world, the Cyclops built a fire
and milked his handsome ewes, all in due order,

255 putting the sucklings to the mothers. Then,
his chores being all <u>dispatched</u>, he caught
another brace[13] of men to make his breakfast,
and whisked away his great door slab
to let his sheep go through—but he, behind,

260 reset the stone as one would cap a quiver.[14]
There was a din[15] of whistling as the Cyclops
rounded his flock to higher ground, then stillness.
And now I pondered how to hurt him worst,
if but Athena[16] granted what I prayed for.

Vocabulary Development

dispatched (di SPACHT) *v.* finished quickly

12. **Poseidon** (poh SY duhn) *n.* god of the sea, earthquakes, horses, and storms at sea.

13. **brace** (brays) *n.* pair.

14. **cap a quiver** (KWIV er) close a case holding arrows.

15. **din** (din) *n.* loud, continuous noise; uproar.

16. **Athena** (uh THEE nuh) *n.* goddess of wisdom, skills, and warfare.

TAKE NOTES

Stop to Reflect

Why do you think Odysseus lies in lines 227–231?

_____

_____

_____

Literary Analysis

An **epic hero** shows qualities that are admired by his or her society. Why does Odysseus decide not to attack the Cyclops?

_____

_____

_____

Underline the part of the bracketed passage that shows Odysseus' wisdom.

Reading Skill

Use background and prior knowledge to analyze the influence of the **historical and cultural context**. Read lines 263–264. Odysseus prays to Athena. Based on your knowledge of Greek history and culture, why would Odysseus pray to Athena?

_____

_____

_____

Literary Analysis

Read the bracketed passage. What heroic qualities does the **epic hero** Odysseus show as he prepares to fight the Cyclops?

_____

_____

_____

Stop to Reflect

Odysseus often involves himself in dangerous tasks. Do you think he is telling the truth about his role in the tasks? Why or why not?

_____

_____

_____

Reading Skill

Use background and prior knowledge to analyze the influence of the **historical and cultural context** in lines 299–300. What does Odysseus' comment tell you about his culture? Explain.

_____

_____

_____

Reading Check

Who will help Odysseus blind the Cyclops? Underline the line that tells you.

265   Here are the means I thought would serve my turn:

    a club, or staff, lay there along the fold—
    an olive tree, felled green and left to season[17]
    for Cyclops' hand. And it was like a mast
    a lugger[18] of twenty oars, broad in the beam—
270   a deep-sea-going craft—might carry:
    so long, so big around, it seemed. Now I
    chopped out a six foot section of this pole
    and set it down before my men, who scraped it;
    and when they had it smooth, I hewed again
275   to make a stake with pointed end. I held this
    in the fire's heart and turned it, toughening it,
    then hid it, well back in the cavern, under
    one of the dung piles in profusion there.
    Now came the time to toss for it: who ventured
280   along with me? whose hand could bear to thrust
    and grind that spike in Cyclops' eye, when mild
    sleep had mastered him? As luck would have it,
    the men I would have chosen won the toss—
    four strong men, and I made five as captain.

285   At evening came the shepherd with his flock,
    his woolly flock. The rams as well, this time,
    entered the cave: by some sheepherding whim—
    or a god's bidding—none were left outside.
    He hefted his great boulder into place
290   and sat him down to milk the bleating ewes
    in proper order, put the lambs to suck,
    and swiftly ran through all his evening chores.
    Then he caught two more men and feasted on them.
    My moment was at hand, and I went forward
295   holding an ivy bowl of my dark drink,
    looking up, saying:

               'Cyclops, try some wine.
    Here's liquor to wash down your scraps of men.
    Taste it, and see the kind of drink we carried
    under our planks. I meant it for an offering
300   if you would help us home. But you are mad,
    unbearable, a bloody monster! After this,
    will any other traveler come to see you?'

    He seized and drained the bowl, and it went down
    so fiery and smooth he called for more:

305   'Give me another, thank you kindly. Tell me,
    how are you called? I'll make a gift will please you.

---

17. **felled green and left to season** chopped down and exposed to the weather to age the wood.
18. **lugger** (LUG er) n. small sailing vessel.

Even Cyclopes know the wine grapes grow
out of grassland and loam in heaven's rain,
but here's a bit of nectar and ambrosia!'[19]

310 Three bowls I brought him, and he poured
          them down.
I saw the fuddle and flush come over him,
then I sang out in cordial tones:

                              'Cyclops,
you ask my honorable name? Remember
the gift you promised me, and I shall tell you.
315 My name is Nohbdy: mother, father, and friends,
everyone calls me Nohbdy.'
                              And he said:
'Nohbdy's my meat, then, after I eat his friends.
Others come first. There's a noble gift, now.'

Even as he spoke, he reeled and tumbled backward,
320 his great head lolling to one side; and sleep
took him like any creature. Drunk, hiccuping,
he dribbled streams of liquor and bits of men.

Now, by the gods, I drove my big hand spike
deep in the embers, charring it again,
325 and cheered my men along with battle talk
to keep their courage up: no quitting now.
The pike of olive, green though it had been,
reddened and glowed as if about to catch.
I drew it from the coals and my four fellows
330 gave me a hand, lugging it near the Cyclops
as more than natural force nerved them; straight
forward they sprinted, lifted it, and rammed it
deep in his crater eye, and leaned on it
turning it as a shipwright turns a drill
335 in planking, having men below to swing
the two-handled strap that spins it in the groove.
So with our brand we bored[20] that great eye socket
while blood ran out around the red-hot bar.
Eyelid and lash were seared; the pierced ball
340 hissed broiling, and the roots popped.

                              In a smithy
one sees a white-hot axehead or an adze
plunged and wrung in a cold tub, screeching steam—
the way they make soft iron hale and hard—:
just so that eyeball hissed around the spike.
345 The Cyclops bellowed and the rock roared round him,
and we fell back in fear. Clawing his face

19. **nectar** (NEHK ter) and ambrosia (am BROH zhuh) drink and food of the gods.

20. **bored** (bawrd) v. made a hole in.

Stop to Reflect

We usually do not think of dishonesty as a heroic quality. Defend Odysseus' actions in the bracketed section. What reasons can you offer for the hero to lie in this situation?

_____

_____

_____

_____

Reading Skill

Use background and prior knowledge to analyze the influence of the **historical and cultural context** in line 323. What cultural values are represented in Odysseus' reference to "the gods"?

_____

_____

_____

_____

How does Odysseus' reference to the gods contrast him with the Cyclops?

_____

_____

Reading Check

The Cyclops brags about what he plans to do to Odysseus and his men. Underline the lines that describe the Cyclops' plans.

Reading Skill

Use background and prior knowledge to analyze the influence of the **historical and cultural context** in the bracketed passage. Read the reply of the other Cyclopes. What might this suggest about the attitude that Greeks had toward health and sickness?

_____

_____

_____

Literary Analysis

What does Odysseus' gleeful response to his successful trick reveal about the character of the **epic hero**?

_____

_____

_____

Reading Check

What does Polyphemus do after the other Cyclopes leave? Circle the sentence that tells the answer.

he tugged the bloody spike out of his eye,
threw it away, and his wild hands went groping;
then he set up a howl for Cyclopes
350 who lived in caves on windy peaks nearby.
Some heard him; and they came by divers[21] ways
to clump around outside and call:
                  'What ails you,
Polyphemus?[22] Why do you cry so sore
in the starry night? You will not let us sleep.
355 Sure no man's driving off your flock? No man
has tricked you, ruined you?'
                   Out of the cave
the <u>mammoth</u> Polyphemus roared in answer:

'Nohbdy, Nohbdy's tricked me, Nohbdy's ruined me!'

To this rough shout they made a sage[23] reply:

360 'Ah well, if nobody has played you foul
there in your lonely bed, we are no use in pain
given by great Zeus. Let it be your father,
Poseidon Lord, to whom you pray.'
                   So saying
they trailed away. And I was filled with laughter
365 to see how like a charm the name deceived them.
Now Cyclops, wheezing as the pain came on him,
fumbled to wrench away the great doorstone
and squatted in the breach with arms thrown wide
for any silly beast or man who bolted—
370 hoping somehow I might be such a fool.
But I kept thinking how to win the game:
death sat there huge; how could we slip away?
I drew on all my wits, and ran through tactics,
reasoning as a man will for dear life,
375 until a trick came—and it pleased me well.
The Cyclops' rams were handsome, fat, with heavy
fleeces, a dark violet.
                 Three abreast
I tied them silently together, twining
cords of willow from the ogre's bed;
380 then slung a man under each middle one
to ride there safely, shielded left and right.
So three sheep could convey each man. I took

Vocabulary Development
mammoth (MAM uhth) *adj.* enormous

21. **divers** (DY vuhrz) *adj.* several; various.
22. **Polyphemus** (pahl i FEE muhs)
23. **sage** (sayj) *adj.* wise.

the woolliest ram, the choicest of the flock,
and hung myself under his kinky belly,
385   pulled up tight, with fingers twisted deep
in sheepskin ringlets for an iron grip.
So, breathing hard, we waited until morning.

When Dawn spread out her fingertips of rose
the rams began to stir, moving for pasture,
390   and peals of bleating echoed round the pens
where dams with udders full called for a milking.
Blinded, and sick with pain from his head wound,
the master stroked each ram, then let it pass,
but my men riding on the pectoral[24] fleece
395   the giant's blind hands blundering never found.
Last of them all my ram, the leader, came,
weighted by wool and me with my meditations.
The Cyclops patted him, and then he said:

'Sweet cousin ram, why lag behind the rest
400   in the night cave? You never linger so,
but graze before them all, and go afar
to crop sweet grass, and take your stately way
leading along the streams, until at evening
you run to be the first one in the fold.
405   Why, now, so far behind? Can you be grieving
over your Master's eye? That carrion rogue[25]
and his accurst companions burnt it out
when he had conquered all my wits with wine.
Nohbdy will not get out alive, I swear.
410   Oh, had you brain and voice to tell
where he may be now, dodging all my fury!
Bashed by this hand and bashed on this rock wall
his brains would strew the floor, and I should have
rest from the outrage Nohbdy worked upon me.'

415   He sent us into the open, then. Close by,
I dropped and rolled clear of the ram's belly,
going this way and that to untie the men.
With many glances back, we rounded up
his fat, stiff-legged sheep to take aboard,
420   and drove them down to where the good ship lay.
We saw, as we came near, our fellows' faces
shining; then we saw them turn to grief
tallying those who had not fled from death.
I hushed them, jerking head and eyebrows up,
425   and in a low voice told them: 'Load this herd;
move fast, and put the ship's head toward the
      breakers.'
They all pitched in at loading, then embarked

© Pearson Education

24. **pectoral** (PEHK tuh ruhl) *adj.* located in or on the chest.
25. **carrion** (KAR ee uhn) rogue (rohg) repulsive scoundrel.

TAKE NOTES

Literary Analysis

Which important heroic qualities does the **epic hero** Odysseus show by coming up with his plan for escape?

_____

_____

_____

_____

Stop to Reflect

The Greeks valued cleverness and frowned upon ignorance. Read the bracketed passage. Do you think Odysseus is more clever than Polyphemus? Explain. Underline the details that show your answer.

_____

_____

_____

Reading Skill

Odysseus and his men steal Polyphemus' sheep. **Use background and prior knowledge** to explain what their actions say about Greek attitudes toward property.

_____

_____

_____

_____

Literary Analysis

An **epic hero** is larger than life but usually also has some human failings. What is Odysseus doing in lines 430–435?

_____

_____

_____

What human weakness does Odysseus' behavior reveal?

_____

_____

_____

Reading Skill

Odysseus shows human weakness, even though he was viewed as a great hero. Use **background and prior knowledge** to explain what this kind of epic hero suggests about Greek beliefs and values?

_____

_____

_____

Reading Check

Does the crew agree with Odysseus' taunting of the Cyclops? Circle the text that tells the answer.

and struck their oars into the sea. Far out,
as far off shore as shouted words would carry,
430 I sent a few back to the adversary:
'O Cyclops! Would you feast on my companions?
Puny, am I, in a cave man's hands?
How do you like the beating that we gave you,
you damned cannibal? Eater of guests
435 under your roof! Zeus and the gods have paid you!'

The blind thing in his doubled fury broke
a hilltop in his hands and heaved it after us.
Ahead of our black prow it struck and sank
whelmed in a spuming geyser, a giant wave
440 that washed the ship stern foremost back to shore.
I got the longest boathook out and stood
fending us off, with furious nods to all
to put their backs into a racing stroke—
row, row, or perish. So the long oars bent
445 kicking the foam sternward, making head
until we drew away, and twice as far.
Now when I cupped my hands I heard the crew
in low voices protesting:

              'Godsake, Captain!
Why bait the beast again? Let him alone!'

450 'That tidal wave he made on the first throw
all but beached us.'

                    'All but stove us in!'
'Give him our bearing with your trumpeting,
he'll get the range and lob a boulder.'

                      'Aye
He'll smash our timbers and our heads together!'
455 I would not heed them in my glorying spirit,
but let my anger flare and yelled:

                     'Cyclops,
if ever mortal man inquire
how you were put to shame and blinded, tell him
Odysseus, raider of cities, took your eye:
460 Laertes' son, whose home's on Ithaca!'

At this he gave a mighty sob and rumbled:
'Now comes the weird[26] upon me, spoken of old.
A wizard, grand and wondrous, lived here—Telemus,[27]
a son of Eurymus;[28] great length of days

26. **weird** (wird) *n.* fate or destiny.
27. **Telemus** (tehl EH muhs)
28. **Eurymus** (yoo RIM uhs)

465　he had in wizardry among the Cyclopes,
　　　and these things he foretold for time to come:
　　　my great eye lost, and at Odysseus' hands.
　　　Always I had in mind some giant, armed
　　　in giant force, would come against me here.
470　But this, but you—small, pitiful and twiggy—
　　　you put me down with wine, you blinded me.
　　　Come back, Odysseus, and I'll treat you well,
　　　praying the god of earthquake[29] to befriend you—
　　　his son I am, for he by his avowal
475　fathered me, and, if he will, he may
　　　heal me of this black wound—he and no other
　　　of all the happy gods or mortal men.'

　　　Few words I shouted in reply to him:

　　　'If I could take your life I would and take
480　your time away, and hurl you down to hell!
　　　The god of earthquake could not heal you there!'

　　　At this he stretched his hands out in his darkness
　　　toward the sky of stars, and prayed Poseidon:

　　　'O hear me, lord, blue girdler of the islands,
485　if I am thine indeed, and thou art father:
　　　grant that Odysseus, raider of cities, never
　　　see his home: Laertes' son, I mean,
　　　who kept his hall on Ithaca. Should destiny
　　　intend that he shall see his roof again
490　among his family in his father land,
　　　far be that day, and dark the years between.
　　　Let him lose all companions, and return
　　　under strange sail to bitter days at home.'

　　　In these words he prayed, and the god heard him.
495　Now he laid hands upon a bigger stone
　　　and wheeled around, titanic for the cast,
　　　to let it fly in the black-prowed vessel's track.
　　　But it fell short, just aft the steering oar,
　　　and whelming seas rose giant above the stone
500　to bear us onward toward the island.
　　　　　　　　　　　　　　　　　　There
　　　as we ran in we saw the squadron waiting,
　　　the trim ships drawn up side by side, and all
　　　our troubled friends who waited, looking seaward.
　　　We beached her, grinding keel in the soft sand,
505　and waded in, ourselves, on the sandy beach.
　　　Then we unloaded all the Cyclops' flock
　　　to make division, share and share alike,

29. **god of earthquake** Poseidon.

Stop to Reflect

Polyphemus calls on Poseidon to curse Odysseus. What do you think will happen as a result?

_____

_____

_____

_____

Reading Skill

What do lines 472–493 suggest about ancient Greek beliefs about the gods' involvement in the mortal world? **Use background and prior knowledge** to answer this question.

_____

_____

_____

Reading Check

Polyphemus explains how a prophecy has come to pass. Why is Polyphemus surprised that Odysseus fulfilled the prophecy? Circle the text that tells the answer.

_____

_____

_____

_____

_____

© Pearson Education

Literary Analysis

What admirable qualities does the **epic hero** Odysseus show in what he does with the stolen sheep in lines 509–513?

_____

_____

_____

Reading Skill

Odysseus is punished by Zeus for his actions. What does this suggest about Greek values and beliefs? **Use background and prior knowledge** to answer this question.

_____

_____

_____

_____

Reading Check

Underline the words that tell what the future holds for Odysseus' ship and his companions.

only my fighters voted that my ram,
the prize of all, should go to me. I slew him
510 by the seaside and burnt his long thighbones
to Zeus beyond the stormcloud, Cronus'[30] son,
who rules the world. But Zeus disdained my offering:
destruction for my ships he had in store
and death for those who sailed them, my
    companions.
515 Now all day long until the sun went down
we made our feast on mutton and sweet wine,
till after sunset in the gathering dark
we went to sleep above the wash of ripples.

When the young Dawn with fingertips of rose
520 touched the world, I roused the men, gave orders
to man the ships, cast off the mooring lines;
and filing in to sit beside the rowlocks
oarsmen in line dipped oars in the gray sea.
So we moved out, sad in the vast offing,[31]
525 having our precious lives, but not our friends.

Reader's Response: What part of the story did you find most exciting? Explain.

_____

_____

_____

_____

Vocabulary Development

disdained (dis DAYND) *v.* rejected angrily

30. **Cronus** (KROH nuhs) Titan who was ruler of the universe until he was overthrown by his son Zeus.
31. **offing** (AWF ing) *n.* distant part of the sea visible from the shore.

from the Odyssey, Part 1

1. **Respond:** If you were one of Odysseus' crew, how would you feel about having him as your leader? Explain your response.

   _____

   _____

2. **Evaluate:** The *Odyssey* has entertained people for thousands of years. Why do you think it has been such an enduring work of literature?

   _____

   _____

3. **Literary Analysis:** Use the chart below to identify three actions that the **epic hero** Odysseus performs. For each action, identify the character trait that it reveals.

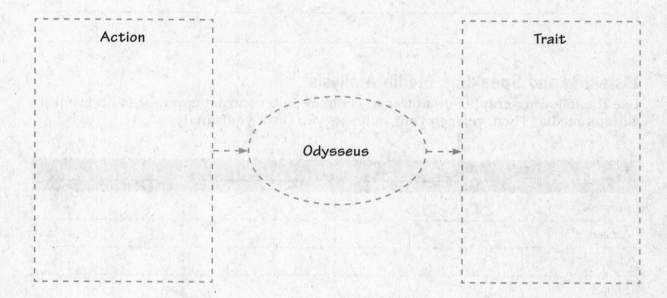

4. **Reading Skill:** What abilities or features of modern technology could have helped Odysseus on his journey if they had been available in ancient times? Explain your answers.

   _____

   _____

Writing: Everyday Epic

Write an **everyday epic**. Choose an everyday event, and write an account that makes it seem larger than life. Answer the following questions to help you draft your epic:

- How can I make this ordinary event extraordinary?

  _____

  _____

- What types of characters will appear in my epic?

  _____

  _____

- What cultural values and beliefs will I display in the hero?

  _____

  _____

- What flaws will I display?

  _____

  _____

Listening and Speaking: Media Analysis

Use the following graphic organizer to compare and contrast coverage of an event in various media. Then, refer to your notes as you draft your analysis.

Media Form:	_____	_____	_____
Purpose			
Audience			
Visuals			
Sound			

from the Odyssey, Part 2

Literary Analysis

An **epic simile** is an elaborate comparison that may extend for several lines. It might recall an entire place or story. As you read, notice how Homer uses epic similes to bring descriptions to life.

Reading Skill

The **historical and cultural context** of a work is the backdrop of details of the time and place in which the work is set or was written. When you **identify influences on your own reading and responses**, the historical and cultural context reflected in a work becomes more apparent.

Use the chart below to note the differences between your own influences and those reflected in the *Odyssey*. An example is shown for you.

Detail in Text

Odysseus says he and his crew plundered Ismarus.

Meaning for Characters

Winners can take valuables from the defeated.

Meaning in My Culture

Looting is shameful.

from the Odyssey, Part 2
Homer

Summary Odysseus has returned home after twenty years. Intruders have taken over his home. They want to kill his son and marry his wife. The goddess Athena has disguised Odysseus as an old beggar. Odysseus kills the intruders and takes back his home and his family.

 Writing About the Big Question

Do heroes have responsibilities? In Part 2 of the Odyssey, Homer tells of Odysseus' arrival at home and the confrontation with suitors, there to marry his wife and steal his lands. Complete this sentence:

The true character of a hero can be seen in _____.

Note-taking Guide

In this plot diagram, record the events of the epic and describe the conflict, the exposition, the climax, and the resolution.

Climax: _____

Event: _____   Event: _____
_____   _____

Event: The bow and arrow challenge   Event: _____

Event: Odysseus meets with   _____
Penelope

Rising Action   Falling Action

Resolution

Exposition

Conflict: _____

from the Odyssey, Part 2

Homer
Translated by Robert Fitzgerald

Penelope

In the evening, Penelope interrogates the old beggar.

"Friend, let me ask you first of all:
who are you, where do you come from, of what nation
and parents were you born?"

                            And he replied:
"My lady, never a man in the wide world
1290 should have a fault to find with you. Your name
has gone out under heaven like the sweet
honor of some god-fearing king, who rules
in equity over the strong: his black lands bear
both wheat and barley, fruit trees laden bright,
1295 new lambs at lambing time—and the deep sea
gives great hauls of fish by his good strategy,
so that his folk fare well.

                            O my dear lady,
this being so, let it suffice to ask me
of other matters—not my blood, my homeland.
1300 Do not enforce me to recall my pain.
My heart is sore; but I must not be found
sitting in tears here, in another's house:
it is not well forever to be grieving.
One of the maids might say—or you might think—
1305 I had got maudlin over cups of wine."

And Penelope replied:

                            "Stranger, my looks,
my face, my carriage,[1] were soon lost or faded
when the Achaeans crossed the sea to Troy,
Odysseus my lord among the rest.
1310 If he returned, if he were here to care for me,
I might be happily renowned!
But grief instead heaven sent me—years of pain.
Sons of the noblest families on the islands,

Vocabulary Development

equity (EHK wit ee) *n.* fairness; justice

maudlin (MAWD lin) *adj.* tearfully and foolishly sentimental

---

1. **carriage** (KAR ij) *n.* posture.

© Pearson Education

Activate Prior Knowledge

Describe the characteristics of a hero.

_____

_____

_____

_____

_____

Literary Analysis

An **epic simile** is an elaborate comparison that may extend over several lines. Read the bracketed passage. To what is the old beggar comparing Penelope's name or reputation?

_____

_____

Reading Skill

The **historical and cultural context** of a work is the details of the time and place in which the work is set or was written. Penelope takes a stranger into her home. What does this tell you about her culture?

_____

_____

_____

Reading Check

What reason does the beggar give Penelope for his silence about himself and his past? Underline the text that tells the answer.

Reading Skill

The **historical and cultural context** of a work becomes more clear when you **identify influences on your own reading and responses**. How do the ancient Greek ideas in Penelope's speech about honoring the dead compare with modern ideas?

_____

_____

_____

_____

Stop to Reflect

Penelope succeeds in tricking her suitors and avoiding marriage for three years. What do her actions tell you about her?

_____

_____

_____

_____

Reading Check ✎

Circle the passage that tells why Penelope no longer fights her suitors.

1315 Dulichium, Same, wooded Zacynthus,[2]
with native Ithacans, are here to court me,
against my wish; and they consume this house.
Can I give proper heed to guest or suppliant
or herald on the realm's affairs?
                          How could I?
wasted with longing for Odysseus, while here
1320 they press for marriage.
                          Ruses[3] served my turn
to draw the time out—first a close-grained web
I had the happy thought to set up weaving
on my big loom in hall. I said, that day:
'Young men—my suitors, now my lord is dead,
1325 let me finish my weaving before I marry,
or else my thread will have been spun in vain.
It is a shroud I weave for Lord Laertes
when cold Death comes to lay him on his bier.
The country wives would hold me in dishonor
1330 if he, with all his fortune, lay unshrouded.'
I reached their hearts that way, and they agreed.
So every day I wove on the great loom,
but every night by torchlight I unwove it;
and so for three years I deceived the Achaeans.
1335 But when the seasons brought a fourth year on,
as long months waned, and the long days were spent,
through impudent folly in the slinking maids
they caught me—clamored up to me at night;
I had no choice then but to finish it.
1340 And now, as matters stand at last,
I have no strength left to evade a marriage,
cannot find any further way; my parents
urge it upon me, and my son
will not stand by while they eat up his property.
1345 He comprehends it, being a man full-grown,
able to oversee the kind of house
Zeus would endow with honor.
                          But you too
confide in me, tell me your ancestry.
You were not born of mythic oak or stone."

Penelope again asks the beggar to tell about himself. He makes up a tale in which Odysseus is mentioned and declares that Penelope's husband will soon be home.

1350 "You see, then, he is alive and well, and headed
homeward now, no more to be abroad
far from his island, his dear wife and son.
Here is my sworn word for it. Witness this,
god of the zenith, noblest of the gods,[4]

2. **Zacynthus** (za KIHN thuhs) _n._ a Greek island.

3. **ruses** (ROOZ ihz) _n._ tricks.

4. **god of the zenith, noblest of the gods** Zeus.

1355 and Lord Odysseus' hearthfire, now before me:
I swear these things shall turn out as I say.
Between this present dark and one day's ebb,
after the wane, before the crescent moon,
Odysseus will come."

The Challenge

Pressed by the suitors to choose a husband from among them, Penelope says she will marry the man who can string Odysseus' bow and shoot an arrow through twelve axhandle sockets. The suitors try and fail. Still in disguise, Odysseus asks for a turn and gets it.

                                    And Odysseus took his time,
1360 turning the bow, tapping it, every inch,
for borings that termites might have made
while the master of the weapon was abroad.
The suitors were now watching him, and some
jested among themselves:

                                        "A bow lover!"

1365 "Dealer in old bows!"
                        "Maybe he has one like it
at home!"

                "Or has an itch to make one for himself."

"See how he handles it, the sly old buzzard!"

And one disdainful suitor added this:
"May his fortune grow an inch for every inch he
        bends it!"

1370 But the man skilled in all ways of contending,
satisfied by the great bow's look and heft,
like a musician, like a harper, when
with quiet hand upon his instrument
he draws between his thumb and forefinger
1375 a sweet new string upon a peg: so effortlessly
Odysseus in one motion strung the bow.
Then slid his right hand down the cord and
        plucked it,
so the taut gut vibrating hummed and sang
a swallow's note.

                        In the hushed hall it smote the suitors
1380 and all their faces changed. Then Zeus thundered
overhead, one loud crack for a sign.
And Odysseus laughed within him that the son
of crooked-minded Cronus had flung that omen
        down.

Reading Skill

Read lines 1356–1359, in which the beggar predicts when Odysseus will return. He predicts the time based on the phases of the moon. How is this an example of the **historical and cultural context** of the story?

_____

_____

_____

_____

Literary Analysis ✏️

Underline the **epic simile** in the bracketed passage. Which of Odysseus' qualities is highlighted in this epic simile?

_____

_____

_____

_____

_____

Reading Check

What test does Penelope decide she will use to choose a husband? Underline the sentence that tell you.

Stop to Reflect

Why do you think Penelope set this test for her suitors?

_____

_____

_____

_____

Reading Skill

Odysseus passes Penelope's test. Consider the **historical and cultural context** of this detail. What does Odysseus' success tell you about Greek values?

_____

_____

_____

_____

Reading Check

Read Odysseus' words to Telemachus. What time does he say has arrived? Underline the answer in the text.

1385   He picked one ready arrow from his table
        where it lay bare: the rest were waiting still
        in the quiver for the young men's turn to come.
        He nocked[5] it, let it rest across the handgrip,
        and drew the string and grooved butt of the arrow,
        aiming from where he sat upon the stool.
                                        Now flashed
1390   arrow from twanging bow clean as a whistle
        through every socket ring, and grazed not one,
        to thud with heavy brazen head beyond.
                                        Then quietly
        Odysseus said:

                        "Telemachus, the stranger
        you welcomed in your hall has not disgraced you.
1395   I did not miss, neither did I take all day
        stringing the bow. My hand and eye are sound,
        not so contemptible as the young men say.
        The hour has come to cook their lordships' mutton—
        supper by daylight. Other amusements later,
1400   with song and harping that adorn a feast."

        He dropped his eyes and nodded, and the prince
        Telemachus, true son of King Odysseus,
        belted his sword on, clapped hand to his spear,
        and with a clink and glitter of keen bronze
1405   stood by his chair, in the forefront near his father.

Odysseus' Revenge
        Now shrugging off his rags the wiliest[6] fighter of
            the islands
        leapt and stood on the broad doorsill, his own bow
            in his hand.
        He poured out at his feet a rain of arrows from the
            quiver
        and spoke to the crowd:

                        "So much for that. Your clean-cut game is over.
1410   Now watch me hit a target that no man has hit
            before,
        if I can make this shot. Help me, Apollo."

        He drew to his fist the cruel head of an arrow for
            Antinous
        just as the young man leaned to lift his beautiful
            drinking cup,
        embossed, two-handled, golden: the cup was in his
            fingers:

---

5. **nocked** (nahkt) set an arrow into the bowstring.

6. **wiliest** (WY lee uhst) _adj._ craftiest; slyest.

1415   the wine was even at his lips: and did he dream of
        death?
    How could he? In that revelry[7] amid his throng of
        friends
    who would imagine a single foe—though a strong
        foe indeed—
    could dare to bring death's pain on him and
        darkness on his eyes?
    Odysseus' arrow hit him under the chin
1420   and punched up to the feathers through his throat.

    Backward and down he went, letting the winecup fall
    from his shocked hand. Like pipes his nostrils jetted
    crimson runnels, a river of mortal red,
    and one last kick upset his table
1425   knocking the bread and meat to soak in dusty blood.
    Now as they craned to see their champion where
        he lay
    the suitors jostled in uproar down the hall,
    everyone on his feet. Wildly they turned and scanned
    the walls in the long room for arms; but not a shield,
1430   not a good ashen spear was there for a man to take
        and throw.
    All they could do was yell in outrage at Odysseus:

    "Foul! to shoot at a man! That was your last shot!"
    "Your own throat will be slit for this!"
                    "Our finest lad is down!
    You killed the best on Ithaca."
                 "Buzzards will tear your eyes out!"
1435   For they imagined as they wished—that it was a
        wild shot,
    an unintended killing—fools, not to comprehend
    they were already in the grip of death.
    But glaring under his brows Odysseus answered:

    "You yellow dogs, you thought I'd never make it
1440   home from the land of Troy. You took my house to
        plunder. . .
    You dared bid for my wife while I was still alive.
    Contempt was all you had for the gods who rule
        wide heaven,
    contempt for what men say of you hereafter.
    Your last hour has come. You die in blood."

© Pearson Education

Vocabulary Development

contempt (kuhn TEHMPT) *n.* disdain or scorn

7. **revelry** (REHV uhl ree) *n.* noisy festivity.

TAKE NOTES

Reading Skill

When you **identify influences on your own reading and responses**, you can better understand the **historical and cultural context** of a work. Read the passage in which Odysseus kills Antinous. Does the way in which Odysseus kills Antinous agree with your idea of a "fair fight"? Explain.

_____

_____

_____

_____

_____

_____

Literary Analysis ✎

Circle the passage that describes Antinous as he is dying. Is this an **epic simile**? Why or why not?

_____

_____

_____

_____

_____

Reading Check ✎

At first, do the young men think Odysseus killed Antinous on purpose or not? Underline the text that tells you.

Reading Skill

Eurymachus blames Antinous for what happened at Odysseus' home. Consider the **historical and cultural context** of this work. Do you think this behavior of blaming another person is valued by the ancient Greeks? Why or why not?

_____

_____

_____

_____

Stop to Reflect

Odysseus does not accept Eurymachus' apology. Would you accept it? Why or why not?

_____

_____

_____

_____

_____

Reading Check

What items does Eurymachus offer Odysseus to try to calm his anger? Underline the text that tells you.

1445   As they all took this in, sickly green fear
       pulled at their entrails, and their eyes flickered
       looking for some hatch or hideaway from death.
       Eurymachus[8] alone could speak. He said:

       "If you are Odysseus of Ithaca come back,
1450   all that you say these men have done is true.
       Rash actions, many here, more in the countryside.
       But here he lies, the man who caused them all.
       Antinous was the ringleader, he whipped us on
       to do these things. He cared less for a marriage
1455   than for the power Cronion has denied him
       as king of Ithaca. For that
       he tried to trap your son and would have killed him.
       He is dead now and has his portion. Spare
       your own people. As for ourselves, we'll make
1460   restitution of wine and meat consumed,
       and add, each one, a tithe of twenty oxen
       with gifts of bronze and gold to warm your heart.
       Meanwhile we cannot blame you for your anger."

       Odysseus glowered under his black brows
1465   and said:
               "Not for the whole treasure of your fathers,
       all you enjoy, lands, flocks, or any gold
       put up by others, would I hold my hand.
       There will be killing till the score is paid.
       You forced yourselves upon this house. Fight your
           way out,
1470   or run for it, if you think you'll escape death.
       I doubt one man of you skins by."

       They felt their knees fail, and their hearts—but heard
       Eurymachus for the last time rallying them.
       "Friends," he said, "the man is implacable.
1475   Now that he's got his hands on bow and quiver
       he'll shoot from the big doorstone there
       until he kills us to the last man.
                                   Fight, I say,
       let's remember the joy of it. Swords out!
       Hold up your tables to deflect his arrows.
1480   After me, everyone: rush him where he stands.
       If we can budge him from the door, if we can pass
       into the town, we'll call out men to chase him.
       This fellow with his bow will shoot no more."

       He drew his own sword as he spoke, a broadsword
           of fine bronze,

---

8. **Eurymachus** (yoo RI muh kuhs)

1485   honed like a razor on either edge. Then crying
        hoarse and loud
    he hurled himself at Odysseus. But the kingly man
        let fly
    an arrow at that instant, and the quivering
        feathered butt
    sprang to the nipple of his breast as the barb stuck
        in his liver.
    The bright broadsword clanged down. He lurched
        and fell aside,
1490   pitching across his table. His cup, his bread and
        meat,
    were spilt and scattered far and wide, and his head
        slammed on the ground.
    Revulsion, anguish in his heart, with both feet
        kicking out,
    he downed his chair, while the shrouding wave of
        mist closed on his eyes.

    Amphinomus now came running at Odysseus,
1495   broadsword naked in his hand. He thought to make
    the great soldier give way at the door.
    But with a spear throw from behind Telemachus
        hit him
    between the shoulders, and the lancehead drove
    clear through his chest. He left his feet and fell
1500   forward, thudding, forehead against the ground.
    Telemachus swerved around him, leaving the long
        dark spear
    planted in Amphinomus. If he paused to yank it out
    someone might jump him from behind or cut him
        down with a sword
    at the moment he bent over. So he ran—ran from
        the tables
1505   to his father's side and halted, panting, saying:

    "Father let me bring you a shield and spear,
    a pair of spears, a helmet.
    I can arm on the run myself; I'll give
    outfits to Eumaeus and this cowherd.
1510   Better to have equipment."

                    Said Odysseus:
    "Run then, while I hold them off with arrows
    as long as the arrows last. When all are gone
    if I'm alone they can dislodge me."
                        Quick
    upon his father's word Telemachus
1515   ran to the room where spears and armor lay.
    He caught up four light shields, four pairs of spears,
    four helms of war high-plumed with flowing manes,
    and ran back, loaded down, to his father's side.

Literary Analysis

Why is the comparison of Eurymachus' sharp sword to a razor only a simile and not an **epic simile**?

_____

_____

_____

_____

Reading Check

How does Odysseus kill Eurymachus? Underline the text that tells you.

Reading Skill

Consider the **historical and cultural context** of this work. What cultural values are reflected by Telemachus when he helps his father by gathering weapons and by fighting?

_____

_____

_____

Read the first bracketed passage. What do the contrasting descriptions of Odysseus' and the suitors' actions tell you about the **historical and cultural context** of this epic?

_____

_____

_____

_____

Literary Analysis 🔍

Read the description of Odysseus in the second bracketed passage. Which details in this **epic simile** compare Odysseus' hair to a work of art?

_____

_____

_____

_____

_____

_____

Reading Check

Who helps Odysseus defeat the suitors? Underline the text that tells you.

He was the first to pull a helmet on
1520 and slide his bare arm in a buckler strap.
The servants armed themselves, and all three took
   their stand
beside the master of battle.
                While he had arrows
he aimed and shot, and every shot brought down
one of his huddling enemies.
1525 But when all barbs had flown from the bowman's
   fist,
he leaned his bow in the bright entryway
beside the door, and armed: a four-ply shield
hard on his shoulder, and a crested helm,
horsetailed, nodding stormy upon his head,
1530 then took his tough and bronze-shod spears. . . .

*Aided by Athena, Odysseus, Telemachus, Eumaeus, and
other faithful herdsmen kill all the suitors.*

And Odysseus looked around him, narrow-eyed,
for any others who had lain hidden
while death's black fury passed.
                In blood and dust
he saw that crowd all fallen, many and many slain.

1535 Think of a catch that fishermen haul in to a
   half-moon bay
in a fine-meshed net from the whitecaps of the sea:
how all are poured out on the sand, in throes for
   the salt sea,
twitching their cold lives away in Helios' fiery air:
so lay the suitors heaped on one another.

Penelope's Test
Penelope tests Odysseus to prove he really is her husband.

1540 Greathearted Odysseus, home at last,
was being bathed now by Eurynome
and rubbed with golden oil, and clothed again
in a fresh tunic and a cloak. Athena
lent him beauty, head to foot. She made him
1545 taller, and massive, too, with crisping hair
in curls like petals of wild hyacinth
but all red-golden. Think of gold infused
on silver by a craftsman, whose fine art
Hephaestus[9] taught him, or Athena: one
1550 whose work moves to delight: just so she lavished
beauty over Odysseus' head and shoulders.
He sat then in the same chair by the pillar,
facing his silent wife, and said:

---

9. **Hephaestus** (heh FEHS tuhs) god of fire and metalworking.

         "Strange woman,
the immortals of Olympus made you hard,

1555 harder than any. Who else in the world
would keep aloof as you do from her husband
if he returned to her from years of trouble,
cast on his own land in the twentieth year?

Nurse, make up a bed for me to sleep on.
1560 Her heart is iron in her breast."

         Penelope
spoke to Odysseus now. She said:

         "Strange man,
if man you are . . . This is no pride on my part
nor scorn for you—not even wonder, merely.
I know so well how you—how he—appeared
1565 boarding the ship for Troy. But all the same . . .

Make up his bed for him, Eurycleia.
Place it outside the bedchamber my lord
built with his own hands. Pile the big bed
with fleeces, rugs, and sheets of purest linen."

1570 With this she tried him to the breaking point,
and he turned on her in a flash raging:

"Woman, by heaven you've stung me now!
Who dared to move my bed?
No builder had the skill for that—unless
1575 a god came down to turn the trick. No mortal
in his best days could budge it with a crowbar.
There is our pact and pledge, our secret sign,
built into that bed—my handiwork
and no one else's!

         An old trunk of olive
1580 grew like a pillar on the building plot,
and I laid out our bedroom round that tree,
lined up the stone walls, built the walls and roof,
gave it a doorway and smooth-fitting doors.
Then I lopped off the silvery leaves and branches,
1585 hewed and shaped that stump from the roots up
into a bedpost, drilled it, let it serve
as model for the rest. I planed them all,
inlaid them all with silver, gold and ivory,
and stretched a bed between—a pliant web
1590 of oxhide thongs dyed crimson.
         There's our sign!
I know no more. Could someone else's hand
have sawn that trunk and dragged the frame away?"

Stop to Reflect

Penelope tests Odysseus by telling the servant to move the bed out of her room, even though Odysseus has already revealed himself. Would you test him if you were Penelope? Explain.

_____

_____

_____

_____

_____

Reading Check

How does Odysseus describe Penelope's attitude toward him? Underline the text that tells you.

Literary Analysis

Why is the simile comparing the olive trunk to a pillar not an **epic simile**?

_____

_____

_____

_____

_____

Reading Skill

Consider the **historical and cultural context** of this work. What Greek values has Penelope shown in testing the men?

_____

_____

_____

_____

Literary Analysis

Odysseus returns after more than twenty years of sailing the Mediterranean, trying to reach his home. All of his men have been lost, and he was nearly drowned at sea. Why is the **epic simile** in the bracketed passage a powerful image for the ending of the *Odyssey*?

_____

_____

_____

_____

_____

_____

Reading Check

Circle the passage that shows how Penelope reacts after Odysseus describes their bed.

Their secret! as she heard it told, her knees
grew tremulous and weak, her heart failed her.
1595   With eyes brimming tears she ran to him,
throwing her arms around his neck, and kissed him,
murmuring:

        "Do not rage at me, Odysseus!
No one ever matched your caution! Think
what difficulty the gods gave: they denied us
1600   life together in our prime and flowering years,
kept us from crossing into age together.
Forgive me, don't be angry. I could not
welcome you with love on sight! I armed myself
long ago against the frauds of men,
1605   impostors who might come—and all those many
whose underhanded ways bring evil on! . . .
But here and now, what sign could be so clear
as this of our own bed?
No other man has ever laid eyes on it—
1610   only my own slave, Actoris, that my father
sent with me as a gift—she kept our door.
You make my stiff heart know that I am yours."

Now from his breast into his eyes the ache
of longing mounted, and he wept at last,
1615   his dear wife, clear and faithful, in his arms,
longed for as the sunwarmed earth is longed for
   by a swimmer
spent in rough water where his ship went down
under Poseidon's blows, gale winds and tons of sea.
Few men can keep alive through a big surf
1620   to crawl, clotted with brine, on kindly beaches
in joy, in joy, knowing the abyss[10] behind:
and so she too rejoiced, her gaze upon her husband,
her white arms round him pressed as though forever.

The Ending

Odysseus is reunited with his father. Athena commands that peace prevail between Odysseus and the relatives of the slain suitors. Odysseus has regained his family and his kingdom.

Reader's Response: How does Odysseus compare with your ideas of what a hero should be? Explain.

_____

_____

10. **abyss** (uh BIS) *n.* ocean depths.

from the Odyssey, Part 2

1. **Respond:** Who do you think faced greater hardships while Odysseus was away from home—Odysseus or Penelope? Explain your response.

   _____

   _____

   _____

2. **Infer:** Why does Penelope believe that she must test Odysseus even though he has removed his disguise?

   _____

   _____

3. **Literary Analysis:** Use a chart like the one shown to analyze the **epic simile** in lines 1613–1624.

Items Being Compared	Details of Epic Simile	Purpose

4. **Reading Skill:** Do you think that Odysseus' values are unique to his culture, or are they universal? Explain.

   _____

   _____

   _____

Writing: Biography of Odysseus

Write a short **biography** of Odysseus. A biography is a description of someone's life. Base the biography on what you know from your reading of the *Odyssey*. Describe dramatic situations in gripping detail. These descriptions will capture your reader's attention. Use the chart below to help you write your biography of Odysseus.

Dramatic Events	Gripping Detail

Listening and Speaking: Debate

Make notes for your debate on the prosecution of Odysseus for killing Penelope's suitors.

Debate Teams: _____

Arguments for the Prosecution

_____

_____

_____

Arguments for the Defense

_____

_____

_____

Articles

About Articles

Articles are short pieces of expository text—they provide information on a particular topic. There are many types of articles, including magazine articles, newspaper articles, and articles published on Web sites. Most articles feature:

- a title
- a byline—the article author's name
- a friendly, relaxed tone—the sound of the author's voice
- text written for a general audience with language they will easily understand

Reading Skill

An **opinion** is a statement of what a person believes. Sometimes writers state opinions as if they were facts. When, in an article or other text, an author shares an opinion, he or she should also **substantiate** it—offer facts to support that opinion. If the author does not offer support, the opinion is **unsubstantiated**.

An author will sometimes introduce an opinion with phrases such as "I believe" or "In my opinion," but this is not always the case. Being able to separate substantiated opinions from unsubstantiated opinions allows you to judge whether or not a text is a reliable source of information.

As you read the magazine article, use the organizer below to evaluate the opinions the author presents.

Opinion	Support	Substantiated (supported) or Unsubstantiated (not supported)

The Sticker Bur

Into each and every barefoot Texas childhood a little sticker bur must fall.

Magazine Article

Features:
- title and byline
- friendly, relaxed tone
- text written for a general audience

Mimi Schwartz

I was in my early teens before I realized that children in other parts of the country could run barefoot through tall grass without fear. Any child who attempted to do so in Central Texas—or in most parts of the state, for that matter—was either very brave or just plain foolish. For Texas fields and lawns had little in common with the velvety expanses of, say, Massachusetts or Northern California. Here defenseless children had to contend with grass that concealed chiggers, mesquite thorns, hackberry branches, and, grizzliest of all, a small brown barb known to connoisseurs[1] as the sticker bur, land mine of the backyard. No instep, no matter how proudly toughened on sizzling pavement, could endure it.

The sticker bur served notice to suburban children that the Texas landscape, however well fenced, watered, graveled, or gardened, remained untamed and inhospitable. As part of a roving band of neighborhood kids, I learned to survey yards like a point man heading into dangerous territory. A dry, patchy lawn was best avoided, though a healthy-looking turf of Bermuda grass held no promise of safety either. Sticker grass was usually paler and spinier than Bermuda, but that difference was discernible only at very close range.

Our gang may not have known where stickers came from (I believed they were prickly pear burs, blown in from the desert), but we knew full well what they could do. When little Stan Shaw, one of our bravest members, would show off by racing up the street through the grass, the rest of us would wait to hear his strangled yelp—akin to that of a betrayed cocker spaniel. Then we knew the sticker had struck, and another yard was off-limits. Those were tragic moments for us because alternate routes were scarce: Even in October the asphalt was searing, and armies of red ants patrolled the curbs. Of course, no self-respecting Texas child would be caught dead doing the sensible thing, which was to put on a pair of shoes.

> The author expresses the opinion that children who ran through tall grass were "brave or just plain foolish." **Is this opinion substantiated or unsubstantiated? Explain.**

> Here, the author expresses an opinion about Stan Shaw and substantiates the opinion with examples as support.

---

1. **connoisseurs** (kän´ə sʉrs´) *n., pl.* people who have expert knowledge and keen discrimination in some field.

The sticker comes from a lateral and low-growing grasslike weed called the sandbur, which has been causing trouble for quite some time. It was first identified in the eighteenth century by Swedish botanist Carolus Linnaeus, author of *Species Plantarum*, the seminal work in plant taxonomy. The burs are actually spiny seeds that mature in the summer, just in time to torture tiny feet. "No other grassy plant has this...lance armed bur, and a description therefore is almost useless," writes Edwin Rollin Spencer in *All About Weeds.* "He who finds a sand bur does not have to be told what it is."

Today there are several kinds of sandbur, including southern, longspine, and field sandbur (whose Latin name, *Cenchrus incertus,* is particularly apt). The most cursory study of a botanical map will reveal why the plants are so familiar to Texans. Sandburs prefer the sandy soil of the southern U.S., especially that beside highways and baseball diamonds, where sand containing sandbur seeds is dumped as fill. Some infested states may have one kind of sandbur but not another, but Texas has all three common kinds, and they all thrive here. In this case, more is clearly not better.

It's hard to find anyone who doesn't hate the sandbur. Weed specialists use words like "nuisance," "pernicious," "noxious," and "hateful" to describe it. "It's considered one of the real bad grasses," says Texas A&M extension weed specialist Rupert Palmer. Cows and sheep dislike sandbur because it is painful to eat; commercial stockmen hate sandbur because it contaminates wool and mohair and is grounds for docking at time of sale. Suburbanites hate sandbur because it hides and breeds in their Bermuda grass.

The author presents opinions about the sandbur from a range of sources. **Are these opinions substantiated or unsubstantiated? Explain.**

Herbicides can be used to keep the seeds from germinating, but the best ways to get rid of sandbur are (a) mow and water your Bermuda grass frequently, (b) plant St. Augustine grass, which shades and crowds out sandbur, or (c) pull the sandbur out. One A&M specialist confessed that it took him three years to get his yard sticker-free using the last method, but it worked.

Still, there's one thing to be said for the loathsome sticker. It breeds cautiousness, a quality not widely admired here but useful in a state that features both jellyfish and rattlesnakes. The wise Texan learns to pick and choose his fights with the landscape. Nowadays, for instance, I do run through moderately high grass. But only with my boots on.

Do heroes have responsibilities?
THE BIG **?**
The author mentions that the sticker "breeds cautiousness." Do you think this sort of carefulness encourages personal responsibility? Explain.

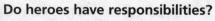

Thinking About the Article

1. What are sticker burs?

   _____

2. What problems do sticker burs cause?

   _____

Reading Skill

3. The author says "It's hard to find anyone who doesn't hate the [sticker bur]." What support does she offer for this opinion?

   _____

   _____

4. Give an example of an opinion the author offers. Tell whether the opinion is substantiated or unsubstantiated and explain why.

   _____

   _____

WRITE ABOUT IT Timed Writing: Critique (40 minutes)

Write a critique—a short essay—in which you analyze and give your opinion about the magazine article. In your critique, tell whether the author proves her overall opinion about sticker burs. Give examples of the support she uses for her ideas. Complete the sentence starters below before you begin writing. Then, refer to these notes as you draft your critique.

The author thinks sticker burs are _____.

She thinks this because _____.

She gives these facts to support her opinion:

_____

_____

_____

Three Skeleton Key • The Red-headed League

Literary Analysis

The **protagonist** is the chief character in a literary work. Some literary works also have an **antagonist**—a character or force that opposes the protagonist. The antagonist can be another character or an external force, such as nature.

- The protagonist's motives may be universally understood feelings and goals such as curiosity or the search for love.
- The protagonist's conflict with the antagonist may represent a universal struggle, such as the conflict between good and evil.

As you read, fill in the chart below.

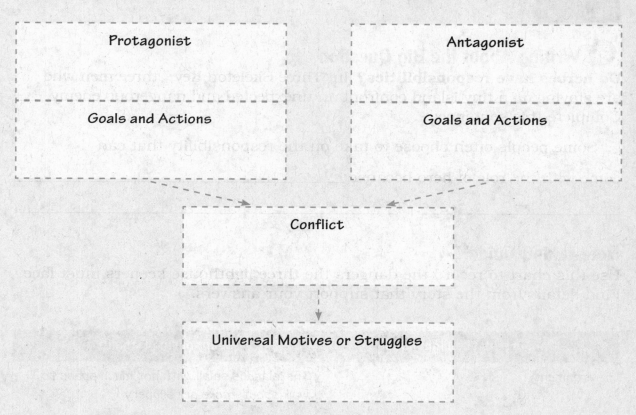

Protagonist

Goals and Actions

Antagonist

Goals and Actions

Conflict

Universal Motives or Struggles

Reading Skill

Comparing and contrasting characters is recognizing and thinking about their similarities and differences. **Generate questions after reading** about each character whom you are comparing.

- What are the character's actions?
- What are the character's reasons for his or her actions?
- What qualities does the character demonstrate?

Three Skeleton Key
George G. Toudouze

Summary Three lighthouse keepers become trapped in the lighthouse when a ship full of rats wrecks on Three Skeleton Key. The rats are hungry, and they will not go away until they have attacked the three men. The men are finally rescued eleven days after they were first trapped.

Writing About the Big Question

Do heroes have responsibilities? In "Three Skeleton Key," three men who are staying on a tiny island confront an unexpected and dangerous enemy. Complete this sentence:

Some people often choose to take on the responsibility that can

come with the role of hero because _____

_____.

Note-taking Guide

Use this chart to record the dangers the three lighthouse keepers must face. Find details from the story that support your answers.

Dangers at the Lighthouse	Supporting Details
Environment	The island is small, with not much space to walk about; rocks are slippery

Three Skeleton Key
George G. Toudouze

My most terrifying experience? Well, one does have a few in thirty-five years of service in the Lights, although it's mostly monotonous routine work—keeping the light in order, making out the reports.

When I was a young man, not very long in the service, there was an opening in a lighthouse newly built off the coast of Guiana,[1] on a small rock twenty miles or so from the mainland. The pay was high, so in order to reach the sum I had set out to save before I married, I volunteered for service in the new light.

Three Skeleton Key, the small rock on which the light stood, bore a bad reputation. It earned its name from the story of the three convicts who, escaping from Cayenne[2] in a stolen dugout canoe, were wrecked on the rock during the night, managed to escape the sea but eventually died of hunger and thirst. When they were discovered, nothing remained but three heaps of bones, picked clean by the birds. The story was that the three skeletons, gleaming with phosphorescent light,[3] danced over the small rock, screaming. . . .

But there are many such stories, and I did not give the warnings of the old-timers at the Isle de Sein[4] a second thought. I signed up, boarded ship, and in a month I was installed at the light.

Picture a grey, tapering cylinder, welded to the solid black rock by iron rods and concrete, rising from a small island twenty odd miles from land. It lay in the midst of the sea, this island, a small, bare piece of stone, about one hundred fifty feet long, perhaps forty wide. Small, barely large enough for a man to walk about and stretch his legs at low tide.

This is an advantage one doesn't find in all lights, however, for some of them rise sheer from the waves, with no room for one to move save within the light itself. Still, on our island, one must be careful, for the rocks were treacherously smooth. One misstep and down you would fall into the sea—not that the risk of drowning was so great, but the waters about our island swarmed with huge sharks who kept an eternal patrol around the base of the light.

Still, it was a nice life there. We had enough provisions to last for months, in the event that the sea should become too rough for the supply ship to reach us on schedule.

1. **Guiana** (gee AN uh) region on the northern coast of South America.
2. **Cayenne** (ky EHN) capital city of French Guiana.
3. **phosphorescent** (faws fuh RES uhnt) **light** a glowing light produced by certain natural chemical reactions.
4. **Isle de Sein** (EEL duh sehn) island off the northwestern coast of France.

Activate Prior Knowledge

What type of creatures do you find most frightening? Imagine that you have found yourself surrounded and trapped by these creatures. Explain how you might feel.

_____

_____

_____

Literary Analysis

The **protagonist** is the chief character of a literary work. The **antagonist** is a character or force that opposes the protagonist. Underline details in the bracketed paragraphs that show that the narrator is the protagonist in this story.

Reading Check

Are the waters surrounding Three Skeleton Key dangerous? Circle the text that tells you.

Stop to Reflect

The narrator says he and the other two lighthouse-keepers live on the lighthouse for eighteen weeks at a time without leaving. Would you like having such a job? What are the advantages of such a job? What are the disadvantages?

_____

_____

_____

_____

Reading Skill

Comparing and contrasting characters is recognizing their similarities and differences. What difference in the characters' ages does the narrator point out?

_____

_____

Reading Check

What surprising sight does Itchoua show his companions in the middle of the night? Underline the text that tells you.

During the day we would work about the light, cleaning the rooms, polishing the metalwork and the lens and reflector of the light itself, and at night we would sit on the gallery and watch our light, a twenty thousand candle-power lantern, swinging its strong, white bar of light over the sea from the top of its hundred-twenty-foot tower. Some days, when the air would be very clear, we could see the land, a thread-like line to the west. To the east, north and south stretched the ocean. Landsmen, perhaps, would soon have tired of that kind of life, perched on a small island off the coast of South America for eighteen weeks, until one's turn for leave ashore came around. But we liked it there, my two fellow-tenders and myself—so much so that, for twenty-two months on end with the exception of shore leaves, I was greatly satisfied with the life on Three Skeleton Key.

I had just returned from my leave at the end of June, that is to say mid-winter in that latitude, and had settled down to the routine with my two fellow-keepers, a Breton[5] by the name of Le Gleo and the head-keeper, Itchoua, a Basque[6] some dozen years or so older than either of us.

Eight days went by as usual, then on the ninth night after my return, Itchoua, who was on night duty, called Le Gleo and me, sleeping in our rooms in the middle of the tower, at two in the morning. We rose immediately and, climbing the thirty or so steps that led to the gallery, stood beside our chief.

Itchoua pointed, and following his finger, we saw a big three-master, with all sail set, heading straight for the light. A queer course, for the vessel must have seen us, our light lit her with the glare of day each time it passed over her.

Now, ships were a rare sight in our waters, for our light was a warning of treacherous reefs, barely hidden under the surface and running far out to sea. Consequently we were always given a wide berth, especially by sailing vessels, which cannot maneuver as readily as steamers.

No wonder that we were surprised at seeing this three-master heading dead for us in the gloom of early morning. I had immediately recognized her lines, for she stood out plainly, even at the distance of a mile, when our light shone on her.

She was a beautiful ship of some four thousand tons, a fast sailor that had carried cargoes to every part of the world, plowing the seas unceasingly. By her lines she was identified as Dutch—built, which was understandable as Paramaribo and Dutch Guiana are very close to Cayenne.

Watching her sailing dead for us, a white wave boiling under her bows, Le Gleo cried out:

---

5. **Breton** (BRET uhn) person born or living in Brittany, a region on the northwestern coast of France.
6. **Basque** (bask) member of a group of people who inhabit a region between Spain and France on the Bay of Biscay.

"What's wrong with her crew? Are they all drunk or insane? Can't they see us?"

Itchoua nodded soberly, looked at us sharply as he remarked: "See us? No doubt—if there is a crew aboard!"

"What do you mean, chief?" Le Gleo had started, turned to the Basque, "Are you saying that she's the Flying Dutchman?"[7]

His sudden fright had been so evident that the older man laughed:

"No, old man, that's not what I meant. If I say that no one's aboard, I mean she's a derelict."

Then we understood his queer behavior. Itchoua was right. For some reason, believing her doomed, her crew had abandoned her. Then she had righted herself and sailed on, wandering with the wind.

The three of us grew tense as the ship seemed about to crash on one of our numerous reefs, but she suddenly lurched with some change of the wind, the yards swung around, and the derelict came clumsily about and sailed dead away from us.

In the light of our lantern she seemed so sound, so strong, that Itchoua exclaimed impatiently:

"But why the devil was she abandoned? Nothing is smashed, no sign of fire—and she doesn't sail as if she were taking water."

Le Gleo waved to the departing ship:

"Bon voyage![8]" he smiled at Itchoua and went on. "She's leaving us, chief, and now we'll never know what—"

"No she's not!" cried the Basque. "Look! She's turning!"

As if obeying his words, the derelict three-master stopped, came about and headed for us once more. And for the next four hours the vessel played around us—zigzagging, coming about,[9] stopping, then suddenly lurching forward. No doubt some freak of current and wind, of which our island was the center, kept her near us.

Then suddenly, the tropic dawn broke, the sun rose and it was day, and the ship was plainly visible as she sailed past us. Our light extinguished, we returned to the gallery with our glasses and inspected her.

The three of us focused our glasses on her poop,[10] saw standing out sharply, black letters on the white background of a life-ring, the stenciled name:

Vocabulary Development

lurched (lercht) *v.* moved awkwardly and suddenly

7. **Flying Dutchman** fabled ghost ship doomed to sail forever.

8. **bon voyage** (bawn voy AWZH) French for "pleasant journey;" a farewell to a traveler.

9. **coming about** changing direction according to the direction of the wind.

10. **poop** (poop) *n.* raised deck at the rear of a sailing ship.

TAKE NOTES

Literary Analysis

What details on this page make you interested in what will happen to the **protagonist?**

_____

_____

_____

Reading Skill

Compare the three **characters'** reactions to the ship. Which one of the characters seems most frightened? Explain.

_____

_____

_____

Reading Check

How does the narrator explain why the ship stays near the lighthouse? Circle the text that tells you.

Reading Skill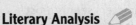

Compare and contrast the reactions of the narrator and Le Gleo to the doomed ship. How are their reactions similar? How are they different?

_____

_____

_____

_____

_____

Literary Analysis

Underline three details that show that the rats are fierce **antagonists**.

Reading Skill

How do the rats on the _Cornelius-de-Witt_ **contrast** with other rats in the world?

_____

_____

_____

_____

"*Cornelius-de-Witt*, Rotterdam."

We had read her lines correctly, she was Dutch. Just then the wind rose and the *Cornelius-de-Witt* changed course, leaned to port and headed straight for us once more. But this time she was so close that we knew she would not turn in time.

"Thunder!" cried Le Gleo, his Breton soul aching to see a fine ship doomed to smash upon a reef, "She's going to pile up! She's gone!"

I shook my head:

"Yes, and a shame to see that beautiful ship wreck herself. And we're helpless."

There was nothing we could do but watch. A ship sailing with all sail spread, creaming the sea with her forefoot as she runs before the wind, is one of the most beautiful sights in the world—but this time I could feel the tears stinging my eyes as I saw this fine ship headed for her doom.

All this time our glasses were riveted on her, and we suddenly cried out together:

"The rats!"

Now we knew why this ship, in perfect condition, was sailing without her crew aboard. They had been driven out by the rats. Not those poor specimens of rats you see ashore, barely reaching the length of one foot from their trembling noses to the tip of their skinny tails, wretched creatures that dodge and hide at the mere sound of a footfall.

No, these were ships' rats, huge, wise creatures, born on the sea, sailing all over the world on ships, transferring to other, larger ships as they multiply. There is as much difference between the rats of the land and these maritime rats as between a fishing smack and an armored cruiser.

The rats of the sea are fierce, bold animals. Large, strong and intelligent, clannish and seawise, able to put the best of mariners to shame with their knowledge of the sea, their uncanny ability to foretell the weather.

And they are brave, these rats, and vengeful. If you so much as harm one, his sharp cry will bring hordes of his fellows to swarm over you, tear you and not cease until your flesh has been stripped from the bones.

The ones on this ship, the rats of Holland, are the worst, superior to other rats of the sea as their brethren are to the land rats. There is a well-known tale about these animals.

A Dutch captain, thinking to protect his cargo, brought aboard his ship—not cats—but two terriers, dogs trained in the hunting, fighting and killing of vicious rats. By the time the ship, sailing from Rotterdam, had passed the Ostend light, the dogs were gone and never seen again. In twenty-four hours they had been overwhelmed, killed and eaten by the rats.

At times, when the cargo does not suffice, the rats attack the crew, either driving them from the ship or eating them alive. And studying the *Cornelius de Witt*, I turned sick, for her small boats were all in place. She had not been abandoned.

Over her bridge, on her deck, in the rigging, on every visible spot, the ship was a writhing mass—a starving army coming towards us aboard a vessel gone mad!

Our island was a small spot in that immense stretch of sea. The ship could have grazed us, passed to port or starboard with its ravening cargo—but no, she came for us at full speed, as if she were leading the regatta at a race, and impaled herself on a sharp point of rock.

There was a dull shock as her bottom stove in, then a horrible crackling as the three masts went overboard at once, as if cut down with one blow of some gigantic sickle. A sighing groan came as the water rushed into the ship, then she split in two and sank like a stone.

But the rats did not drown. Not these fellows! As much at home in the sea as any fish, they formed ranks in the water, heads lifted, tails stretched out, paws paddling. And half of them, those from the forepart of the ship, sprang along the masts and onto the rocks in the instant before she sank. Before we had time even to move, nothing remained of the three-master save some pieces of wreckage floating on the surface and an army of rats covering the rocks left bare by the receding tide.

Thousands of heads rose, felt the wind and we were scented, seen! To them we were fresh meat, after possible weeks of starving. There came a scream, composed of innumerable screams, sharper than the howl of a saw attacking a bar of iron, and in the one motion, every rat leaped to attack the tower!

We barely had time to leap back, close the door leading onto the gallery, descend the stairs and shut every window tightly. Luckily the door at the base of the light, which we never could have reached in time, was of bronze set in granite and was tightly closed.

The horrible band, in no measurable time, had swarmed up and over the tower as if it had been a tree, piled on the embrasures of the windows, scraped at the glass with thousands of claws, covered the lighthouse with a furry mantle and reached the top of the tower, filling the gallery and piling atop the lantern.

Their teeth grated as they pressed against the glass of the lantern-room, where they could plainly see us, though they could not reach us. A few millimeters of glass, luckily very strong, separated our faces from their gleaming, beady eyes, their sharp claws and teeth. Their odor filled the tower, poisoned our lungs and rasped our nostrils with a pestilential, nauseating smell. And there we were, sealed alive in our own light, prisoners of a horde of starving rats.

© Pearson Education

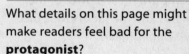

Stop to Reflect

Read the bracketed paragraph. How might you feel if you were the narrator at this time? Explain.

_____

_____

_____

Literary Analysis

What details on this page might make readers feel bad for the **protagonist**?

_____

_____

_____

_____

Reading Check

What tells the men that the crew of the *Cornelius-de-Witt* did not escape the ship? Circle the text that tells the answer.

Literary Analysis

Read the bracketed passage. With what external force are the **protagonist** and his companions now in conflict?

_____

_____

Reading Skill

Compare the behavior of the sharks and the rats. How is their behavior similar?

_____

_____

_____

Stop to Reflect

Does the narrator make you believe that rats would be capable of the actions he describes? Explain.

_____

_____

_____

Reading Check

Do the rats like the lighthouse light? Underline the text that tells you.

> That first night, the tension was so great that we could not sleep. Every moment, we felt that some opening had been made, some window given away, and that our horrible besiegers were pouring through the breach. The rising tide, chasing those of the rats which had stayed on the bare rocks, increased the numbers clinging to the walls, piled on the balcony—so much so that clusters of rats clinging to one another hung from the lantern and the gallery.

With the coming of darkness we lit the light, and the turning beam completely maddened the beasts. As the light turned, it successively blinded thousands of rats crowded against the glass, while the dark side of the lantern-room gleamed with thousands of points of light, burning like the eyes of jungle beasts in the night.

All the while we could hear the enraged scraping of claws against the stone and glass, while the chorus of cries was so loud that we had to shout to hear one another. From time to time, some of the rats fought among themselves and a dark cluster would detach itself, falling into the sea like a ripe fruit from a tree. Then we would see phosphorescent streaks as triangular fins slashed the water—sharks, permanent guardians of our rock, feasting on our jailors.

The next day we were calmer, and amused ourselves by teasing the rats, placing our faces against the glass which separated us. They could not fathom the invisible barrier which separated them from us, and we laughed as we watched them leaping against the heavy glass.

But the day after that, we realized how serious our position was. The air was foul; even the heavy smell of oil within our stronghold could not dominate the fetid odor of the beasts massed around us, and there was no way of admitting fresh air without also admitting the rats.

The morning of the fourth day, at early dawn, I saw the wooden framework of my window, eaten away from the outside, sagging inwards. I called my comrades and the three of us fastened a sheet of tin in the opening, sealing it tightly. When we had completed the task, Itchoua turned to us and said dully:

"Well—the supply boat came thirteen days ago, and she won't be back for twenty-nine." He pointed at the white metal plate sealing the opening through the granite—"If that gives way—" he shrugged—"they can change the name of this place to Six Skeletons Key."

The next six days and seven nights, our only distraction was watching the rats whose holds were insecure fall a hundred and twenty feet into the maws of the sharks— but they were so many that we could not see any <u>diminution</u> in their numbers.

Vocabulary Development

diminution (DIM uh noo shuhn) _n._ lessening

Thinking to calm ourselves and pass the time, we attempted to count them, but we soon gave up. They moved incessantly, never still. Then we tried identifying them, naming them.

One of them, larger than the others, who seemed to lead them in their rushes against the glass separating us, we named "Nero";[11] and there were several others whom we had learned to distinguish through various peculiarities.

But the thought of our bones joining those of the convicts was always in the back of our minds. And the gloom of our prison fed these thoughts, for the interior of the light was almost completely dark, as we had to seal every window in the same fashion as mine, and the only space that still admitted daylight was the glassed-in lantern-room at the very top of the tower.

Then Le Gleo became morose and had nightmares in which he would see the three skeletons dancing around him, gleaming coldly, seeking to grasp him. His maniacal, raving descriptions were so vivid that Itchoua and I began seeing them also.

It was a living nightmare, the raging cries of the rats as they swarmed over the light, mad with hunger; the sickening, strangling odor of their bodies—

True, there is a way of signaling from light-houses. But to reach the mast on which to hang the signal we would have to go out on the gallery where the rats were.

There was only one thing left to do. After debating all of the ninth day, we decided not to light the lantern that night. This is the greatest breach of our service, never committed as long as the tenders of the light are alive; for the light is something sacred, warning ships of danger in the night. Either the light gleams, a quarter hour after sundown, or no one is left alive to light it.

Well, that night, Three Skeleton Light was dark, and all the men were alive. At the risk of causing ships to crash on our reefs, we left it unlit, for we were worn out—going mad!

At two in the morning, while Itchoua was dozing in his room, the sheet of metal sealing his window gave way. The chief had just time enough to leap to his feet and cry for help, the rats swarming over him.

But Le Gleo and I, who had been watching from the lantern-room, got to him immediately, and the three of us battled with the horde of maddened rats which flowed through the gaping window. They bit, we struck them down with our knives—and retreated.

We locked the door of the room on them, but before we had time to bind our wounds, the door was eaten through and gave way, and we retreated up the stairs, fighting off the rats that leaped on us from the knee-deep swarm.

11. **Nero** (NIR oh) (A.D.37–68) Roman emperor who was notoriously cruel.

Literary Analysis

The **protagonist** names some of the rats. What does this detail tell you about his situation?

_____

_____

Stop to Reflect

What happens in Le Gleo's nightmares? Underline the text that tells you. How do his nightmares affect the other men?

_____

_____

_____

Literary Analysis

What do you think motivates the **protagonist** and Le Gleo to risk their lives to help Itchoua?

_____

_____

_____

_____

Reading Check

What do the men decide to do on the ninth day of their captivity? Underline the text that tells you.

Literary Analysis

Are the **antagonists** vicious, mindless animals or are they intelligent and organized?

_____

Underline two details that support your answer.

Reading Skill

Read the bracketed passage. **Contrast** the reactions of the narrator and Le Gleo. What do the differences in their reactions make clear?

_____

_____

_____

_____

_____

Reading Check

Why does the patrol ship arrive? Circle the text that tells you.

I do not remember, to this day, how we ever managed to escape. All I can remember is wading through them up the stairs, striking them off as they swarmed over us; and then we found ourselves, bleeding from innumerable bites, our clothes shredded, sprawled across the trapdoor in the floor of the lantern-room—without food or drink. Luckily, the trapdoor was metal set into the granite with iron bolts.

The rats occupied the entire light beneath us, and on the floor of our retreat lay some twenty of their fellows, who had gotten in with us before the trapdoor closed, and whom we had killed with our knives. Below us, in the tower, we could hear the screams of the rats as they devoured everything edible that they found. Those on the outside squealed in reply, and writhed in a horrible curtain as they stared at us through the glass of the lantern-room.

Itchoua sat up, stared silently at his blood trickling from the wounds on his limbs and body, and running in thin streams on the floor around him. Le Gleo, who was in as bad a state (and so was I, for that matter) stared at the chief and me vacantly, started as his gaze swung to the multitude of rats against the glass, then suddenly began laughing horribly:

"Hee! Hee! The Three Skeletons! Hee! Hee! The Three Skeletons are now six skeletons! Six skeletons!"

He threw his head back and howled, his eyes glazed, a trickle of saliva running from the corners of his mouth and thinning the blood flowing over his chest. I shouted to him to shut up, but he did not hear me, so I did the only thing I could to quiet him—I swung the back of my hand across his face.

The howling stopped suddenly, his eyes swung around the room, then he bowed his head and began weeping softly, like a child.

Our darkened light had been noticed from the mainland, and as dawn was breaking, the patrol was there to investigate the failure of our light. Looking through my binoculars, I could see the horrified expression on the faces of the officers and crew when, the daylight strengthening, they saw the light completely covered by a seething mass of rats. They thought, as I afterwards found out, that we had been eaten alive.

But the rats had also seen the ship, or had scented the crew. As the ship drew nearer, a solid phalanx[12] left the light, plunged into the water and, swimming out, attempted to board her. They would have succeeded, as the ship was hove to, but the engineer connected his steam to a hose on the deck and scalded the head of the attacking column, which slowed them up long enough for the ship to get underway and leave the rats behind.

12. **phalanx** (FAY langks) *n.* group of individuals advancing in a close, compact formation.

Then the sharks took part. Belly up, mouths gaping, they arrived in swarms and scooped up the rats, sweeping through them like a sickle through wheat. That was one day that sharks really served a useful purpose.

The remaining rats turned tail, swam to the shore, and emerged dripping. As they neared the light, their comrades greeted them with shrill cries, with what sounded like a <u>derisive</u> note predominating. They answered angrily and mingled with their fellows. From the several tussles that broke out, they resented being ridiculed for their failure to capture the ship.

But all this did nothing to get us out of our jail. The small ship could not approach, but steamed around the light at a safe distance, and the tower must have seemed fantastic, some weird, many—mouthed beast hurling defiance at them.

Finally, seeing the rats running in and out of the tower through the door and the windows, those on the ship decided that we had perished and were about to leave when Itchoua, regaining his senses, thought of using the light as a signal. He lit it and, using a plank placed and withdrawn before the beam to form the dots and dashes, quickly sent out our story to those on the vessel.

Our reply came quickly. When they understood our position—how we could not get rid of the rats, Le Gleo's mind going fast, Itchoua and myself covered with bites, cornered in the lantern-room without food or water—they had a signalman send us their reply.

His arms, swinging like those of a windmill, he quickly spelled out:

"Don't give up. Hang on a little longer! We'll get you out of this!"

Then she turned and steamed at top speed for the coast, leaving us little reassured.

She was back at noon, accompanied by the supply ship, two small coast guard boats, and the fire boat—a small squadron. At twelve-thirty the battle was on.

After a short reconnaissance,[13] the fire boat picked her way slowly through the reefs until she was close to us, then turned her powerful jet of water on the rats. The heavy stream tore the rats from their places, hurled them screaming into the water where the sharks gulped them down. But for every ten that were dislodged, seven swam ashore, and the stream could do nothing to the rats within the tower. Furthermore, some of them, instead of returning to the rocks, boarded the fire boat, and the men were

© Pearson Education

Vocabulary Development
derisive (di RI siv) *adj.* mocking

13. **reconnaissance** (ri KAWN uh suhns) *n.* explanatory survey or examination.

Stop to Reflect

Read the bracketed passage. The narrator suggests that the rats resent being made fun of by the other rats. In this description, what power does the narrator suggest that the rats possess?

_____

_____

_____

_____

Literary Analysis

How does the conflict between the **protagonist** and the rats represent the universal struggle for survival?

_____

_____

_____

_____

Reading Check ✏

How do the men signal the rescue ship? Underline the text that tells you.

Read the underlined sentence. What is the narrator saying about the **antagonists**?

_____

_____

_____

Stop to Reflect 📖

Does human intelligence win out in the conflict and overcome the rats' brutality in the end? Explain.

_____

_____

_____

_____

Reading Skill 📖

Generating questions after reading can help you **compare and contrast**. What is one question you could ask about the narrator?

_____

_____

What is one question you could ask about the rats?

_____

_____

forced to battle them hand to hand. They were true rats of Holland, fearing no man, fighting for the right to live!

Nightfall came, and it was as if nothing had been done, the rats were still in possession. One of the patrol boats stayed by the island; the rest of the flotilla[14] departed for the coast. We had to spend another night in our prison. Le Gleo was sitting on the floor, babbling about skeletons, and as I turned to Itchoua, he fell unconscious from his wounds. I was in no better shape and could feel my blood flaming with fever.

Somehow the night dragged by, and the next afternoon I saw a tug, accompanied by the fire boat, coming from the mainland with a huge barge in tow. Through my glasses, I saw that the barge was filled with meat.

Risking the treacherous reefs, the tug dragged the barge as close to the island as possible. To the last rat, our besiegers deserted the rock, swam out and boarded the barge reeking with the scent of freshly cut meat. The tug dragged the barge about a mile from shore, where the fire boat drenched the barge with gasoline. A well placed incendiary shell from the patrol boat set her on fire.

The barge was covered with flames immediately, and the rats took to the water in swarms, but the patrol boat bombarded them with shrapnel from a safe distance, and the sharks finished off the survivors.

A whaleboat from the patrol boat took us off the island and left three men to replace us. By nightfall we were in the hospital in Cayenne.

What became of my friends? Well, Le Gleo's mind had cracked and he was raving mad. They sent him back to France and locked him up in an asylum,[15] the poor devil; Itchoua died within a week; a rat's bite is dangerous in that hot, humid climate, and infection sets in rapidly.

As for me—when they fumigated[16] the light and repaired the damage done by the rats, I resumed my service there. Why not? No reason why such an incident should keep me from finishing out my service there, is there?

Besides—I told you I liked the place—to be truthful, I've never had a post as pleasant as that one, and when my time came to leave it forever, I tell you that I almost wept as Three Skeleton Key disappeared below the horizon.

14. **flotilla** (floh TIL uh) _n._ small fleet.

15. **asylum** (uh SY luhm) _n._ institution for the care of the mentally ill.

16. **fumigated** (FYOO muh gayt id) _v._ disinfected with fumes.

Three Skeleton Key

1. **Infer:** Consider how the rats come to the island. What impression of the rats does this method of arrival create?

   _____

   _____

2. **Infer:** Itchoua remarks, "If that [window] gives way, they can change the name of this place to Six Skeletons Key." What does Itchoua mean by this remark?

   _____

   _____

3. **Literary Analysis:** What universal struggle does the conflict between the **protagonist** and the **antagonist** represent?

   _____

   _____

4. **Reading Skill:** Complete the Venn diagram below to **compare and contrast** the narrator's outlook at the beginning of the story with his outlook at the end of the story.

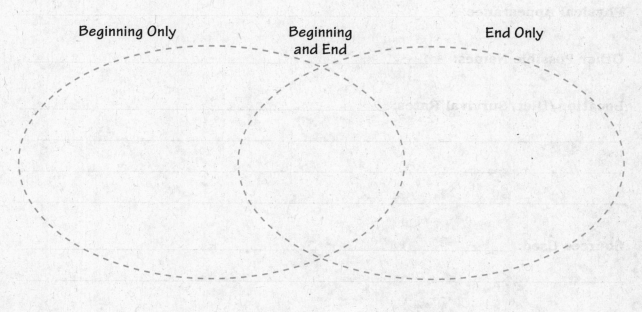

Beginning Only   Beginning and End   End Only

Writing: Journal Entries

Imagine that you are one of the characters in "Three Skeleton Key" other than the narrator. Write three **journal entries** describing the events in the story as they unfold.

- Choose three situations from the story.

  _____

  _____

- Describe how the character feels in each situation.

  _____

  _____

- Describe how the character reacts in each situation.

  _____

  _____

Use your notes to write your journal entries.

Research and Technology: Oral Report

Use the following lines to jot down notes for your **oral report** on ship rats. Try to use both print and non-print sources in your research.

Physical Appearance: _____

Other Possible Names: _____

Location/Diet/Survival Rates: _____

_____

_____

_____

Sources Used: _____

_____

The Red-headed League
Sir Arthur Conan Doyle

Summary Jabez Wilson, a pawnbroker, consults Sherlock Holmes about the mysterious "Red-headed League." The League employed him for a short time and then disappeared overnight. Holmes discovers that criminals invented the League. He must use his powers of observation to stop a daring robbery plan.

 Writing About the Big Question

Do heroes have responsibilities? In "The Red-headed League," Sherlock Holmes sets out to solve a peculiar mystery involving men with brilliant red hair. Complete these sentences:

When a crime is being committed, a hero will _____.

The heroes involvement may show his or her character because

_____.

Note-taking Guide
Use this sequence-of-events chart to record the plot of the story.

The Red-headed League employs Jabez Wilson.	→		→		→		→	Holmes traps the criminals.

The Red-headed League

1. **Infer:** Why does Holmes find Wilson's story interesting?

   _____

   _____

2. **Analyze Cause and Effect:** Which clues found at Saxe-Coburg Square lead to Holmes's solution of the mystery?

   _____

   _____

3. **Literary Analysis:** Identify the **protagonist**. What is the protagonist's goal?

   _____

   _____

4. **Reading Skill:** Fill in the Venn diagram below to **compare and contrast** Holmes's character at the beginning of the story with his character at the end of the story.

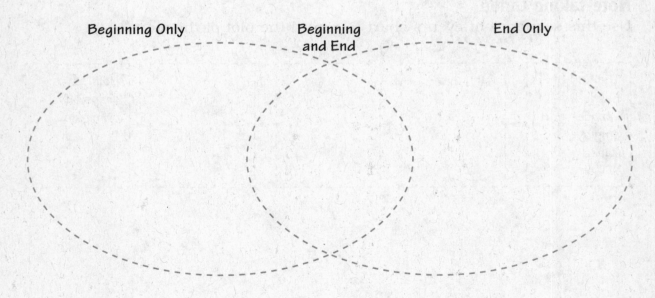

Beginning Only   Beginning   End Only
                      and End

Writing: Journal Entries

Imagine that you are one of the characters in "The Red-headed League" other than Dr. Watson. Write three **journal entries** describing the events in the story as they unfold.

- Choose three situations from the story.

  _____

  _____

- Describe how the character feels in each situation.

  _____

  _____

- Describe how the character reacts in each situation.

  _____

  _____

Use your notes to write your journal entries.

Research and Technology: Oral Report

Use the following lines to jot down notes for your **oral report** on the science of detective work. Try to use both print and non-print sources in your research.

Fingerprinting: _____

Lie Detectors: _____

Other Techniques Used to Gather Information: _____

_____

_____

_____

Sources Used: _____

_____

There Is a Longing • Glory and Hope

Literary Analysis

An author's **purpose**, or goal, is shaped by his or her **philosophical assumptions**, or basic beliefs. These philosophical assumptions may be political ideology, moral or ethical beliefs, or assumptions about human nature. The author may use these basic beliefs as support for his or her argument. The response of the **audience**, or readers, to the author's work will depend on whether the audience shares the basic beliefs underlying the author's purpose.

Identify the basic beliefs and assumptions in the author's work to read critically. Determine whether you accept them and whether others in the intended audience would be likely to accept them. Then, evaluate whether these assumptions help the author achieve his or her purpose. Use the chart below to record your ideas as you read.

Philosophical Assumptions	Evaluation

Reading Skill

Comparing and contrasting is recognizing similarities and differences. Authors often use a compare-and-contrast organization to show the similarities and differences between one point of view and another in persuasive writing. Use self-monitoring techniques like the ones shown to make sure that you understand the comparisons.

- Identify the things or ideas being compared.
- Restate the similarities and differences in your own words.
- Explain the significance of the similarities and differences.

If you cannot identify, restate, or explain the author's points, reread to clarify or to find words or phrases that were unclear.

There Is a Longing
Chief Dan George

Summary The speaker believes that Native Americans must hold on to their cultural values and traditions. They must also take part in "the white man's success" in order to survive. He wants to see his people rise up and be great once more. He asks the Great Spirit to help him guide his people to a better life.

Writing About the Big Question

Do heroes have responsibilities? In his speech, Chief Dan George says his power to make war is gone, but he longs to serve his people. Complete these sentences:

Not all heroes know they are heroes because _____

_____. A leader can be a true hero when he or she

_____.

Note-taking Guide

Use this chart to record the longings of Chief Dan George and his people.

The Speaker's Longings
for his people to have what they need to survive

Activate Prior Knowledge

What qualities do you think an individual must have in order to succeed in society? Explain.

_____

_____

_____

_____

Literary Analysis

A writer's **purpose** is his or her reason for writing. **Philosophical assumptions** are basic beliefs. What is Chief George's purpose for writing?

_____

_____

What are the philosophical assumptions that help shape his purpose?

_____

_____

Reading Skill

Comparing and contrasting is recognizing similarities and differences. How are new warriors different from old warriors?

_____

_____

_____

Reading Check

What is the only weapon left to Chief Dan George? Circle the text that tells you.

There Is a Longing
Chief Dan George

There is a longing in the heart of my people
to reach out and grasp that which is needed
for our survival. There is a longing among
the young of my nation to secure for themselves
5 and their people the skills that will
provide them with a sense of worth and
purpose. They will be our new warriors.
Their training will be much longer and
more demanding than it was in olden days.
10 The long years of study will demand more
determination; separation from home and
family will demand endurance. But they
will emerge with their hand held forward,
not to receive welfare, but to grasp the
15 place in society that is rightly ours.

I am a chief, but my power to make war
is gone, and the only weapon left to me
is speech. It is only with tongue and speech
that I can fight my people's war.
20 Oh, Great Spirit![1] Give me back the courage
of the olden Chiefs. Let me wrestle with
my surroundings. Let me once again,
live in harmony with my environment.
Let me humbly accept this new culture
25 and through it rise up and go on. Like
the thunderbird[2] of old, I shall rise again
out of the sea; I shall grab the instruments
of the white man's success—his
education, his skills. With these new tools
30 I shall build my race into the proudest
segment of your society. I shall see our
young braves and our chiefs sitting in
the houses of law and government, ruling
and being ruled by the knowledge and
35 freedoms of our great land.

Vocabulary Development

determination (dee ter mi NAY shuhn) _n._ firm intention
endurance (ehn DOOR uhns) _n._ ability to withstand hardship

1. **Great Spirit** for many Native Americans, the greatest power or god.
2. **thunderbird** powerful supernatural creature that was thought to produce thunder by flapping its wings and to produce lightning by opening and closing its eyes. In the folklore of some Native American nations, the thunderbird is in constant warfare with the powers beneath the waters.

There Is a Longing

1. **Analyze:** Why does Chief Dan George believe that it is necessary for the "new warriors" to endure new training?

   _____

   _____

   _____

2. **Interpret:** What does Chief Dan George mean when he refers to fighting a war "with tongue and speech"?

   _____

   _____

   _____

3. **Literary Analysis:** Do you think that Chief Dan George's intended audience shares his basic beliefs? Support your answer with details from the text.

   _____

   _____

   _____

4. **Reading Skill:** Use this chart to record the ideas that Chief Dan George presents about the past, present, and future.

Past	Present	Future

Writing: Letter

Write a **letter** to Chief Dan George telling him how you feel about "There Is a Longing." Find the four passages that you think are most inspiring. Discuss those passages in your letter. Use the chart below to write notes for your letter.

Passage	What the Passage Means	Why It Is Inspiring

Listening and Speaking: Media Analysis

Use the graphic organizer below to gather ideas for your media analysis.

Web Site:	_____	_____
Audience	small children	adults
Purpose		
Formality		
Tone		

Glory and Hope
Nelson Mandela

Summary "Glory and Hope" is a speech that Nelson Mandela gave when he became president of South Africa. He talks about his vision for South Africa. He urges his listeners to face the challenges of the future with hope and determination.

? Writing About the Big Question

Do heroes have responsibilities? In his speech, Nelson Mandela celebrates the liberty newly gained by his country and pleads for national reconciliation and liberty. Complete these sentences:

When a leader promises to serve his or her nation, he or she has an

obligation to follow through because _____.

The leader may become a heroic figure to many because _____

_____.

Note-taking Guide
Use this chart to compare the old South Africa to the new South Africa.

Old South Africa	New South Africa

Glory and Hope

1. **Generalize:** Which ideas in the speech are especially important for safeguarding the human rights of all people throughout today's world?

   _____

   _____

2. **Connect:** How does the title of the speech connect with the ideas Mandela conveys?

   _____

   _____

3. **Literary Analysis:** What are the **philosophical assumptions**, or basic beliefs, that help shape the purpose of Nelson Mandela's speech?

   _____

   _____

4. **Reading Skill:** Use this chart to record the ideas that Nelson Mandela presents about the past, present, and future.

Past	Present	Future

Writing: Letter

Write a **letter** to Nelson Mandela telling him how you feel about "Glory and Hope." Find the four passages that you think are the most inspiring. Discuss those passages in your letter. Use the chart below to write notes for your letter.

Passage	What the Passage Means	Why It Is Inspiring

Listening and Speaking: Media Analysis

Use the graphic organizer below to gather ideas for your media analysis.

Web Site:	_____	_____
Audience	small children	adults
Purpose		
Formality		
Tone		

Expository Texts

About Expository Texts

There are a wide variety of **expository texts**, including newspapers, magazines, Web sites, press releases, and multimedia presentations. Expository texts may be long or short, may contain graphics or just text, and may be written for general or specific audiences. However, all expository texts are written for the general purpose of informing or describing.

Reading Skill

In an expository text, the author's general purpose is to inform or describe. However, the author will also have a specific purpose for writing. When you analyze an author's purpose, consider both the general and the specific purpose. To determine the specific purpose, consider the controlling, or main, idea of the text as well as the details used to support that idea. Those details will also support the author's specific purpose.

An almanac is an expository text that provides facts, dates, and statistics on a particular subject. As you read the almanac entry, use this chart to explain the author's specific purpose.

> **General Purpose**
> to inform

> **Specific Purpose**

> Detail

> Detail

> Detail

> Detail

> **Controlling Idea**

★ TEXAS ALMANAC ★

(from the 1911 Texas Almanac)

Automobiles in Texas

Ten years ago an automobile was a curiosity in the leading cities of Texas. Five years ago the people in many counties had never seen what was then known as the horseless carriage. Today it is estimated that the number of automobiles in actual service in Texas will reach nearly 30,000 and that over $40,000,000 is invested in the machines. Reports, dated August 1, 1910, from 180 counties in the State show a total of 14,276 automobiles. A canvass by the Commercial Secretaries' Association places the number at 30,000, which, at an average value of $1,500 each, would make the investment $45,000,000. This number is constantly increasing, and counting the life of a machine at three years, the new machines purchased to take the place of old ones cost $15,000,000 annually.

Although the automobile is counted a luxury and in the majority of cases, is used for pleasure, or as a means of transportation from the home to the office, the automobile is found in practical everyday life in all parts of the State. In the cities it is taking the place of the hack and the carriage and in many instances of the truck and the delivery wagon.

In the plains country the automobile is used to carry the mail and to cover long distances not traversed by railroads. Commercial travelers use them in making towns in their district or territory, saving time thereby, and in many other ways has the machine been adapted to commercial purposes.

According to the Almanac canvass, Dallas County led all other counties in the number of automobiles registered August 1, 1910. Since that date nearly 200 machines have been added to the list, but August 1 registry is used in comparison with other county statistics secured on that date.

On August 1, Dallas County reported 1,390 automobiles; Harris, 1,031; Bexar, 1,024; Tarrant, 852; McLennan, 546; El Paso, 506; Jefferson, 413; Travis, 375; Potter, 350; Williamson, 275; Galveston, 219; Hale, 200; Tom Green, 190; Taylor, 176; Hunt, 172; Bell, 171; Navarro, 146; Collins, 133; Runnels, 127; Cooke, 125; Lubbock, 125; Johnson, 110. Reports from other counties show less than 100 automobiles registered and are not placed in this list.

Review the content of these sentences. **Explain the specific purpose of this paragraph.**

The details in this paragraph support the author's purpose.

Do heroes have responsibilities?
(a) How have the increasing numbers of automobiles added to the widespread effects of using them? **(b)** How have these increasing numbers and uses of automobiles added responsibility to both automakers and drivers?

Thinking About the Expository Texts

1. How many years ago was the almanac entry written?

_____

2. What changes in automobile use does the almanac entry point out?

_____

TALK ABOUT IT Reading Skill

3. The author's general purpose for writing the almanac entry is to inform. How successful is he or she at achieving this general purpose? Give two reasons for your answer.

_____

_____

4. Why might the author of the almanac entry have included details about the number of automobiles in different cities in Texas?

_____

_____

WRITE ABOUT IT Timed Writing: Essay **(40 minutes)**

Write an essay in which you explain and analyze the specific purpose of the almanac entry. Provide evidence from the text to support your ideas. Use the list below to record ideas to include in your essay.

General Purpose: to inform

Specific Purpose: _____

Textual Evidence of Specific Purpose:

_____

_____

_____

The exercises and tools presented here are designed to help you increase your vocabulary. Review the instruction and complete the exercises to build your vocabulary knowledge. Throughout the year, you can apply these skills and strategies to improve your reading, writing, speaking, and listening vocabulary.

The following list contains common word roots with meanings and examples. On the blank lines, write other words you know that have the same roots. Write the meanings of the new words.

Root	Meaning	Example and Meaning	Your Words	Meanings
-brev-	brief; short	*brevity:* the quality of lasting for a short time		
-cede-	go	*recede:* move or go away or move or go back		
-dict-	say or tell	*predict:* tell what might happen next		
-fac-	make	*factory:* place where things are made		
-fer-	bring; carry	*reference:* something you say or write that mentions another person or thing, something that brings or carries more information		
-ject-	throw	*eject:* push or throw out with force		
-manu-	hand	*manual:* operated or done by hand		

Root	Meaning	Example and Meaning	Your Words	Meanings
-phon-	hearing; sound	*telephone:* a device that brings sound over long distances		
-port-	carry	*support:* carry or hold something up		
-scrib-	write	*scribble:* write something quickly in a messy way		
-sequ-	follow	*consequence:* effect that follows a cause		
-similis-	same	*similar:* alike in some way		
-spec-	look; see	*inspect:* look carefully at something		
-sum-	take; use	*assumption:* something that you think is true or take as true		
-tele-	far; distant	*telescope:* instrument that makes distant objects look larger		
-vali-	strong; worth	*valid:* true, based on strong reasons or facts		
-ver-	truth	*verify:* make sure something is true		

The following list contains common prefixes with meanings and examples. On the blank lines, write other words you know that begin with the same prefixes. Write the meanings of the new words.

Prefix	Meaning	Example and Meaning	Your Words	Meanings
anti-	against	*antisocial:* not liking to meet and talk to people; against friendliness		
aud-	hearing; sound	*auditorium:* a room for hearing concerts or speeches		
con-	with; together	*concur:* agree with		
de-	down; from	*decrease:* become less		
dis-	not	*disorganized:* not organized		
in-	without; not	*incapable:* not able		
inter-	between	*intermission:* short period of time between the parts of a play or concert		
ir-	without; not	*irregular:* not regular		

Prefix	Meaning	Example and Meaning	Your Words	Meanings
mis-	wrong; bad	*misspell:* spell wrong; spell incorrectly		
multi-	many	*multicolored:* having many colors		
non-	without; not	*nonfat:* without fat		
ob-	against	*obstacle:* something that works against another, something that makes it difficult for you to succeed		
post-	after	*post-test:* a test given after instruction		
pre-	before	*preview:* look before		
re-	again	*remake:* make again		
sub-	below, under	*submarine:* a ship that moves under the ocean		
super-	above; over	*superior:* better than another		
un-/an-/a-	not	*unbelievable:* not believable		

© Pearson Education

The following list contains common suffixes with meanings and examples. On the blank lines, write other words you know that have the same suffixes. Write the meanings of the new words.

Suffix	Meaning	Example and Meaning	Your Words	Meanings
-able/-ible	able to be	*movable*: able to be moved		
-al	relating to	*financial*: relating to money		
-ance/-ence	act of; state of; quality of	*assistance*: act of giving help		
-ate	make	*motivate*: make someone feel eager to do something		
-en	make	*weaken*: make something less strong		
-er/-or	one who	*actor*: person who acts		
-ful	filled with	*joyful*: filled with happiness		
-hood	state or quality of	*manhood*: the state of being an adult male		

Suffix	Meaning	Example and Meaning	Your Words	Meanings
-ic	like; pertaining to	*heroic:* like a hero; brave		
-ish	resembling	*foolish:* not sensible		
-ist	one who	*violinist:* person who plays the violin		
-ize/-yze	make	*publicize:* make public; tell people about		
-less	without	*powerless:* without power		
-ly	in a way	*quickly:* done in a short amount of time		
-ment	act or quality of	*excitement:* feeling of being excited		
-ness	state or quality of	*kindness:* friendly and caring behavior		
-ous	having; full of	*famous:* having fame; known and recognized by many people		
-sion/-tion	act or process of	*persuasion:* act of convincing someone		

Use a **dictionary** to find the correct spelling, the meaning, the pronunciation, and the part of speech of a word. The dictionary will show you how the plural is formed if it is irregular. You can also find the word's history, or *etymology*, in a dictionary. Etymology explains how words change, how they are borrowed from other languages, and how new words are invented, or "coined."

Here is a sample entry from a dictionary. Notice what it tells about the word. Then, follow the instructions.

---

lemon (lem´ ən) **n.** [ME *lymon* < MFr *limon* < Ar *laimūn* < Pers *līmūn*]
1 a small, egg-shaped, edible citrus fruit with a yellow rind and a juicy, sour pulp, rich in ascorbic acid **2** the small, spiny, semitropical evergreen citrus tree (*Citrus limon*) bearing this fruit **3** pale yellow **4** [slang] something, esp. a manufactured article, that is defective or imperfect

---

1. Circle the *n.* in the dictionary entry. It stands for *noun.* Write what these other parts of speech abbreviations mean: *v.* _____, *adv.* _____, *adj.* _____, *prep.* _____.

2. Underline the origins of the word *lemon.* ME stands for Middle English, Ar stands for Arabic, and Pers. stands for Persian. What do you think MFr stands for? _____

3. Put a box around the pronunciation.

4. How many noun definitions does the entry have? _____

5. Which definition is slang? _____

6. Which definition of *lemon* is used in the following sentence? _____

   The car that my dad bought turned out to be a lemon.

Activity: Use a dictionary to learn about the origins of these words.

Activity: Use a dictionary to learn about the origins of these words.

1. literature _____ / _____ / _____
           pronunciation   main part of speech   original language(s)
_____ / _____
      1st meaning   other meanings

_____

_____

_____

_____

2. language _____ / _____ / _____
           pronunciation   main part of speech   original language(s)
_____ / _____
      1st meaning   other meanings

_____

_____

_____

Activity: Look up each of the following words in a dictionary. Then, write a definition of the word and a sentence using the word.

moment _____

_____

popular _____

_____

remedy _____

_____

blur _____

_____

lazy _____

_____

Use these word study cards to break big words into their parts. Write the word at the top of the card. Then, divide the word into its prefix, root, and suffix. Note that not all words have prefixes and suffixes. List the meaning of each part of the word. Next, find three words with the same root and write them on the card. Finally, write the word's part of speech and its definition. Use a dictionary to help you. One example has been done for you.

Word:	invisible	
Prefix	**Root**	**Suffix**
in: not	**vis:** see	**ible**-able to be

Root-related Words
1. vision
2. revise
3. visibility

Definition: invisible *adj.* not able to be seen

Word:		
Prefix	**Root**	**Suffix**

Root-related Words
1.
2.
3.

Definition:

Word:

Prefix	Root	Suffix

Root-related Words
1.
2.
3.

Definition:

Word:

Prefix	Root	Suffix

Root-related Words
1.
2.
3.

Definition:

Word:

Prefix	Root	Suffix

Root-related Words
1.
2.
3.

Definition:

appreciate (uh PREE shee ayt) *v.* recognize; understand and be grateful for

contemporary (kuhn TEM puh rer ee) *adj.* recent or current; living or happening at the same time

contribute (kuhn TRIB yoot) *v.* give, add, provide

detect (dee TEKT) *v.* discover

display (di SPLAY) *v.* exhibit; show

involve (in VAHLV) *v.* include, require

participate (pahr TIS uh payt) *v.* take part in, join

specific (spuh SIF ik) *adj.* precise, or definite

trivial (TRIV ee uhl) *adj.* of little or no importance

vital (VYT uhl) *adj.* necessary

A. True/False For each of the following, mark T or F to indicate whether the italicized vocabulary word has been used correctly in the sentence. If you have marked F, correct the sentence by changing the words that make the statement wrong.

1. _____ William Shakespeare is considered to be a *contemporary* author.

2. _____ We will *contribute* twelve cans of soup to the food drive.

3. _____ Two characters *participate* in the conflict over the farm.

4. _____ Life-or-death situations are considered *trivial*.

5. _____ I *appreciate* it when my shoes are stolen from my locker.

6. _____ Air is *vital* for humans to live.

7. _____ Most people will *display* their faults in public.

8. _____ To *detect* a change in the mood, you must pay attention to the details.

9. _____ Do not *involve* James in the argument you are having.

10. _____ Alice was being *specific* when she said she would be home around noon.

B. Original Sentences Use each academic vocabulary word in an original sentence that illustrates its meaning.

appreciate _____

_____

contemporary _____

_____

contribute _____

_____

detect _____

_____

display _____

_____

involve _____

_____

participate _____

_____

specific _____

_____

trivial _____

_____

vital _____

_____

aspect (AS pekt) *n.* an element or a part

attitude (AT uh tood) *n.* a way of acting that shows a disposition or opinion

categorize (KAT uh guh ryz) *v.* classify; place within a group

circumstance (SER kuhm stans) *n.* a fact or event

emotion (ee MOH shuhn) *n.* a feeling

imply (im PLY) *v.* hint at or suggest

motive (MOHT iv) *n.* the reason a person acts in a certain way

sequence (SEE kwuhns) *n.* an arrangement in which one follows another

topic (TAHP ik) *n.* the subject or a work or talk

verify (VER uh fy) *v.* test whether something is true

A. Completions Complete each sentence that has been started for you. Your sentence completion should be logical and illustrate the meaning of the vocabulary word in italics.

1. he scientist ran tests to *verify* _____

2. Please, *categorize* these facts into _____

3. The *circumstance* that would most likely make me scream would be _____
_____

4. His *motive* for stealing the car was _____

5. The *aspect* of her personality that I like the most is _____
_____

6. You will get along with people better if you have an *attitude* that is _____
_____

7. The most powerful *emotion* is _____

8. My favorite *topic* for group discussion is _____
_____

9. When I got home, the front door was open, which *implies* _____
_____

10. An example of a logical *sequence* is _____

B. Original Sentences Use each academic vocabulary word in an original sentence that illustrates its meaning.

aspect _____

_____

attitude _____

_____

categorize _____

_____

circumstance _____

_____

emotion _____

_____

imply _____

_____

motive _____

_____

sequence _____

_____

topic _____

_____

verify _____

_____

C. Write new words that you come across in your reading. Define each word.

_____

_____

_____

abstract (AB strakt) *n.* summary

anticipate (an TIS uh payt) *v.* expect something

contemplate (KAHN tuhm playt) *v.* consider or think about

derive (di RYV) *v.* get from a source

equivalent (ee KWIV uh luhnt) *adj.* equal in meaning

hence (HENS) *adv.* as a result; therefore

illuminate (i LOO muh nayt) *v.* make clear

internal (in TER nuhl) *adj.* on the inside

signify (SIG nuh fy) *v.* be a sign of something

texture (TEKS chuhr) *n.* arrangement or structure of something

A. Code Name Use the code to figure out each vocabulary word. Each letter is represented by a number or symbol.

%	5	•	*	2	#	!	7	^	&	9	¶	£	$	3	¥	+	=	?	÷	4	¢	6	§	«	ç
a	b	c	d	e	f	g	h	i	j	k	l	m	n	o	p	q	r	s	t	u	v	w	x	y	z

1. ÷ 2 § ÷ 4 = 2   _____

2. ^ $ ÷ 2 = $ %   _____

3. % 5 ? ÷ = % • ÷   _____

4. 7 2 $ • 2   _____

5. % $ ÷ ^ • ^ ¥ % ÷ 2   _____

6. * 2 = ^ ¢ 2   _____

7. ? ^ ! $ ^ # «   _____

8. ^ ¶ ¶ 4 £ ^ $ % ÷ 2   _____

9. • 3 $ ÷ 2 £ ¥ ¶ % ÷ 2   _____

10. 2 + 4 ^ ¢ % ¶ 2 $ ÷   _____

B. Use each academic vocabulary word in an original sentence that illustrates its meaning.

abstract _____

_____

anticipate _____

_____

contemplate _____

_____

derive _____

_____

equivalent _____

_____

hence _____

_____

illuminate _____

_____

internal _____

_____

signify _____

_____

texture _____

_____

C. Write new words that you come across in your reading. Define each word.

_____

_____

_____

abstract (AB strakt) *adj.* not concrete; of thought

considerable (kuhn SID er uh buhl) *adj.* much or large; worth noting

concept (KAHN sept) *n.* idea

deliberation (di lib uhr AY shuhn) *n.* act of carefully thinking about an issue

distinct (di STINKT) *adj.* separate; well defined

emphasize (EM fuh syz) *v.* stress

impact (IM pakt) *n.* force of a collision; shock

mechanism (MEK uh niz uhm) *n.* system or means of doing something; working parts of a machine

transition (tran ZISH uhn) *n.* passing from one to another

usage (YOO sij) *n.* way of using something

A. Completions Complete each sentence that has been started for you. Your sentence completion should be logical and illustrate the meaning of the vocabulary word in italics.

1. Two examples of *abstract* words are _____

2. Careful *deliberation* is necessary before deciding to _____
_____

3. When reading poetry, you should *emphasize* _____

4. The teenage years are a *transition* from _____
_____

5. An object of *considerable* weight is _____

6. In science class, I learned the *concept* of _____
_____

7. The scientist invented a *mechanism* that would _____
_____

8. When giving a speech, you should demonstrate correct *usage* of _____
_____

9. Part of my *distinct* style is my _____

10. An event that might cause a huge *impact* is _____

B. Use each academic vocabulary word in an original sentence that illustrates its meaning.

abstract _____

_____

considerable _____

_____

concept _____

_____

deliberation _____

_____

distinct _____

_____

emphasize _____

_____

impact _____

_____

mechanism _____

_____

transition _____

_____

usage _____

_____

C. Write new words that you come across in your reading. Define each word.

_____

_____

_____

ambiguous (am BIG yoo uhs) *adj.* having numerous possible meanings

compile (kuhm PYL) *v.* put together; compose by gathering materials

condense (kuhn DENS) *v.* shorten or make concise

convince (kuhn VINS) *v.* overcome doubts; persuade

elaborate (ee LAB uh rayt) *v.* work out in detail

elaborate (ee LAB uh rit) *adj.* extremely detailed

illuminate (i LOO muh nayt) *v.* make clear; provide insight

implement (IM pluh ment) *v.* put into action; fulfill or accomplish

relevant (REL uh vuhnt) *adj.* related to

revise (ri VYZ) *v.* read carefully to correct

strategy (STRAT uh jee) *n.* science of managing or planning; plan

A. Answer each question. Then, explain your answer.

1. Would an *ambiguous* answer be clear?

   _____

   _____

2. What would you *compile* if you were creating an anthology?

   _____

   _____

3. Is a heavily decorated room *elaborate*?

   _____

   _____

4. Would a *condensed* book be longer than the original?

   _____

   _____

5. Would a book on raising tigers be *relevant* to your life?

   _____

   _____

   _____

6. If you were asked to *elaborate* on your plan, what would you do?

_____

_____

7. What type of activity might require a *strategy*?

_____

_____

8. If you were asked to *revise* your essay, what would you do?

_____

_____

9. How could you *convince* your younger brother to stop pestering you?

_____

_____

10. Could an explanation *illuminate* a question?

_____

_____

11. Would a general *implement* a flawed battle plan?

_____

_____

B. Write new words that you come across in your reading. Define each word.

_____

_____

_____

_____

_____

appraise (uh PRAYZ) *v.* judge the quality or worth of something; set a value on something

cogent (KOH juhnt) *adj.* convincing; powerfully appealing

coherent (koh HER uhnt) *adj.* orderly or logical; sticking together

compelling (kuhm PEL ing) *v.* forcing or pressuring

complex (kahm PLEKS) *adj.* complicated or intricate

confirm (kuhn FERM) *v.* prove the truth or authenticity

controversy (KAHN truh ver see) *n.* a discussion over opposing viewpoints; a dispute

defect (DEE fekt) *n.* an imperfection

significant (sig NIF uh kuhnt) *adj.* important; full of meaning

technique (tek NEEK) *n.* methods used to create an artistic work

A. True/False For each of the following, mark T or F to indicate whether the italicized vocabulary word has been used correctly in the sentence. If you have marked F, correct the sentence by changing the words that make the statement wrong.

1. _____ If you give a *cogent* explanation of your ideas, everyone will vote for you.

2. _____ To *confirm* the contents of the food, read the ingredients label.

3. _____ Infants can usually complete *complex* tasks.

4. _____ If a computer has a *defect*, it may not run properly.

5. _____ The instructions were *coherent*, so I couldn't build the model.

6. _____ There was *controversy* about the new law, and everyone agreed that the government was right to pass it.

7. _____ To solve a problem, you should ignore the most *significant* parts of the issue.

8. _____ When you practice, you can improve your *technique*.

9. _____ To *appraise* the value of a car, offer the owner more money than it is worth.

10. _____ The details in the story were *compelling* us to keep reading, so we stopped before we were finished.

B. Write original sentences using only the two vocabulary words per sentence that are given to you.

1. appraise / confirm _____

_____

2. cogent / compelling _____

_____

3. defect / significant _____

_____

4. coherent / controversy _____

_____

5. complex / technique _____

_____

C. Write new words that you come across in your reading. Define each word.

_____

_____

_____

Use this page to write down academic words you come across in other subjects, such as social studies or science. When you are reading your textbooks, you may find words that you need to learn. Following the example, write down the word, the part of speech, and an explanation of the word. You may want to write an example sentence to help you remember the word.

dissolve *verb* to make something solid become part of a liquid by putting it in a liquid and mixing it

The sugar *dissolved* in the hot tea.

_____

_____

_____

_____

_____

_____

_____

_____

_____

_____

_____

_____

_____

_____

_____

_____

Use these flash cards to study words you want to remember. The words on this page come from Unit 1. Cut along the dotted lines on pages V25 through V28 to create your own flash cards or use index cards. Write the word on the front of the card. On the back, write the word's part of speech and definition. Then, write a sentence that shows the meaning of the word.

forebears	rancor	atonement
obstinacy	tantalizingly	furtive
reciprocate	elusive	pertinent

noun ancestors His forebears started the family business.	*noun* stubbornness The child refused to clean up, and she was punished for her obstinacy.	*verb* return She refused to reciprocate his anger.
noun bitter hate The rivals fumed with rancor for each other.	*adverb* in a teasing way He held the ball tantalizingly out of reach.	*adjective* hard to grasp or retain mentally The correct answer was elusive to him.
noun act of making up for a wrongdoing or injury He volunteered at a nursing home as atonement for his misbehavior.	*adjective* sneaky With a furtive wink, he let his friend in on the joke.	*adjective* relevant; having a connection to the matter at hand Let's discuss only pertinent information at this meeting.

Use these flash cards to study words you want to remember. Cut along the dotted lines on pages V25 through V28 to create your own flash cards or use index cards. Write the word on the front of the card. On the back, write the word's part of speech and definition. Then, write a sentence that shows the meaning of the word.

VOCABULARY FOLD-A-LIST

Use a fold-a-list to study the definitions of words. The words on this page come from Unit 1. Write the definition for each word on the lines. Fold the paper along the dotted line to check your definition. Create your own fold-a-lists on pages V31 and V32.

tumultuous _____

_____

implications _____

_____

poignant _____

_____

distraught _____

_____

insolent _____

_____

inscrutable _____

_____

bilingual _____

_____

countenance _____

_____

interminably _____

_____

pallid _____

_____

Fold In ↓

© Pearson Education

Write the word that matches the definition on each line.
Fold the paper along the dotted line to check your work.

greatly disturbed;
in an uproar   _____

indirect results   _____

emotionally touching   _____

troubled or confused   _____

boldly disrepectful   _____

baffling; mysterious   _____

using two languages   _____

face   _____

endlessly   _____

pale   _____

Fold In ←

Write the words you want to study on this side of the page. Write the definitions on the back. Then, test yourself. Fold the paper along the dotted line to check your definition.

Word: _____

_____

Word: _____

_____

Word: _____

_____

Word: _____

_____

Word: _____

_____

Word: _____

_____

Word: _____

_____

Word: _____

_____

Word: _____

_____

Word: _____

_____

Fold In ←

Write the word that matches the definition on each line.
Fold the paper along the dotted line to check your work.

Definition: _____

Definition: _____

Definition: _____

Definition: _____

Definition: _____

Definition: _____

Definition: _____

Definition: _____

Definition: _____

Definition: _____

Fold In ←

The list on these pages presents words that cause problems for many people. Some of these words are spelled according to set rules, but others follow no specific rules. As you review this list, check to see how many of the words give you trouble in your own writing. Then, add your own commonly misspelled words on the lines that follow.

abbreviate	auxiliary	census	deficient
absence	awkward	certain	definitely
absolutely	bandage	changeable	delinquent
abundance	banquet	characteristic	dependent
accelerate	bargain	chauffeur	descendant
accidentally	barrel	chief	description
accumulate	battery	clothes	desert
accurate	beautiful	coincidence	desirable
ache	beggar	colonel	dessert
achievement	beginning	column	deteriorate
acquaintance	behavior	commercial	dining
adequate	believe	commission	disappointed
admittance	benefit	commitment	disastrous
advertisement	bicycle	committee	discipline
aerial	biscuit	competitor	dissatisfied
affect	bookkeeper	concede	distinguish
aggravate	bought	condemn	effect
aggressive	boulevard	congratulate	eighth
agreeable	brief	connoisseur	eligible
aisle	brilliant	conscience	embarrass
all right	bruise	conscientious	enthusiastic
allowance	bulletin	conscious	entrepreneur
aluminum	buoyant	contemporary	envelope
amateur	bureau	continuous	environment
analysis	bury	controversy	equipped
analyze	buses	convenience	equivalent
ancient	business	coolly	especially
anecdote	cafeteria	cooperate	exaggerate
anniversary	calendar	cordially	exceed
anonymous	campaign	correspondence	excellent
answer	canceled	counterfeit	exercise
anticipate	candidate	courageous	exhibition
anxiety	capacity	courteous	existence
apologize	capital	courtesy	experience
appall	capitol	criticism	explanation
appearance	captain	criticize	extension
appreciate	career	curiosity	extraordinary
appropriate	carriage	curious	familiar
architecture	cashier	cylinder	fascinating
argument	catastrophe	deceive	February
associate	category	decision	fiery
athletic	ceiling	deductible	financial
attendance	cemetery	defendant	fluorescent

foreign	minuscule	proceed	_____
fourth	miscellaneous	prominent	
fragile	mischievous	pronunciation	_____
gauge	misspell	psychology	
generally	mortgage	publicly	_____
genius	naturally	pursue	
genuine	necessary	questionnaire	_____
government	neighbor	realize	
grammar	neutral	really	_____
grievance	nickel	recede	
guarantee	niece	receipt	_____
guard	ninety	receive	
guidance	noticeable	recognize	_____
handkerchief	nuisance	recommend	
harass	obstacle	reference	_____
height	occasion	referred	
humorous	occasionally	rehearse	_____
hygiene	occur	relevant	
ignorant	occurred	reminiscence	_____
immediately	occurrence	renowned	
immigrant	omitted	repetition	_____
independence	opinion	restaurant	
independent	opportunity	rhythm	_____
indispensable	optimistic	ridiculous	
individual	outrageous	sandwich	_____
inflammable	pamphlet	satellite	
intelligence	parallel	schedule	_____
interfere	paralyze	scissors	
irrelevant	parentheses	secretary	_____
irritable	particularly	siege	
jewelry	patience	solely	_____
judgment	permanent	sponsor	
knowledge	permissible	subtle	_____
lawyer	perseverance	subtlety	
legible	persistent	superintendent	_____
legislature	personally	supersede	
leisure	perspiration	surveillance	_____
liable	persuade	susceptible	
library	phenomenal	tariff	_____
license	phenomenon	temperamental	
lieutenant	physician	theater	_____
lightning	pleasant	threshold	
likable	pneumonia	truly	_____
liquefy	possess	unmanageable	
literature	possession	unwieldy	_____
loneliness	possibility	usage	
magnificent	prairie	usually	_____
maintenance	precede	valuable	
marriage	preferable	various	_____
mathematics	prejudice	vegetable	
maximum	preparation	voluntary	_____
meanness	previous	weight	
mediocre	primitive	weird	_____
mileage	privilege	whale	
millionaire	probably	wield	_____
minimum	procedure	yield	

When you are reading, you will find many unfamiliar words. Here are some tools that you can use to help you read unfamiliar words.

Phonics

Phonics is the science or study of sound. When you learn to read, you learn to associate certain sounds with certain letters or letter combinations. You know most of the sounds that letters can represent in English. When letters are combined, however, it is not always so easy to know what sound is represented. In English, there are some rules and patterns that will help you determine how to pronounce a word. This chart shows you some of the vowel digraphs, which are combinations like *ea* and *oa*. Two vowels together are called vowel digraphs. Usually, vowel digraphs represent the long sound of the first vowel.

Vowel Diagraphs	Examples of Unusual Sounds	Exceptions
ee and *ea*	steep, each, treat, sea	head, sweat, dread
ai and *ay*	plain, paid, may, betray	plaid
oa, *ow*, and *oe*	soak, slow, doe	now, shoe
ie and *igh*	lie, night, delight	friend, eight

As you read, sometimes the only way to know how to pronounce a word with an ea spelling is to see if the word makes sense in the sentence. Look at this example:

The water pipes were made of *lead*.

First, try out the long sound "ee." Ask yourself if it sounds right. It does not. Then, try the short sound "e." You will find that the short sound is correct in that sentence.

Now try this example.

Where you *lead*, I will follow.

Word Patterns

Recognizing different vowel-consonant patterns will help you read longer words. In the following sections, the **V** stands for "vowel" and the **C** stands for "consonant."

Single-syllable Words

CV – go: In two letter words with a consonant followed by a vowel, the vowel is usually long. For example, the word *go* is pronounced with a long *o* sound.

In a single syllable word, a vowel followed only by a single consonant is usually short.

CVC – got: If you add a consonant to the word *go*, such as the *t* in *got*, the vowel sound is a short *o*. Say the words *go* and *got* aloud and notice the difference in pronunciation.

Multi-syllable words

In words of more than one syllable, notice the letters that follow a vowel.

VCCV – robber: A single vowel followed by two consonants is usually short.

VCV — begin: A single vowel followed by a single consonant is usually long.

VCe — beside: An extension of the VCV pattern is vowel-consonant-silent *e*. In these words, the vowel is long and the *e* is not pronounced.

When you see a word with the VCV pattern, try the long vowel sound first. If the word does not make sense, try the short sound. Pronounce the words *model*, *camel*, and *closet*. First, try the long vowel sound. That does not sound correct, so try the short vowel sound. The short vowel sound is correct in those words.

Remember that patterns help you get started on figuring out a word. You will sometimes need to try a different sound or find the word in a dictionary.

As you read and find unfamiliar words, look the pronunciations up in a dictionary. Write the words in this chart in the correct column to help you notice patterns and remember pronunciations.

Syllables	Example	New words	Vowel
CV	go		long
CVC	got		short
VCC	robber		short
V/CV	begin open		long long
VC/V	closet		short

Mnemonics are devices, or methods, that help you remember things. The basic strategy is to link something you do not know with something that you *do* know. Here are some common mnemonic devices:

Visualizing Create a picture in your head that will help you remember the meaning of a vocabulary word. For example, the first four letters of the word *significance* spell *sign.* Picture a sign with the word *meaning* written on it to remember that significance means "meaning" or "importance."

Spelling The way a word is spelled can help you remember its meaning. For example, you might remember that *clarify* means to "make clear" if you notice that both *clarify* and *clear* start with the letters *cl.*

To help you remember how to spell certain words, look for a familiar word within the difficult word. For example:

Believe has a *lie* in it.

Separate is *a rat* of a word to spell.

Your *principal* is your *pal.*

Rhyming Here is a popular rhyme that helps people figure out how to spell *ei* and *ie* words.

i before **e** — except after **c** *or when sounding like* **a** *as in neighbor and weigh.*

List words here that you need help remembering. Work with a group to create mnemonic devices to help you remember each word.

_____	_____
_____	_____
_____	_____
_____	_____

List words here that you need help remembering. Work with a group to create mnemonic devices to help you remember each word.

_____   _____

_____   _____

_____   _____

_____   _____

_____   _____

_____   _____

_____   _____

_____   _____

_____   _____

_____   _____

_____   _____

_____   _____

_____   _____

Use these sentence starters to help you express yourself clearly in different classroom situations.

Expressing an Opinion
I think that _____

I believe that _____

In my opinion, _____

Agreeing
I agree with _____ that _____

I see what you mean.

That's an interesting idea.

My idea is similar to _____'s idea.

My idea builds upon _____'s idea.

Disagreeing
I don't completely agree with you because _____

My opinion is different than yours.

I got a different answer than you.

I see it a different way.

Reporting a Group's Ideas
We agreed that _____

We decided that _____

We had a different approach.

We had a similar idea.

Predicting
I predict that _____

I imagine that _____

Based on _____ I predict that _____

Paraphrasing
So you are saying that _____

In other words, you think _____

What I hear you saying is _____

Offering a Suggestion
Maybe we could _____

What if we _____

Here's something we might try.

Asking for Clarification
I have a question about that.

Could you explain that another way?

Can you give me another example of that?

Asking for a Response
What do you think?

Do you agree?

What answer did you get?

VOCABULARY BOOKMARKS

Cut out each bookmark to use as -a handy word list when you are reading. On the lines, jot down words you want to learn and remember. You can also use the bookmark as a placeholder in your book.

TITLE	
Word	**Page #**
_____	_____
_____	_____
_____	_____
_____	_____
_____	_____
_____	_____
_____	_____
_____	_____
_____	_____
_____	_____
_____	_____
_____	_____
_____	_____

TITLE	
Word	**Page #**
_____	_____
_____	_____
_____	_____
_____	_____
_____	_____
_____	_____
_____	_____
_____	_____
_____	_____
_____	_____
_____	_____
_____	_____
_____	_____

TITLE	
Word	**Page #**
_____	_____
_____	_____
_____	_____
_____	_____
_____	_____
_____	_____
_____	_____
_____	_____
_____	_____
_____	_____
_____	_____
_____	_____
_____	_____

Cut out each bookmark to use as a handy word list when you are reading. On the lines, jot down words you want to learn and remember. You can also use the bookmark as a placeholder in your book.

TITLE		TITLE		TITLE	
Word	**Page #**	**Word**	**Page #**	**Word**	**Page #**
_____	_____	_____	_____	_____	_____
_____	_____	_____	_____	_____	_____
_____	_____	_____	_____	_____	_____
_____	_____	_____	_____	_____	_____
_____	_____	_____	_____	_____	_____
_____	_____	_____	_____	_____	_____
_____	_____	_____	_____	_____	_____
_____	_____	_____	_____	_____	_____
_____	_____	_____	_____	_____	_____
_____	_____	_____	_____	_____	_____
_____	_____	_____	_____	_____	_____
_____	_____	_____	_____	_____	_____

Use these cards to record words you want to remember. Write the word, the title of the story or article in which it appears, its part of speech, and its definition. Then, use the word in an original sentence that shows its meaning

Word: _____ Page _____

Selection: _____

Part of Speech: _____

Definition: _____

_____

My Sentence _____

_____

Word: _____ Page _____

Selection: _____

Part of Speech: _____

Definition: _____

_____

My Sentence _____

_____

Word: _____ Page _____

Selection: _____

Part of Speech: _____

Definition: _____

_____

My Sentence _____

_____

VOCABULARY BUILDER CARDS

Use these cards to record words you want to remember. Write the word, the title of the story or article in which it appears, its part of speech, and its definition. Then, use the word in an original sentence that shows its meaning

Word: _____ Page _____

Selection: _____

Part of Speech: _____

Definition: _____

_____

My Sentence _____

_____

Word: _____ Page _____

Selection: _____

Part of Speech: _____

Definition: _____

_____

My Sentence _____

_____

Word: _____ Page _____

Selection: _____

Part of Speech: _____

Definition: _____

_____

My Sentence _____

_____

Using the Personal Thesaurus

The Personal Thesaurus provides students with the opportunity to make connections between words academic words, familiar words, and even slang words. Students can use the Personal Thesaurus to help them understand the importance of using words in the proper context and also avoid overusing words in their writing.

Use the following routine to foster frequent use of the Personal Thesaurus.

1. After students have read a selection or done some writing, have them turn to the Personal Thesaurus.

2. Encourage students to add new entries. Help them to understand the connection between their personal language, which might include familiar words and even slang, and the academic language of their reading and writing.

3. Call on volunteers to read a few entries aloud. Point out that writers have many choices of words when they write. Help students see that audience often determines word choice.

N

nice

admirable

friendly

agreeable

pleasant

cool

phat

A

B

C

D

E

F

G

H

I

J

K

L

M

N

O

P

Q

R

S

T

U

V

W

X

Y

Z

(Acknowledgments continued from page ii)

Dell Publishing, a div of Random House, Inc.
From *The Giant's House* by Elizabeth McCracken, copyright © 1996 by Elizabeth McCracken. Used by permission of The Dial Press/Dell Publishing, a division of Random House, Inc.

Dunow Carlson Lerner Agency
"Desiderata" by Elizabeth McCracken from *http://www.randomhouse.com/boldtype/0397/mccracken/*. Copyright © 1996 by Elizabeth McCracken. Used by permission of Dunow Carlson Lerner Agency.

Faber and Faber Limited
"Macavity: The Mystery Cat" by T.S. Eliot from *Old Possum's Book of Practical Cats* by T. S. Eliot. Copyright 1939 by T.S. Eliot and renewed 1967 by Esme Valerie Eliot. Used by permission of Faber and Faber Limited.

Farrar, Straus & Giroux, LLC
"Part 1: The Cyclops" from *The Odyssey* by Homer, translated by Robert Fitzgerald. Copyright © 1961, 1963 by Robert Fitzgerald. Copyright renewed 1989 by Benedict R. C. Fitzgerald, on behalf of the Fitzgerald children. Used by permission.

Graywolf Press
"Fifteen" from *The Way It Is: New and Selected Poems* by William Stafford. Copyright © 1966, 1998 by the Estate of William Stafford. Used by permission of Graywolf Press, Saint Paul, MN.

Harcourt, Inc.
"Macavity: The Mystery Cat" from *Old Possum's Book of Practical Cats* by T.S. Eliot. Copyright 1939 by T. S. Eliot and renewed 1967 by Esme Valerie Eliot, Used by permission of Harcourt, Inc. This material may not be reproduced in any form or by any means without the prior written permission of the publisher.

HarperCollins Publishers, Inc.
"Summer" from *Brown Angels: An Album of Pictures and Verse* by Walter Dean Myers. Copyright © 1993 by Walter Dean Myers. Used by permission of HarperCollins Publishers.

Hawaiian Lifeguard Association
"Beach and Ocean Safety Signs" by Staff from *www.aloha.com*. Copyright © 1986, 2001 Hawaiian Lifeguard Association. All rights (and lefts) reserved. Used with permission.

Helmut Hirnschall
"There is a Longing . . ." by Chief Dan George & Helmut Hirnschall from *My Heart Soars*. Copyright © 1974 by Chief Dan George and Helmut Hirnschall. Used by permission of Helmut Hirnschall.

The Barbara Hogenson Agency, Inc.
"The Secret Life of Walter Mitty" by James Thurber from *My World-And Welcome To It*. Copyright © 1942 by James Thurber. Copyright © renewed 1970 by Rosemary A. Thurber. Used by permission from The Barbara Hogenson Agency, Inc.

HowStuffWorks, Inc.
"How Podcasting Works" by Stephanie Watson from *http://computer.howstuffworks.com/podcasting.htm*. Copyright © 1998–2007 HowStuffWorks, Inc. Courtesy of How Stuff Works.com.

Lyndon B. Johnson Library
From *A White House Diary* by Lady Bird Johnson. Used with permission of the Lyndon B. Johnson Library.

The Estate of Dr. Martin Luther King, Jr. c/o Writer's House LLC
"I Have a Dream" by Dr. Martin Luther King, Jr. from *The Words of Martin Luther King, Jr.* Copyright © 1963 Martin Luther King Jr., copyright renewed © 1991 Coretta Scott King. Used by arrangement with The Heirs to the Estate of Martin Luther King Jr., c/o Writers House as agent for the proprietor New York, NY.

Alfred A. Knopf, Inc.
"Dreams" and "Dream Deferred" from *The Collected Poems of Langston Hughes* by Langston Hughes. Copyright © 1994 by The Estate of Langston Hughes. Used by permission of Alfred A. Knopf, a division of Random House, Inc.

Andrew MacAndrew
"The Necklace" by Guy de Maupassant, translated by Andrew MacAndrew, from *Boule De Suif And Selected Stories* by Guy de Maupassant, New York, NAL, 1964, pp. 143–151. Translation copyright © 1964 by Andrew MacAndrew. Used by permission of Marie-Christine MacAndrew.

Methuen Publishing, Ltd.
"The Inspector-General" from *The Sneeze: Plays and Stories* by Anton Chekhov, translated and adapted by Michael Frayn, published by Methuen Drama. Originally from *An Awl in a Sack* by Anton Chekhov, 1885. Used by permission of Methuen Publishing, Ltd.

National Oceanic and Atmospheric Administration
"Tornadoes" from *www.noaa.gov/tornadoes.html*. Used courtesy of U.S. National Oceanic and Atmospheric Administration (NOAA).

NJ TRANSIT
Port Jervis & Pascack Valley Lines from *MTA Train Schedule: Metro-North Railroad*. Copyright © 2006 NJ Transit. Used by permission of NJ TRANSIT.

Northwestern University Press
"Sonnets on Love XIII" from *Sonnets on Love and Death* by Jean de Sponde translated by David R. Slavitt. English translation copyright (C) 2001 by David R. Slavitt. Published 2001. Evanston: Northwestern University Press, 2001. Used by permission of Northwestern University Press. All rights reserved. http://www.nupress.northwester.edu.

PHOTO AND ART CREDITS

Event: Philip Crowson/THE BATTALION; *Play Hard; Play Together; Play Smart from The Carolina Way*: Getty Images, Inc.; *A Hero in Our Midst*: The Picture Desk, Inc./PARAMOUNT PICTURES/THE KOBAL; AP/Wide World Photos; *The Skeleton Key*: Corel Professional Photos CD-ROM™; *The Red-headed League*: Pearson Education; *There Is a Longing*: Library of Congress; *The Sticker Bur*: Getty Images, Andrew McRobb/© Dorling Kindersley, Scott Camazine/Photo Researchers, Inc.: *Glory and Hope*: Corel Professional Photos CD-ROM™; *Automobiles in Texas*: Car Culture/CORBIS, Hulton-Deutsch Collection/CORBIS